RAILWAY DISASTERS

CAUSE AND EFFECT

PRC

Contents

Previous page:
**Bristol Temple Meads: a night view looking east into the
spectacle of the colour-light signals from the end of
Platform 9.** Ian Allan Library

ISBN 1 85648 049 6

This edition combines two books first
published in 1987 and 1989 by Ian Allan
Limited under the titles "Danger Signals" and
"Danger On The Line"

© S Hall 1987, 1989

This edition published 1992 by
The Promotional Reprint Company Limited
exclusively for Bookmart Ltd, Desford Road,
Enderby, Leicester, UK.

Printed in Hong Kong

Foreword

by
Major C. F. Rose MBE, C.Eng, FICE, MCIT,
Chief Inspecting Officer of Railways,
Department of Transport

Railway accidents are always news. Even relatively minor ones reach the front page, whilst more serious ones in other modes of transport might not be mentioned at all. In part this is a reflection of the railways' long history, but there is also the railways' success in achieving such high levels of safety; people do not expect trains to crash and when they do there is often a feeling of shock or bewilderment. However, we have to recognise that there will always be accidents, since there is no such thing as absolute safety. What is important is that the cause of most accidents that do occur is investigated in depth — and not only the immediate cause but also the underlying factors which may have set the scene for the accident. It is on these underlying factors that Stan Hall had concentrated and it is this that makes his book much more than just a catalogue of disasters. I believe that it will be read with interest and profit by professional railwaymen who, whilst they may not agree with all that is written, will find themselves challenged to think about aspects of safety that may have passed unnoticed or been dismissed as irrelevant. The informed amateur will be intrigued by the opportunity to look behind the scenes and follow the sometimes tortuous but always fascinating search for safety, and even those with little knowledge of railways should find much of interest, and reassurance, in the story that unfolds. Stan Hall's long experience as a railwayman, culminating in his position at the centre of British Railways' search for a railway that is efficient, economic and safe, has given him the credentials to write this book. In doing so, I believe he has made a positive contribution to the cause of railway safety.

Left:
Manchester Piccadilly — an orderly array of colour-light signalling amidst the confusion of overhead cables.
British Railways

Introduction

It could be said that I have been preparing this book for the last 40 years or so, ever since I started work with the London Midland & Scottish Railway in April 1943 at the age of 17 as a junior booking clerk at Keighley, on the Midland Division main line between Leeds and Carlisle. I quickly found that I was interested in railway operating, particularly signalling and safety, and in my spare time in those early days I was usually to be found somewhere around the station or in the signalboxes, of which there were no fewer than six. There were two serious accidents in the area about that time, 1943/44, to arouse my interest, one being the derailment on the curve at Thwaites, just south of Keighley, of a number of fish vans at the rear of one of the Up Scotch sleeping car expresses. The other was a collision at Steeton, just north of Keighley, when the Down Edinburgh sleeper crashed into a goods train being set back into the refuge siding. Being wartime, neither of these accidents received much publicity.

My first experience of a Ministry of Transport Public Inquiry was in 1948, when I went to the Crewe Arms Hotel to hear about the Winsford crash, which occurred when the Up Postal express ran into the back of the 5.40pm Glasgow-Euston, the latter being at a standstill after the communication cord had been pulled. Shortly after this I took the first step on the 'Operating' ladder with responsibilities for the safety of trains and passengers, when I became a station master at a small station in the industrial West Riding. The receipts hardly covered the porters' wages, and the station — Battyeford, on the Leeds-Huddersfield 'new' line — was not worth keeping open, but there were five signalboxes, including four on the very busy four-track section between Mirfield and Huddersfield, and it was a good training ground for someone interested in signalling and safety. By chance I discovered that the District Signalmen's Inspector had an extensive collection of Ministry of Transport accident reports, which he lent to me. I devoured them from cover to cover, and so began an admiration for the work and the Reports of the Inspecting Officers of the Ministry of Transport which has lasted to the present day. Throughout the remainder of my career with British Railways in many parts of the country, at station, division, and HQ level, I had responsibilities for safety and accident investigation, culminating in five years at British Railways Board Headquarters as the Signalling & Safety Officer. During that period, or in the preceding years, I managed to visit almost every power signalbox on BR, and had the good fortune to be able to travel in the driving cab, usually with an Inspector, over virtually every main line in Britain. During the course of this I met, and was able to discuss safety problems with, many hundreds of signalmen and drivers. I shall always be grateful to those who helped me to get a better 'feel' of what it is to be a driver or a signalman, and to be able to appreciate their problems and responsibilities. I never cease to be impressed by their quite proper pride in their craft, and their dedication to the railway. They need no lessons in customer care — the customer has always been their first concern.

Those, then, are my qualifications for writing this book. It is a book which I believe needed to be written, not just to explain how accidents happen but also *why* they happen despite the existence of modern safeguards and a great deal of expenditure. I expect that I may have trodden on a few toes in doing so and if I have unwittingly caused hurt or offence, I hope that my apologies will be accepted. I have tried to be objective throughout, not an easy task with the burden of 40 years' loyalty and tradition, and if I have failed in that objectivity the responsibility is mine, and mine alone. This book is in no way an official review of safety standards. The British Railways Board has hardly been involved at all in its preparation, except for the provision of a small amount of information, and that is the way both the Board and I have preferred it. Whilst I would have tried to be objective even with BR's co-operation in assembling the material, there would have been an inevitable suspicion that I was, even if in only a small

Below:

A scene that used to be repeated everywhere on Britain's railways during foggy weather or falling snow. The fog signalman placed a warning fog signal on the rail to explode when a train passed over it. His hut and brazier have now passed into railway history, together with his long overcoat, cloth cap and walrus moustache. Ian Allan Library

Left:
An instructor explains the functions of a signal at Willesden to two drivers during a tour of the yards and sidings.
British Railways (LMR)

measure, presenting the BR case. Happily, that eventuality has not arisen.

Some may feel that my criticisms of railway management are too restrained and that, on the facts I have presented, a harsher criticism would have been justified. Others may take the opposite view. I can only leave readers to judge for themselves. At the same time I have been anxious not to let hindsight colour my judgement, a trap into which it would be very easy to fall. It must also be remembered that a thousand trains arriving safely is not news; the one that does not is. The book deals mainly with recent serious accidents, and then only those with an 'operating' flavour. In general, each chapter considers a different type of accident, and I make no apology for describing accidents in dramatic terms — accidents *are* dramatic — but I have deliberately avoided naming the people involved, because most of them are still alive.

In my descriptions of railway operating procedures, equipment, Rules, etc, I have tried to steer a middle course between long, tedious descriptions on the one hand, which might bore the professional railwayman or knowledgeable amateur, and a degree of brevity on the other hand, which might confuse the layman. The book is not aimed specially at railwaymen, although I hope that they might find it interesting and perhaps of value, but rather at the general public who are often curious to know just how railway accidents are caused, but find technical descriptions of railway procedures a little baffling. I have been anxious not to take the reader's knowledge for granted, and if I have erred too far the other way I ask for your indulgence.

The basis of the book is an examination of the reasons behind the obvious causes of an accident. It is not enough to say that a driver, for example, made an error. One has to ask whether that error could (and should) have been foreseen, what preventive measures or equipment existed, whether more could have been done, and if so, why it had not been done. The research into these questions has been greatly facilitated by the availability of reports on all serious accidents, published by the Ministry of Transport following Public Inquiries held by Inspecting Officers. I am greatly indebted to the Chief Inspecting Officer, Major C. F. Rose MBE, who has readily placed his library of reports at my disposal. My working relationships with Major Rose and his fellow Inspecting Officers have been amongst the most enjoyable and rewarding of my railway career.

I am also indebted to the following for checking the script and for their helpful comments: Mr K. C. Appleby, former Area Manager at York, Mr T. Morgan, a main line driver at Skipton depot, and Mr J. E. Whitehouse MBE, former Divisional Staff Officer at Birmingham. My family and friends have given me unfailing support and encouragement, for which I am extremely grateful.

The utmost care has been taken to ensure factual accuracy as far as possible, but if any errors are detected I should be grateful to be informed. The opinions expressed are mine alone, and I take responsibility for them.

Safety at Signals and the Value of AWS

A few miles west of Manchester, the railway line from Liverpool and the M602 motorway run side by side. Drivers on the M602, faced with all the normal hazards of motorway driving, must often have looked enviously at trains passing in such effortless safety on the adjacent railway and wished that they could change places with the engine driver. Driving a train looks so easy; the signalman does all the steering, and all the driver has to do is stop when required. Or so it must have seemed until the morning of 4 December 1984, when those same motorway drivers were suddenly confronted with a ball of flame spreading across from the railway line, and were showered with burning debris. The 10.05 express Liverpool-Scarborough had plunged into the back of an almost stationary loaded oil tank train at 45-50mph. By great good fortune the front two coaches, which were engulfed in flames, were almost empty and only two passengers were killed, in addition to the driver. It is a tribute to modern coach design and construction that none of the other 150 passengers suffered serious injury.

The cause of the accident was quite clear — the driver passed Eccles Distant signal, which was giving a 'Caution' message, and the Home signal, which was saying 'Danger, Stop', without any apparent reaction, and his train continued forward at unchecked speed until a few seconds before it hit the oil tank train. Why the driver failed to react to the signals will never be known; he was killed at once.

The history of railways is littered with similar crashes, which may indicate that driving a train is perhaps not quite so simple as it looks. The driver must watch out for, and obey, every signal. He must always be on the alert and must never lose his concentration for an instant. It is a tribute to the sense of responsibility and self-discipline of drivers that there are so few lapses of concentration, and when the driver is killed in an accident of this nature it cannot be proved beyond doubt, but can only be assumed, that a lapse of concentration has taken place.

Faced with the likely consequences of human error of this nature, the railways have for many years sought and applied ways and means of guarding against it, and the

Below left:
Tragedy at Eccles. Class 45 locomotive No 45147 is seen here embedded in the rear of the oil tank train into which it crashed at speed on the morning of 4 December 1984, after having run past Eccles Home signal, which was at Danger. A. Sherratt

Bottom left:
Eccles: the burnt-out leading coach of the 10.05 express from Liverpool to Scarborough.
Manchester Evening News

Right:
Another view of the Eccles collision, looking westwards. Having the motorway alongside greatly facilitated the access of the rescue and emergency services. The foam used to fight the fire can clearly be seen.
Roger Kaye

Below:
Eccles: a huge road-transported heavy-lifting crane was used, almost dwarfing the railway breakdown crane beyond.
A. Sherratt

Right:
On 5 December, the day after the accident, Class 31 No 31171 is in attendance with the Newton Heath breakdown train as the remains of the wreckage are removed. David A. Ingham

Below:
Eccles Up Home signal, seen in 1978, with the 11.56 Filey-Liverpool entering the station on the Down main line. This picture shows how the signal merges with the bridge beyond it. Noel Johnston

Below right:
The same signal in August 1986, having been provided with a white back-plate to enable drivers to see it more easily. The DMU entering Eccles station is the 12.50 Manchester-Liverpool. Author

question has to be asked as to why there were no such safeguards at Eccles signalbox. As long as a century ago much thought and ingenuity were being expended on the subject. An interesting experiment was then being conducted at Wimbledon on the London & South Western Railway using an apparatus similar to that later adopted by the Great Western Railway. It consisted of a bar lying between the rails at the Distant signal. When the signal was not in the 'Clear' position, the bar was raised slightly and made contact with a wheel-operated vertical rod on the underside of the locomotive, causing a whistle to sound. This system, known as Kempe & Rowell's patent, was primarily designed to enable the use of fog-signalmen to be discontinued, rather than as a means of assisting the driver in all weathers. Fog-signalling was an occupation attended with some danger, and was expensive. But Kempe could see the value of his and Rowell's apparatus as an additional all-weather safeguard for the driver. There was, however, a school of thought which held the view that nothing should

be done that might in any way distract the driver from his primary duty of observing and obeying signals, and that any mechanical or other aids might eventually and unwittingly lead to a reduction in his overall level of concentration. It was a view that was to prevail in some quarters for another half century and more, but there were exceptions, the Great Western being the most notable. Following a serious collision at Slough in June 1900, when the 1.15pm express from Paddington to Falmouth ran into the back of a passenger train standing in the station after the driver of the express had failed to obey the Distant signals, the Great Western considered what ought to be done to prevent a repetition, following prompting by Col Sir Arthur Yorke in his Report.

In January 1906 experimental apparatus was installed on one of its branch lines. The apparatus was similar to Kempe & Rowell's patent but with the warning being actuated electrically. Instead of the bar between the two rails being raised and lowered, a fixed ramp was provided which made

contact with a spring-loaded shoe on the locomotive. When the Distant signal was 'Clear' an electric current passed through the ramp and rang a bell on the locomotive. When the Distant signal was at 'Caution' no current passed and the raising of the spring-loaded shoe broke an electrical circuit and sounded an alarm. It was thus fail-safe; a fundamental principle of all signalling and safety equipment. The experiment was extended to the line between Paddington and Reading between 1908 and 1910 and the equipment was developed to provide an automatic application of the brake unless the driver intervened. The experiment was so successful that the Great Western extended its use to all its main lines, so that by 1939 it had equipped 3,250 locomotives and 2,850 track miles, contributing greatly to that company's excellent and enviable safety record.

The Great Western was by no means the only pre-Grouping (pre-1923) railway company interested in what became known as Automatic Train Control (ATC). The North Eastern Railway had a mechanical appliance at Distant signals, and equipped 1,528 locomotives and 90 route miles. Among the other railways the Great Central, the Great Eastern, the London, Brighton & South Coast and the London & North Western were all conducting experiments. The Grouping of 120 separate railway companies into the 'Big Four' in 1923, resulting from the Railways Act of 1921, led to many improvements in other fields but it severely set back the advancement of ATC. Was it mere coincidence that the only one of the 'Big Four' that went ahead with a full ATC installation, the Great Western, was the only one that was relatively unaffected by the Grouping? There may be a lesson here that re-organisations delay desirable reforms, but it is significant that almost all the worthwhile experiments in ATC which were in hand on the pre-Grouping railways came to a dead stop at the end of 1922.

But why did the other railway companies not press ahead with ATC? There were plenty of accidents to help them to make up their minds, and Inspecting Officers, in their reports, continued to press for its adoption. Col Pringle was particularly active in this, and in 1920/21 chaired a committee on the subject, whose terms of reference were:

1 To enumerate the possible functions of ATC . . . and prescribe requisites which devices should fulfil.
2 To examine ATC devices under trial and recommend for further trial or for experimental installation . . .
3 To form conclusions on the adoption of ATC, in respect of all or any of its possible functions, having regard to advantages . . . and cost.

The Report, dated April 1922, ranged over the whole subject and concluded that there was a prima facie case for warning devices to be installed at Distant signals, but that it was more important to provide trip-stop control at selected Stop signals. It suggested that the railway companies should co-operate to provide standard equipment which would allow the employment of fog-signalmen at Distant signals to be dispensed with, and which would provide for three effects — Danger, Warning and Clear. The committee was unanimous in its opposition to visual cab-signalling.

Below:
The Great Western Railway and its successor the Western Region had a remarkably good safety record, thanks to Automatic Train Control, but here is one that slipped through the net. A forlorn-looking BR Standard 'Britannia' class locomotive No 70026 *Polar Star* after its derailment at Milton, near Didcot, on 20 November 1955 whilst hauling an excursion from Treherbert to Paddington. The driver was not used to this type of locomotive and failed to react to ATC warnings, entering Milton loop at too high a speed. This is one example of many where new equipment is a contributory cause of accidents. British Railways (WR)

It might be thought that with such definite recommendations the railway companies would have acted promptly and equipped all main lines within a few years, leading to a considerable reduction in the number of serious accidents, but it did not happen. The upheaval and distraction of Grouping had some effect, although with only four companies instead of 120 it ought to have been somewhat easier to devise standard equipment. Probably the new 'Big Four' thought that the cost was too great in the more difficult financial conditions following World War 1 — the total cost was put at £4,660,000 to equip 24,000 distant signals, 38,000 stop signals and 23,000 locomotives. The proposals suffered from being too ambitious and wide-ranging, with their emphasis on train-stop equipment at Stop signals rather than warning equipment at Distant signals, whereas if the terms of reference and resulting recommendations had concentrated on the Distant signal, and if the other companies could have swallowed their pride and adopted the Great Western system, the cost would have been very much reduced and the future quite different. In the event the Great Western went its own way and the others did nothing. Accidents caused by drivers failing to react to adverse Distant signals continued to occur. If Col Pringle had expected his committee to achieve anything, he must have been very disappointed, but undaunted, and anxious to achieve something before he retired, he chaired another ATC committee in 1928/29. Its terms of reference this time were: 'To review the recommendations made by the ATC Committee of 1922 and to consider and report what alterations, if any, should be made in that Committee's conclusions and recommendations having regard to the developments that have taken place since that date.'

The membership of the committee was even more high-powered than before. The table at the top of this page details its eminent membership.

Only a few days after the committee had its first meeting on 1 October 1928, there was yet another accident of the type that ATC could have prevented, and which had disastrous results. It occurred at Charfield, between Gloucester and Bristol, on the West of England main line of the London Midland & Scottish Railway's Midland Division in the early hours of 13 October 1928, when the 10.00pm express and mail from Leeds to Bristol, hauled by ex-Midland Railway Class 3P 4-4-0 No 714, crashed at full speed into a goods train which was being set back into the down lie-by. The coaches of the express had wooden bodies and were gas-lit. An empty wagon train was passing on the next line at the precise moment and was involved in the crash, the wooden wagons helping to feed the fire which broke out. Fifteen lives were lost. It was a dramatic and spectacular accident which must have done much to concentrate the minds of the committee, whose eventual recommendations, published in 1930, proposed both 'Direct' and 'Indirect' methods of increasing security. This time the committee made a firm recommendation in favour of the Great Western fixed-ramp system at Distant signals, and whilst it proposed increased

security at Stop signals this was rather a secondary consideration. The Distant signal had won the day.

The 'Indirect' methods proposed were designed to assist enginemen 'to carry out their duties of observation of, and obedience to, signals. To improve sighting facilities from the cab by designing and constructing locomotives and glasses so that steam and smoke may be cleared from the

line of vision; and by positioning signals so that having regard to their background, height, etc, they will most readily come into line with the view obtainable from the engine cab. To increase the illuminative and penetrative power of signal lights themselves'.

It was also proposed that Block Signalling controls of the type referred to in Chapter 6 should be extended on 'important traffic roads'. Finally, there was mention of a recently-developed inductive control system (known as the Hudd system) which impressed the committee sufficiently for it to persuade the Southern Railway to give the necessary facilities for its first trial under working conditions at Byfleet.

What were the results of the second Pringle Committee? The Great Western, pleased that the Report had endorsed its ATC system so emphatically, went ahead and expanded its use over all its main lines, aided by Government Guaranteed Loan Schemes, but it refused to have much to do with colour-light signals. The London, Midland & Scottish Railway held perfunctory trials of the Hudd system at Millers Dale, but put its faith in 'Indirect'

Left:
The Strowger-Hudd inductive control system in the driving cab. The warning hooter sounded a short or continuous blast depending on whether the signal was in the Clear position, or against the driver. Next to the hooter can be seen the device by which the driver could stop the hooter sounding, and release the brake if appropriate. Ian Allan Library

Below left:
Strowger-Hudd warning magnets in experimental use in 1931. They operated the warning hooter in the engine cab, and applied the brakes throughout the train if the signal was at Caution. Ian Allan Library

Below:
Northallerton signalbox, seen in 1984. It houses one of the first electrical-relay interlocking systems, and came into operation on the day that World War 2 broke out — 3 September 1939. L. Abram

methods, by embarking, among other things, on a major programme to replace semaphore Distant signals with electrically-lit colour-light signals. The Southern Railway went in extensively for multiple-aspect colour-light signalling to assist the working of its intensive and growing electrified suburban and main line services. The London & North Eastern Railway took little action on the recommendations in the Report, but was very progressive in one sphere. In the 1930s it introduced an electrical relay interlocking system on the main line between York and Northallerton, complete with continuous track-circuiting, route-setting switches on a panel instead of cumbersome signal levers, and automatic colour-light signals. ATC was virtually ignored by all the railway companies except the Great Western, despite the high-powered signatories of the recommendations of the ATC Committee Report, and despite the Charfield accident, and one cannot escape the feeling that the railway companies had merely taken part in the committee for the sake of appearances, and never had any real intention of actually doing anything. Financially the railways were in difficulties, and there was little money to spare for investment of a type whose effects could not easily be measured by accountants. The 1921 Railways Act had fixed at about £50 million the standard net revenue which Parliament had decided was a fair remuneration to railway share-holders. The actual results for 1929 were £45 million, for 1930 they were £38 million and for 1931 £33 million. The lowest point was reached in 1932 when net revenue was only £26 million, in the depths of the trade depression, and there was only a slow improvement in succeeding years to £38 million in 1937. The LNER was hit particularly hard by the depression because it depended so much on heavy industries for its business. In such circumstances it is not difficult to imagine railway boards of management looking bleakly on proposals for additional investment in safety, given the generally high standards which already existed.

As already explained, except on the GWR only very small-scale experiments and trials were embarked on, a

situation which was aggravated by the doubts and indecision which surrounded the subject and which may be summarised as:

1 Which ought to have first priority for investment, Distant signals or Stop signals?
2 What indications should ATC give to the driver at the Distant signal?
3 Should ATC be installed at colour-light signals?
4 How should double-yellow colour-light signals be dealt with?
5 How should ATC, conversion of semaphore signals to colour-light or intensified light, and installation of Block Controls in signalboxes, rank with each other for priority of treatment for investment?

There was a further factor. Conversion to colour-light signalling brought not only increased safety but also other benefits. Maintenance costs were reduced, the need to change oil-lamps weekly was avoided, and the signals could be operated normally during fog because of their penetrating beam, so avoiding the need for fog-signalmen. Given all this, plus the increase in safety which was thought to follow from the more visually-arresting colour-light signal, especially at night and during poor visibility, it can be seen how easily a strong case could be made out for the extension of colour-light signalling rather than the adoption of ATC, when there was not sufficient money available for both. Much faith was put in colour-light signalling on its own as an increased safety factor. How much that faith was justified is impossible to judge; it can only be pointed out that colour-light distants were involved in some of the worst accidents in railway history:

Bourne End	30 September 1945	43 killed
Harrow and Wealdstone	8 October 1952	112 killed
St Johns, Lewisham	4 December 1957	90 killed

There were others, but supporters of colour-light signals could argue that there might have been even more if semaphore signals had not been converted to colour-light, and that intensive electrified suburban services could not have been operated without multiple-aspect colour-light signalling. Both schools of thought were correct; colour-light signalling and ATC are complementary, not competitive. It is interesting to note that the railways considered it safe to discontinue the use of fog-signalmen at colour-light Distant signals (despite some evidence to the contrary), yet persisted with their employment at the relatively safer semaphore Distant signal equipped with ATC right up to the 1980s.

By the outbreak of World War 2, enthusiasm for train-stops at selected Stop signals had completely evaporated and the various concepts of ATC were merging in favour of warning control at the Distant signal. The LMSR had been slowly developing the Hudd system and in 1935 it decided to equip the former London, Tilbury & Southend line between Campbell Road Junction (Bow) and Shoeburyness, because of its proneness to fog. By the outbreak of war the experimental work was approaching completion but the system was still not in full use. Overall, very slow progress had been made with ATC in the nine years since the Report of the second Pringle Committee. On the LNER almost nothing had been done, although that company had been stung into belated action by the crash at Castlecary on the Glasgow-Edinburgh main line on 10 December 1937 (see Appendix for details of this and other collisions not described in the text), and had started making preparations for trials of Hudd apparatus on that line. All work ceased during the war, and after it there were more urgent matters to concern railway boards of management. The railway system had been severely overworked and under-maintained during the war, and with the return of a Labour Government in the summer of 1945 there was the prospect of Nationalisation.

The collision at Ecclefechan on 23 July 1945 and the derailment at Bourne End on 30 September 1945 focussed attention on the subject yet again. Once more the Inspecting Officer, Lt-Col Sir Alan Mount, made the now standard plea for ATC. Once more it fell on deaf ears, indeed it seemed that the railways had virtually set their face against ATC when they replied that:

'apart from the question of finance, the general installation of ATC, even of the warning type, on main lines where this does not already exist, would occupy a considerable time and employ a large number of skilled men. The supply of such staff is strictly limited, and its employment on this installation would therefore necessarily delay the execution of other work such as the modernisation of signalling, the extension of track circuiting and other similar works.'

This reply was in some ways understandable. The railway companies could not get enough staff of the right calibre, new equipment was in short supply, and, as always, there wasn't enough money. It was all the railways could do just to keep abreast of their very heavy freight traffic. ATC must necessarily have been well down their list of priorities, except of course on the Great Western, who must have been grateful for their prewar foresight. On a minor note, however, the Hudd system on the London Tilbury & Southend line had proved its reliability and was approved by the Minister of Transport in 1947.

And so matters stood when the four main line companies were nationalised on 1 January 1948 and the Railway Executive was formed. This new body initially took a more positive view, aided by reduced financial worries and the early optimism of the new undertaking. In the next five years there were studies, experiments and trials to decide the final form that ATC should take on British Railways. At first the Great Western system was favoured but it was thought to have problems if adopted in other parts of the country, especially on electrified lines, and a preference emerged for a modified Hudd system. However, it proved very difficult to embody the modifications desired and the years slipped by. Progress was disappointingly slow and it was not until August 1952 that the drawings were ready for what was hoped would be the final prototype design. The first set of equipment was fitted to a locomotive and put into service on 17 October 1952, nine days after the Harrow & Wealdstone disaster. The appalling nature of that accident obviously impressed itself upon the Railway Executive, which announced almost at once that as soon as the equipment was proved to be satisfactory, it would embark upon a five-year plan to equip 1,332 miles of the most important main lines, followed by a longer term plan to equip a further 4,000 route miles, in addition to the 1,400 route miles already equipped. This was indeed a comprehensive plan. Unfortunately, the satisfactory proving of equipment again took longer than expected, and the system was not finally approved until November 1956, four

Right:
The pile of wreckage after the worst peace-time accident in British railway history — the high-speed collision of three passenger trains at Harrow & Wealdstone station on 8 October 1952 which left 112 people dead, and which could have been prevented by Automatic Train Control. Ian Allan Library

14

years later, and 26 years after the second Pringle Committee Report. An allocation of £20 million was included in the British Transport Commission Plan for the Modernisation and Re-equipment of British Railways, issued in 1955.

Progress was still not very rapid — the original plans of 1953 had envisaged over 6,700 route miles being equipped, but because of delays in the supply of equipment it was 1958 before work got under way. It had originally been planned to equip 568 route miles by the end of 1959, but this was not to be achieved. The awful disasters of Harrow (1952) and St Johns (1957) might have been expected to provide an incentive to quicker progress, but the railways were gradually becoming even safer in other ways, and they could point with pride to the years 1949, 1954 and 1956 in which no passenger had been killed in a train accident. Against the background of such a superb safety record, Harrow and St Johns might have been thought of as aberrations — tragic enough but not indicative of widespread shortcomings in British Railways' safety defences. However, during the 1960s, work on the installation of ATC, now known as the Automatic Warning System (AWS), went ahead rapidly, aided by a number of large-scale re-resignalling schemes, so that by the end of 1972 nearly 3,000 route miles had been equipped with British Railways standard AWS. Progress continued to be made throughout the 1970s, and by the end of 1985 a total of 6,313 route miles had been equipped, which included the replacement of all the former Great Western equipment in order to achieve standardisation. So, almost exactly a hundred years after the trials of Kempe & Rowell's patent apparatus at Wimbledon, the programme to equip all important lines on British Railways is approaching completion, but as long as there are important lines without AWS, safety will be at risk, as was demonstrated so spectacularly at Eccles.

It might be instructive to look back to Lt-Col G. R. S. Wilson's Report on the Harrow accident to see what reservations and doubts he might have had, and whether these have been borne out in practice. No doubt Lt-Col Wilson was anxious not to dilute the force of his recommendations by expressing doubts, or suggesting variations, but the following comments are of interest:

'there should be no objection to the same footplate indication for the caution and danger indications of a multi-aspect signal, bearing in mind that ATC must always be regarded as an auxiliary to personal observation of the signals, and not as a substitute for it . . . I consider that, from the safety point of view, there is no need for differentiation on the footplate between the Yellow and Double Yellow indications at a four-aspect signal.'

Perhaps he had the Southern Region particularly in mind. It had followed the tradition of its predecessor, the Southern Railway, in extending the use of multiple-aspect colour-light signalling, which it believed yielded more benefit in terms of safety than other forms of investment, and which had contributed greatly to the Southern's excellent safety record. Coupled with the greatly improved forward view which the driver has from an electric multiple-unit train compared with a steam locomotive, the Southern considered AWS to be lower on the scale of priorities than continuous track-circuiting and colour-light signalling, a view which was also held by some operators outside the Southern. Despite Lt-Col Wilson's remarks, the Southern had misgivings about a warning system which had the same effect at signals showing two yellows, one yellow or red, as much of their intensive suburban service was worked on signals showing one or two yellows — inevitable with the close running of trains — and they feared that continuous acknowledgement of AWS warnings by the driver might lead to subconscious automatic cancellation and eventual disaster, as was to be demonstrated at Wembley on 11 October 1984, when an electric multiple-unit train from Euston to Bletchley ran past a Danger signal and collided with a Freightliner train which was just leaving Willesden sidings.

Progress in installing the Automatic Warning System on the Southern Region was very slow. In addition to the doubts which the Southern had about the standard British Railways AWS there was the technical difficulty of

Above left:
Removing GWR Automatic Train Control installations on the North Warwick line between Birmingham Moor Street and Stratford-upon-Avon in 1979, prior to their replacement by standard BR AWS equipment. This photograph was taken at Stratford-upon-Avon. British Rail (LMR)

Above:
The missing link — the warning magnet now installed on the approach to Eccles Distant signal. Had it been there on 4 December 1984 the collision would almost certainly not have happened. Author

installing it on lines electrified on the conductor rail system, which was not overcome until 1963. Even then little progress was made. To overcome the fears about repetitive cancellation, work was started on a more advanced system which gave individual signal aspects in the driving cab and required the driver to acknowledge each indication by a separate and distinct action, but the project was beset by technical difficulties and by 1973 no fully proven system was available, whilst the cost was estimated to be nearly three times that of the standard British Railways system. By this time there was pressure from all sides for the Southern to install AWS without further delay, and development work on the Southern's own AWS finally came to a halt. A belated start was then made in equipping the electrified lines with the British Railways standard AWS, after which fairly rapid progress was made, although the work is not expected to be complete until 1988/89.

The gap in the Southern's safety defences was cruelly exposed on the Brighton main line just before midnight on 19 December 1978 between Hassocks and Preston Park when the 21.50 electric multiple-unit train from London Victoria to Brighton, which was standing at a signal, was run into at almost full speed by a similar train, the 21.40 Victoria-Littlehampton. Three people were killed, including the driver of the 21.40. The Inspecting Officer, Maj Rose, in his Report, stated that if the signals had been provided with AWS, he thought the accident would not have occurred. He also commented that:

'after years of well-intentioned although, in the end, fruitless delay, during which time the Southern Region has been less well protected against the possibility of serious rear-end collisions than other Regions, there is now a firm and realistic programme for bringing the Region up to standard. It is to be hoped that neither technical difficulty nor financial stringency will be allowed to stand in the way of the successful completion of the programme within the planned timescale.'

The urgent need to complete the programme was emphasised by further collisions on the Southern, which would almost certainly have been prevented by AWS. Among them were:

1 At Parks Bridge Junction near Lewisham on 18 August 1981 the 07.49 Charing Cross-Bromley North passed a signal at Danger and came into contact with the rear of the 06.18 Dover-Cannon Street, which was crossing from the Up Fast line to the Up Slow line in front of it. Fortunately there were no injuries but a few seconds the wrong way could have resulted in tragedy.
2 At Bromley Junction on 13 November 1981 the 08.22 West Croydon-London Bridge passed a signal at Danger and came into side-long collision with the 08.23 Beckenham-Victoria. Fortunately again, there were no serious injuries.
3 At East Croydon on 16 January 1982 the 23.18 empty van train from Brighton to London Bridge, which was standing in platform 1, was run into in the rear at about 30mph by an Engineer's works train, whose driver had passed the protecting signal at Danger. Damage was estimated to be in excess of £¾ million.

Only systems such as AWS can provide a safeguard against a driver's error or inattention. Very soon now, when the installation of AWS on selected routes has been completed, Col Pringle and all the other Inspecting Officers who have pressed for so long and so hard for ATC and later for AWS (together with those Railway Officers who had faith in it) against what must often have seemed intransigent and obstructive railway managements, will have been vindicated. Only the Great Western emerges from this story with credit. The other railway companies and their successors have since 1923 almost consistently dragged their feet. Yet during the hundred years that this story has covered, the art of signalling has progressed from the simple and rudimentary to the most technically advanced, with computers and solid-state interlocking; in fact signal engineering is in the vanguard of progress, and a shining example of the application of scientific discovery and knowledge to railways. So what is the reason for this apparent paradox? It is perhaps to be found in the membership of Pringle's committees, which consisted of a Civil Engineer, a Signalling Engineer, a Locomotive Engineer and an Operating Superintendent.

With so many departments concerned there was ample scope for delay, vacillation and lack of whole-hearted commitment. If Automatic Train Control had been considered to be an integral part of the signalling system and directly and totally the responsibility of the Signal Engineer, it is surely impossible to believe that it would have taken more than 100 years to equip the railways with this simple safeguard. Have Signal Engineers assumed that their responsibilities finish at the lens of the colour-light signal or the arm of the semaphore signal, without ensuring that the message those signals give is correctly received, interpreted and acted upon by the driver? If so, many people would think that those responsibilities ought to be extended and that they should not end until the signal's instruction is correctly obeyed by the driver. After all, the

Signal Engineer has provided the signalman with every conceivable safeguard to ensure that he operates his signals safely; why has the driver, who must obey those signals correctly if safety is to be achieved, been excluded from the process?

The present Automatic Warning System is a quite simple concept, designed for Absolute Block signalling with separate Distant and Stop signals. Its application to multiple-aspect signals capable of displaying two yellows, one yellow and red is not entirely satisfactory, as we have seen, because the same warning indications are given if the signal is showing anything other than green. Lt-Col Wilson in his comments on the Harrow crash (1952) thought there was no objection to it, possibly on the realistic grounds that it was better to have reasonable protection now rather than perfection at some unknown date in the future. In view of the lack of progress up to that date he can hardly be criticised for his view. The Southern saw difficulties, and their fears have not been entirely groundless. The collision at Wembley in 1984 was only one example of several cases where crashes have occurred despite all modern safeguards including AWS being provided. On 22 July 1981 the 16.10 High Speed Train (HST) from Bristol to Paddington passed a signal at Danger and collided with a parcels train which was standing at the next signal near Hayes & Harlington. Fortunately the driver had reacted to the AWS warning at the red signal and had managed to reduce his speed from 100mph to 15/20mph at the time of the collision, but the warnings which were given at the two previous signals were ineffective. There were no serious injuries but all the components of a major disaster were there. All high speed trains carry a driver and co-driver when travelling at speeds over 100mph but the extra driver was of no avail in this case. On 31 May 1985, near Battersea Park, the 09.20 'Gatwick Express' ran into the back of the 08.51 East Grinstead-Victoria. At the Public Inquiry it was stated that the driver of the train from Gatwick had passed a succession of double-yellow and yellow signals, properly cancelling the AWS warning in each case, but when he finally received the same warning sound at the Red signal protecting the East Grinstead train he failed to notice the difference in the signal.

The weakness of the AWS might be thought to be the ability of the driver to over ride the automatic application of the brake at a Caution signal. Without that ability, Wembley and the other collisions just mentioned would not have happened, so is it feasible to remove that ability? Unfortunately it is not, because the result would be widespread disruption and delay to the train service every day. Trains frequently run on successive double-yellow Caution signals with little reduction in speed, and often the next signal in front of a driver may change to Proceed after he has received a Caution at the previous signals. It would be intolerable for trains to be brought to a stand every time

Above right & right:
Disaster on the Southern Region. Scenes at Sweethill Bridge on the Brighton main line on 20 December 1978 after the previous evening's 21.40 EMU from London Victoria to Littlehampton had run into the 21.50 EMU from Victoria to Brighton, which was standing at a signal. AWS could have prevented this.
Colin Burnham

Above:
The remains of the driving trailer belonging to unit No 7333, at the rear of the 21.50 Victoria-Brighton which was struck by the 21.40 Victoria-Littlehampton. The additional danger in the event of an accident involving vehicles with blue asbestos insulation can readily be appreciated.
Colin Burnham

Year	Location	Passenger fatalities	Speed on impact	Observations
1978	Hassocks-Preston Park (SR)	1	45/50mph	Preventable by AWS, now installed
1979	Paisley (ScR)	5	35/40mph	AWS not involved
1979	Invergowrie (ScR)	3	60mph	AWS not involved
1981	Seer Green (LMR)	3	30mph	AWS not involved
1983	Wrawby Junction (ER) (Lincs)	1	20/25mph	AWS not involved
1984	Wembley (LMR)	3	50/55mph	Preventable by improved AWS
1984	Eccles (LMR)	2	45/50mph	Preventable by AWS, now installed

in such circumstances. What is needed is a system where the automatic brake application cannot be over ridden by a thoughtless driver, in that it requires a specific choice of action by the driver depending on the precise signal aspect. Alternatively, monitoring apparatus is needed to check that a driver has correctly responded to the signal's message, and interposes if he has not. The present AWS system is showing its age and something better is going to be needed in the future, especially if speeds are to rise. To some extent the reservations of the Southern have been shown to be well-founded, but whether British Railways has either the will or the money for a better system remains to be seen, yet it seems inconceivable that the railways of Britain might enter the 21st century with a protection system which started in the 19th century.

Finally, a glance at the list of collisions at the top of this page that have resulted in the deaths of passengers in the 10 years 1976-85 may serve to show how much is owed to AWS.

Is it mere chance that the Western Region is absent, or a tribute to the foresight of its predecessor?

Less than one fatal collision, and only two passengers killed, on average each year, shows a very high safety standard indeed. One cannot say how much longer the list would have been without AWS — it is a matter of conjecture, but the very small number of fatalities in each collision is also very notable — only as many as are killed in a single car crash on the roads of this country every day of the year. We have to go back as far as 1962 to find more than 10 passenger deaths in a collision; a record of which coach designers and builders, as well as all railwaymen, can be very proud.

Because of the widespread installation of AWS there were only two collision in which passengers were killed where there was no AWS, and which AWS could have prevented, in the 10-year period 1976-85, and both locations have now been equipped. An examination of the period before AWS started to be installed (based on train accidents into which Government inquiries were held) gives an interesting comparison:

1930-37 (eight years): 13 accidents preventable by AWS. 63 fatalities.

1938-52 (15 years): 15 accidents preventable by AWS. 241 fatalities.

1976-85 (10 years): two accidents preventable by AWS. Three passengers and three staff killed.

The figures speak for themselves, although it has to be remembered that there were many collisions without fatalities, but nevertheless resulting in injuries, and in very costly damage and delay.

Appendix 1

Automatic Warning Systems, ATC, Hudd and AWS

The Great Western Railway Automatic Train Control System

Track equipment:
A fixed ramp approximately 50ft long lying in the 'four-foot' between the rails, near the Distant signal. When the signal is 'Clear' an electric current is applied to the ramp.

Locomotive equipment:
A pick-up shoe is located beneath the locomotive, which engages the ramp. When the signal is at Caution a magnetically-operated valve, normally held closed by a current from a battery on the locomotive, is opened and allows air to enter the brake pipe and apply the brakes. A siren also sounds as a warning. When the signal is 'Clear' the electric current which passes through the ramp is picked up by the shoe and holds the valve closed. It also sounds a bell.

Cab equipment:
A siren, to sound a warning.
A bell, to sound 'Clear'.
Equipment to overcome the automatic application of the brake when a Warning is received.
No visual indicator.

Later developments:
Additional electrical equipment to differentiate between two yellows and one yellow at a Distant signal. The ramp is energised with the opposite polarity and sounds both the siren and a horn at a double-yellow signal.

Below:
BR Standard AWS equipment. A permanent magnet and an electro-magnet laid in the 'four-foot'. British Railways (LMR)

Left:
Cab layout of an electric locomotive. The AWS visual indicator is to the left of the driver's windscreen. AEI

Above:
Close-up of the AWS visual indicator. Author

The Hudd Non-Contact System of Automatic Train Control

The original Strowger-Hudd system had a permanent magnet and an electro-magnet in the 'four-foot' 200ft before the Distant signal, and a combined permanent and electro-magnet at the Stop signal. On the locomotive there was a receiver, a hooter, and an acknowledgement plunger. At a Clear Distant signal a short hoot was given, at a Caution Distant signal a long hoot was given, and at a Stop signal no indication was given. At a Caution Distant signal and a Danger Stop signal there was an automatic brake application, which the driver could override with his acknowledgement plunger only at the Distant signal. There was no visual indicator in the cab.

As later developed by the LMS Railway the system was installed only at Distant signals, and worked as follows:
Track equipment:
A permanent magnet and an electro-magnet are located in the 'four-foot' at the approach to a Distant signal. When the signal is 'Clear' the electro-magnet is energised.
Locomotive equipment:
A receiver fixed underneath the locomotive reacts to the magnets on the track. When it passes over the permanent magnet it sounds a siren and applies the brake after a short delay. If the electro-magnet is energised the siren is shut off and the brake application does not take place. The driver can override the brake application, in which case a visual indicator in the cab will display a segmented disc coloured alternately black and yellow.

The British Railways standard Automatic Warning System of Train Control (AWS)

Track equipment:
A permanent magnet and an electro-magnet are installed in

the 'four-foot' about 200yd on the approach side of those signals which can display a Caution aspect.
Locomotive equipment:
A receiver is fixed underneath the locomotive and reacts to the magnets fixed in the track. If the signal is 'Clear' the electro-magnet is energised and a bell sounds in the driving cab. If the signal is not 'Clear' the electro-magnet remains not energised, a horn sounds in the driving cab and the brake is applied. The driver can stop the horn sounding and override the brake application by pressing a cancelling plunger, in which case a visual indicator in the cab will display a segmented disc coloured alternately black and yellow.

Solid-state equipment is used in the most recent builds of locomotives and multiple-units, replacing the mechanical bell and visual indicator, but the principle is unchanged.

Appendix 2

Standards which BR adopts to decide whether or not a line should be equipped with AWS

AWS is to be provided on the following:

1 Lines on which speeds of 75mph and over are allowed, with a substantial volume of express passenger trains.
2 Lines with a high density of suburban passenger trains.
3 Lines with a substantial density of passenger and freight trains, and lines scheduled to carry heavy freight trains.
4 Lines which are often foggy.
5 Short stretches of line between routes equipped under other criteria, which together form part of a through route.
6 Lines on which there is more than one train per hour in either direction between midnight and 06.00 (lines must be at least 20 miles long and speeds at least 40mph).

Condition **5** is designed to give AWS safeguards to drivers working trains on parts of different trunk routes already equipped, connected by lines which would not otherwise qualify. Condition **6** is designed to give AWS safeguards to drivers during those hours when there is most likelihood of drowsiness.

Appendix 3

Details of accidents not otherwise explained in the text

Castlecary (between Glasgow and Edinburgh LNER): 10 December 1937

In the late afternoon an Edinburgh-Glasgow express hauled by Gresley Pacific locomotive No 2744 *Grand Parade* ran past the signals at Danger at Castlecary during a snowfall, and collided at almost full speed with a Dundee-Glasgow express which had come to an emergency stop a little way beyond the signalbox. Although there was some dispute about the position of the Distant signal arm, Automatic Train Control would have prevented the accident if the Distant signal had been properly in the Caution position. 35 passengers were killed.

Ecclefechan (near Gretna LMSR): 23 July 1945

The 1.0pm express from Glasgow to Euston, hauled by Stanier Pacific locomotive No 6231 *Duchess of Atholl*, crashed sidelong at 60/65mph into a freight train which was setting back into the refuge siding at Ecclefechan. The driver had run past the Outer and Inner Home signals at Danger. The driver and fireman were both killed but fortunately there were no passenger fatalities. All the signals concerned were upper-quadrant semaphores.

Bourne End (near Berkhamsted LMSR): 30 September 1945

Engineering work was in progress on the Fast line and Up trains were being diverted to the Slow line through a 20mph crossover at Bourne End. The 8.20pm sleeping car express from Perth to Euston, hauled by 'Royal Scot' 4-6-0 locomotive No 6157 *The Royal Artilleryman*, became derailed when passing through the crossover at a speed of about 50/60mph. The Distant signal was a colour-light showing two yellows which meant: 'Pass next signal at restricted speed, and the points may be set through the speed-restricted crossover'. The speed of the train was not reduced in time, but Automatic Train Control might have alerted the driver and prevented the accident. 43 people were killed.

Harrow & Wealdstone (LMSR): 8 October 1952

The 8.15pm sleeping car express from Perth to Euston (the same train as at Bourne End above), hauled by Stanier Pacific No 46242 *City of Glasgow* ran past the colour-light Distant signal at Caution and the Outer and Inner Home signals at Danger and crashed at 50/60mph into the 7.31am local passenger train from Tring to Euston which was standing in the station at Harrow. Almost immediately a double-headed express, the 8.0am from Euston to Liverpool and Manchester crashed into the wreckage at about 60mph. The result was devastating and 112 people were killed, a death roll exceeded only once by the double collision at

Quintinshill near Gretna on 22 May 1915 in which 227 people were killed. Automatic Train Control would almost certainly have prevented the Harrow crash.

Lewisham St John's (Southern Region): 4 December 1957

In foggy weather the 4.56pm express from Cannon Street to Folkestone and Ramsgate hauled by a 'Battle of Britain' class Pacific locomotive No 34066 *Spitfire* ran past a colour-light signal at Red, preceded by two Caution colour-light signals showing respectively two yellows and one yellow, and crashed into the rear of the 5.18pm electric multiple-unit train from Charing Cross to Hayes which was standing at a signal at Parks Bridge Junction. The effects of the collision brought down on to the wreckage the 350ton girder bridge carrying the Nunhead loop-line. 90 people

Left:
Bourne End (LMS) 30 September 1945. 'Royal Scot' class 4-6-0 No 6157 *The Royal Artilleryman* is being prepared for re-railing after plunging down an embankment. It had attempted to negotiate a crossover at too high a speed. C. R. L. Coles

Below:
The ultimate horror. Harrow & Wealdstone station on the morning of 8 October 1952. The newly-rebuilt Pacific No 46202 *Princess Anne* (the former 'Turbomotive') lies across a heap of wreckage in Britain's worst-ever peace-time crash. Ian Allan Library

were killed. This accident would almost certainly have been prevented by automatic warning signalling.

Between Hassocks and Preston Park (Southern Region): 19 December 1978

The 21.50 12-car electric multiple-unit train from London Victoria to Brighton had been standing at a Red signal for two or three minutes just north of Patcham Tunnel when it was run into in the rear by the 21.40 Victoria to Littlehampton 8-car electric multiple-unit travelling at 45/50mph. The time was 23.22. One passenger and two railwaymen, including the driver of the 21.40, lost their lives. The second train had passed a Caution colour-light signal 1½ miles away, but there was no light in the next

Right:
The scene of the accident at Lewisham St Johns, showing the collapsed girders which were brought down by the effects of the collision, when the tender of No 34066 and the leading coach of the 4.56pm Cannon Street-Ramsgate struck and dislodged a steel column supporting them. The girders collapsed on to the front coaches of the Ramsgate train, causing many deaths. British Railways (SR)

Above right:
The bridge at Lewisham St Johns (SR) which collapsed on the wreckage of the two trains involved in the collision on 4 December 1957. Ian Allan Library

Below:
A view of the flyover at Lewisham St Johns on 12 December 1957 after the damaged section of the flyover had been removed, with the tracks beneath once again open for traffic. British Rail (SR)

Left and below:
A clear demonstration that BR's Automatic Warning System is not foolproof. The scene at Wembley Station (LMR) after an evening commuter train from Euston to Bletchley had run past a Danger signal and collided with a Freightliner train which was leaving Willesden sidings on 11 October 1984.
Mick Roberts

signal, ¾-mile away, which should have been showing Red, protecting the stationary train. In modern colour-light installations the failure of a light in one signal will automatically switch to Danger the next signal in rear, but the signalling on the Brighton line dated from 1932 and was not so equipped, nor was AWS provided which would have operated correctly and warned the driver even if the signal light were out. The signalling has since been modernised under the Brighton line resignalling scheme, and AWS has been provided.

Wembley (London Midland Region): 11 October 1984

The 17.54 electric multiple-unit train from Euston to Bletchley, after passing several colour-light signals showing one or two yellows, ran past one at Red and collided at about 60mph with a Freightliner train which was just leaving Willesden sidings. This route is equipped with multiple-aspect colour-light signalling, continuous track circuiting and automatic warning signalling. The Inspecting Officer, Maj C. F. Rose, concluded that: 'It is entirely possible that [the driver] allowed his mind to wander or otherwise lost concentration, and cancelled the AWS warnings . . . without realising what he was doing. On the other hand, a distinguished panel of medical specialists, having examined [the driver] and studied all the available evidence, have concluded that, on the balance of probabilities [the driver's] behaviour was due to a rare but well recognised medical condition . . ., I believe he should be given the benefit of any doubt. But whatever the cause, the BR AWS was ineffective in preventing the collision.'

② Protecting the Stranded Train

The date was 22 October 1979. The weather was quite reasonable for the time of year but on board the 08.44 passenger train from Glasgow to Dundee things were not going well. By the time the train passed Longforgan signalbox, about six miles short of its destination, it was already 25 minutes late due to mechanical difficulties with the diesel locomotive, No 25083. Power had been lost intermittently on the journey but after the driver had reset and isolated the earth fault switch he found he could obtain power satisfactorily, and a fitter at Perth said that it would be in order for the train to continue to Dundee.

After leaving Perth the train made the normal station stops at Errol and Invergowrie, but on restarting from the latter something seemed to be holding the train. The driver stopped just beyond the platform and examined the locomotive. The brakes appeared to be binding on the leading bogie and as he could not free them he decided to continue the journey, hoping to be able to reach Dundee, only three miles away. However, when he had travelled only a few hundred yards one of the traction motors was seen to be on fire, so the train was stopped again. It was then standing on the curve along the bank of the Firth of Tay, with five coaches. The engine had been shut down and after the usual sounds of the journey everything was quiet and

still, almost eerily so, with the silence punctuated only by the cries of wheeling gulls. The passengers may have felt a slight irritation at the further delay but they surely didn't feel vulnerable sitting there waiting.

Suddenly in the distance behind them could be heard the deep throb of a Class 47 locomotive being worked hard with the roar of its engine becoming ever more insistent. The guard and secondman of the 08.44 looked on horrified and helplessly as the 09.35 express from Glasgow to Aberdeen burst into view round the curve and rushed on unchecked towards them. Seconds later it hurtled into an appalling collision with their own train.

The force of the impact threw the last two coaches of the standing train over the sea wall on to the muddy foreshore, killing both occupants of the last coach. The cab of the Class 47 was completely crushed and both the driver and secondman were killed. One other passenger was fatally injured. It was fortunate that the 08.44 was not heavily loaded or the death toll would inevitably have been greater. It was also fortunate that no train was approaching on the opposite line. Nevertheless 51 people had to be taken to hospital, where 13 were detained, including four with serious injuries.

The guard and secondman of the 08.44 were astonished

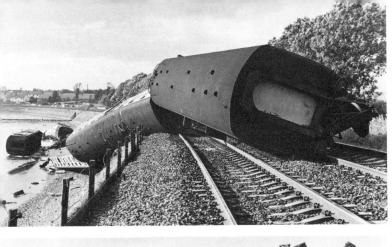

when the second train approached. How could it be? The signalling should surely have prevented it and safeguarded their train. They must have felt much as the crew of the Up Scotch sleeper felt when their train stood short of steam just north of Ais Gill summit, near Kirkby Stephen, on the night of 1 September 1913 and they heard the ominous sound of another Up Scotch express rapidly bearing down on them after it had overrun the Danger signals at Mallerstang. Or similarly at Winsford, near Crewe, in 1948 when an up express was stopped in mid-section by a soldier pulling the communication cord, and was run into by a following postal express.

Such rear-end collisions are becoming rarer, thanks to automatic warning signalling and modern electrical safety-controls in signalboxes, but at one time they were much more frequent, particularly in the 19th century. A second line of defence was therefore devised to safeguard a stranded train if a following one should pass the signalbox in rear in error. The 1883 Rule Book said:

'When a train is stopped out of course from any cause the guard must immediately go back to stop any following train, exhibiting a hand Danger signal, and place detonators on the line, one at 400 yards, one at 800 yards and two at 1,200 yards from his train.' (Railway detonators, also known as fog signals, are small devices intended to be fixed to the top of a rail in an emergency. They are exploded

This page:
Scenes of horror alongside the Firth of Tay on 22 October 1979 after the 09.35 express from Glasgow to Aberdeen had run at full speed into the 08.44 Glasgow-Dundee, which had broken down. The forces unleashed in a high-speed crash are clearly demonstrated here. Fortunately the tide was out and there were not many passengers in the stationary train. Spanphoto

27

by the wheels of a locomotive passing over them, and warn the locomen of a hazard ahead.)

Exactly 100 years later the Rules said much the same but in rather more words. And of course telephones could be used to give earlier warning if there were any nearby. Apart from that nothing had changed much in that direction. Efforts had been concentrated on trying to ensure that a second train did not pass the signalbox in rear in error, reducing the reliance on the other, rather more archaic, forms of train protection.

But why were the arrangements for train protection by detonator ineffective at Invergowrie? The answer is that they were ineffective for the same reason that they had been ineffective so many times previously — the time factor. In principle, as soon as a train stops out of course, owing to failure or derailment for example, the guard should rush off back down the line the instant it stops, with his detonators and flags or lamp, to stop any train approaching. There shouldn't be one of course; the signalling should see to that. But in theory this procedure should be followed just in case, and based on bitter experience.

In practice however it is not like that. Recent history provides few examples where such action on a guard's part has prevented a collision, and an examination of the procedures laid down in the Rule Book shows why. The guard is told that:

'If a train is stopped by accident, failure, obstruction or other exceptional cause and any other line is obstructed, or there is reason to believe this is likely, the first duty of the traincrew is to protect such lines . . . by the quickest possible means . . . when the train comes to a stand the

Above:
Inside a typical manually-operated signalbox. Pictured here is Summit Tunnel signalbox on the ex-L&Y main line from Wakefield to Manchester. The block instruments on the shelf show that the signalman has given 'Line Clear' to the next signalman in rear, and has received 'Line Clear' from the next signalman beyond. Between the block instruments is a switch to allow the signalbox to be closed during quiet periods; it puts the signalboxes at each side into through communication with each other. Below the block shelf on a smaller shelf are indicators showing whether signals out of the signalman's sight are 'On' (Danger or Caution) or 'Off' (Clear).
British Railways (LMR)

Below:
Ancient but effective. A detonator, fixed to the rail by thin strips of lead. It is exploded by the pressure of a wheel passing over it, and the noise warns the driver of an unexpected hazard ahead. Author

driver and guard must confer ... and ascertain whether any other line is obstructed or damaged; if it is the appropriate protection arrangements must be carried out.

Trainmen, when carrying out protection, must exhibit a hand Danger signal and must place detonators . . . on the obstructed line as follows:

   1 detonator ¼ mile from the obstruction
   1 detonator ½ mile from the obstruction
   3 detonators 1 mile from the obstruction (1¼ miles where permissible speed is 100mph or above)

If, before the trainman reaches the full distance, he comes to a signalbox or telephone, he must inform the signalman of the circumstances.'

It can be seen from this extract from the Rule Book that the traincrew's first concern is to see if *any other line* is obstructed. This is exactly as it should be because whilst their own train is protected by the signalling system, an accidental obstruction of an adjoining line may not be so protected and there would be nothing to prevent another train on such a line from running into the wreckage. But in order to find out if any other line is obstructed the guard must walk along the train to see the driver, who should be walking back to meet the guard. If they find that no other line is obstructed (the normal result in the case of the commonest stoppage, engine failure) the urgency of the situation is reduced and they then confer to decide how the failure is to be dealt with. In some cases the driver is likely to say that he expects to be able to rectify the defect within a few minutes, therefore there is no point in the guard setting off to protect his train. He would not have time to get very far before the train was ready to depart and it would only cause additional delay. If the driver is unable to rectify the defect, then the guard will set off to protect his train, and possibly also to seek assistance if it is more effective for him to do so in rear of his train rather than by the driver walking forward.

It can be seen, therefore, how time races by before the guard's protection in rear becomes effective. Possibly 10 minutes to walk down the train, confer with the driver, and return. Another 10 minutes to get at least half a mile from his train in order to give the driver of a wrongly approaching train a reasonable chance of stopping before reaching the stranded train. It is quite likely that if an error has occurred somewhere the second train will be on the scene in less than 20 minutes. Only a few minutes separated the two trains in the Invergowrie collision, and the guard of the stranded train had not even got beyond the rear of his own train. Beyond 20 minutes other safety precautions come into play. The signalmen would have become alert to the possibility of there being something wrong in the section. All trains would be stopped and the driver of the first train in the opposite direction would be told by the signalman to take his train forward cautiously, so that if his line was obstructed he would be able to stop in time.

This procedure would eventually have taken place in the section between the signalboxes at Buckingham Junction (Dundee) and Longforgan, but before it was due to be applied the fatal error had been made. However, before examining the circumstances of that fatal error, it may be appropriate to examine the safeguards which have been devised over the years to make the signalling system more and more foolproof. Let us consider the sort of errors that might occur.

1 *By the driver missing the signals at the signalbox in rear and proceeding into the forward section towards the stranded train at full speed.*
   The Automatic Warning System (AWS) was devised to help drivers to observe signals, as explained in the

Above:

A LNER block instrument, made by Tyer & Co.
1 **Repeater indicator, worked by the signalman at the next signalbox beyond. The inscription 'Train on Line' means the same as 'Train in Section'.**
2 **Indicator worked by this signalman, by rotating handle (4).**
3 **The wheel of the Welwyn Control.**
4 **Rotating handle, for placing the block indicator needle in different positions.**
5 **'Tapper', for sending bell signals to the next signalman.**
6 **Signal indication repeater, for a colour-light signal out of sight of the signalman.**
7 **Signal arm repeater, for a semaphore signal out of sight of the signalman. He must observe the repeater each time he moves the signal lever to ensure that the signal arm obeys the lever.**
British Railways (LMR)

previous chapter. It had already been installed at the Longforgan Distant signal, which is a colour-light.
2 *By the signalman making an error and thinking that a train had already passed clear of the forward section whilst in reality it was still there; then clearing all his signals for a second train.*
The Absolute Block signalling system, as installed between Longforgan and Buckingham Junction signalboxes, is based on the use of block telegraph instruments and bells for passing messages between adjacent signalmen. It is operated in accordance with the Absolute Block regulations, as follows:

Before clearing his signals for a train the signalman must send the appropriate 'is line clear?' bell signal to the

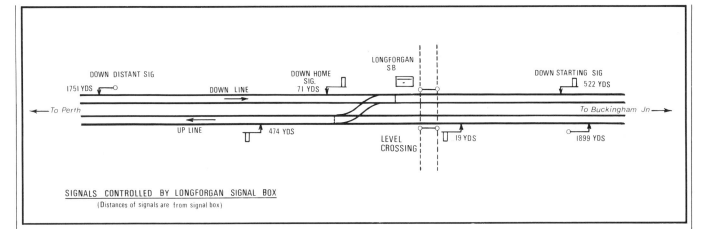

SIGNALS CONTROLLED BY LONGFORGAN SIGNAL BOX
(Distances of signals are from signal box)

signalman at the other end of the forward section. If the line *is* clear the second signalman must repeat the bell signal back to the first signalman and place the telegraph needle on his block instrument to the 'line clear' position. This 'line clear' indication is repeated on a duplicate instrument in the first signalbox and is the authority to the first signalman to clear his signals. As the train passes the first signalbox the signalman there must send the bell signal 'train entering section'. The second signalman then moves the needle on his block instrument to 'train in section'. When the train passes the second signalbox the signalman there sends back the bell signal 'train out of section' and puts the needle to its normal position. The way is now clear for another train.

The actual Absolute Block regulation is necessarily rather more wordy than that, but the above is, in essence, what happens. Provided the signalmen carry out the procedures correctly and are alert, it is absolutely safe, as has been proved times without number over a century or more, but it puts a premium on human nature, and occasionally errors occur. Such errors by their very nature are potentially calamitous and Signal Engineers have

devised various safeguards over the years, sometimes used separately and sometimes in conjunction with each other, depending on the importance of the signalbox and the density of traffic. The safeguards installed between Longforgan signalbox and Buckingham Junction signalbox at the time of the accident were:

1 The Starting signal at Longforgan was electrically locked at Danger and could not be cleared unless the signalman at Buckingham Junction had placed his block instrument to 'line clear'. Once a line-clear release had been obtained, and the signal lever had been pulled in order to clear the signal, and had then been replaced to return the signal to Danger after the train had passed, the signal could not again be cleared until a new line-clear release had been given.

Below:
Longforgan signalbox in September 1986. Class 26 diesel No 26034 running light has just passed the Down Home signal on its way from Perth to Dundee. Author

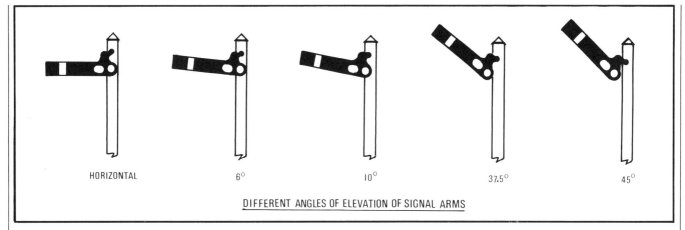

HORIZONTAL   6°   10°   37.5°   45°

DIFFERENT ANGLES OF ELEVATION OF SIGNAL ARMS

2 In order to ensure that the Starting signal was put back to Danger after each train and became electrically locked, a mechanical interlock (known as sequential locking) was provided which locked the Home signal at Danger until the Starting signal lever was replaced.

3 The Home Signal at Longforgan was provided with an electrical contact which prevented the signalman there from placing his block indicator to 'line clear' unless the signal was at Danger.

This combination of line-clear release on the Starting signal, sequential locking and electrical controls required that all the signals at Longforgan were replaced to Danger and that a fresh line-clear release was obtained, before a second train could be allowed to proceed.

There was a further safeguard. Once the block instrument at Buckingham Junction had been placed to 'train in section', it could not be turned to another position until the train had arrived there and had operated an electrical circuit on the track (known as a track circuit), thus effectively preventing a second train from being allowed to come before the first one had cleared the section. (This is known as Welwyn Control.)

With all those safeguards installed it is obvious that something very unusual happened at Longforgan on the day in question. The signalman was operating his equipment correctly, and all his signals were at Danger protecting the 08.44 Glasgow-Dundee, which was in the section ahead, when the following train approached about 10 minutes later. The driver of that train, the 09.35 Glasgow-Aberdeen, will have received an AWS warning at the Distant signal, and he responded correctly, bringing his train nearly to a stand at the Home signal before the signalman cleared it to allow the train to draw down towards the Starting signal 500 yards away in order to await the clearance of the previous train and the acceptance of this one by the signalman at Buckingham Junction. What went wrong then is not clear, because both the driver and secondman were killed and vital evidence is unobtainable. According to the Rule Book the train should have drawn slowly past the Home signal, and as it approached the signalbox the driver should have been watching to see if the signalman wanted him to stop there to give him a message (about a need to travel cautiously in the section ahead for example). If there was no such indication from the signalman the driver should have continued to draw forward slowly, taking his train over the level crossing and stopping just beyond it so that the guard could go to the signalbox to remind the signalman that the train was standing there. He should not have drawn down to the Starting signal.

What actually happened, according to the evidence of the signalman and the guard, followed the instructions in the Rule Book very closely, except for the last fatal act. The guard was travelling in the rear coach and he looked out of his near-side window as the train was just approaching Longforgan signalbox at walking pace. He saw the Home signal move to the Clear position, after which the train continued slowly past the signal and over the level crossing. A moment later the train started to accelerate, and when he looked out again he saw the Starting signal 30-40 yards away. It appeared to be 'half-cocked', that is to say it was not horizontal but was not giving a proper 'Off' (ie Clear) indication. He described it as a 'poor Off'. At the subsequent Department of Transport Public Inquiry he gave his impression of the extent to which the signal arm was above horizontal as he saw it, using a full-size mock-up of a signal arm. He placed it at an angle of 7.4° — hardly 'half-cock', which would require something of the order of 20/25%. In his evidence the guard said that at the time he had not really thought about whether the signal was Clear or not; he knew the driver to be a most experienced and competent man and felt that he would not have passed the signal if it had not been properly 'Off'. In retrospect he realised that the signal was certainly not giving a proper 'Off' indication and he thought that he must have assumed at the time that the signal had been cleared and returned to Danger by the signalman and that the arm had not returned properly to the horizontal position. It is a pity that the guard's evidence on this aspect was somewhat muddled because he was the only surviving witness who had a close view of the signal. Should he have taken some emergency action at the time? It is very difficult to say yes, because the guard did not see the signal when the driver was looking at it. Secondly, when he did look out he had a much less perfect view of it than the driver, and thirdly, he was entitled to rely on the driver's judgement. It is almost unknown for a guard to query a driver's judgement in such circumstances, and although the guard in retrospect thought that he must have assumed at the time that the signal *had* been cleared for the train, and had then been replaced to Danger (without the arm going correctly to horizontal) in the five seconds or so that had elapsed between the driver passing it and the guard looking out at it, such an assumption was not unreasonable either at the time or subsequently. Finally, Maj Rose, the Inspecting Officer who held the Public Inquiry, attached no blame to the guard; a conclusion from which it is difficult to dissent.

The signalman's evidence was similar to the guard's. He said he had replaced the Starting signal after the passage of the previous train, the 08.44 Glasgow-Dundee, and he saw it clearly go back correctly to Danger. The following train, the 09.35 Glasgow-Aberdeen, drew slowly past his signalbox and he thought he might have waved to the locomen. He certainly waved at the guard. As the train approached the Starting signal it started to pick up speed and went past the signal, which as far as he could see was still at Danger. He

Right:
How should the driver interpret this Distant signal? Class 31 No 31423 passes with the 11.33 Norwich-Birmingham on 22 January 1983. John C. Baker

went down on to the track and saw that from there the signal arm appeared to be slightly raised, about 4°.

It will remain for ever a mystery as to why the driver of the 09.35 went past Longforgan's Starting signal at Danger. Could the driver really have taken it for a Clear indication? As soon as the Home signal was cleared (ie moved to the Clear position) he would almost certainly have looked forward to see if the Starting signal was going to be cleared also, and it is evident that at that point he did not think that the Starting signal *was* clear, because he continued to draw forward slowly, past the signalbox and over the level crossing, and as he still did not accelerate it can be deduced that he still thought that the Starting signal was at Danger, or at least that he was undecided as to whether it was at Danger or at Clear. At this point along the line he should have stopped to allow the guard to go to the signalbox, as provided for in the Rules, but for some reason he continued to draw forward slowly. He may have thought that there was a track circuit between the Home signal and the Starting signal, which would have avoided the need for him to stop to allow the guard to go to the signalbox. The existence of such track circuits is indicated at the signal by a white diamond plate fixed to the signal post, but because trains were so rarely stopped at Longforgan it is possible that the situation had never previously arisen for the driver. According to the evidence of both the guard and the signalman the train did not start to accelerate until it was approaching the Starting signal. Possibly the driver had looked away from the signal for some reason and then when he looked up he may have decided that the signal was supposed to be Clear. That seems to be the most likely explanation but we can never be certain. No one will ever know exactly what took place in the driving cab in those last few moments before the fatal mistake was made. Nor shall we ever know whether the driver's assistant concurred with the driver's view, but we do know from experience that a driver's assistant will rarely query his driver's actions or decisions, and there is no evidence on which we can attach any blame to him in this case.

It is fortunately quite rare for accidents to be caused by

Right:
A device which places detonators on the rail when the signalman moves a lever. They may be provided for last-minute emergency purposes, or to act routinely in conjunction with a Danger signal. Ian Allan Library

drivers going past 'half-cocked' signals which are supposed to be at Danger. However, there was such an accident at Winwick Junction, just north of Warrington, on 11 July 1967 when a diesel multiple-unit train went past a 'half-cocked' signal of 17° at Winwick Quay signalbox and collided with a freight train, fortunately without fatalities; but with so few accidents from such a cause it is difficult to justify heavy expenditure on remedial measures. AWS-type magnets at Starting signals, or co-acting detonators, would provide reasonable safeguards but to treat all Starting signals like that would be to incur unjustifiably heavy expenditure. The 'half-cock' problem does not arise with colour-light signals, but to replace all semaphore Starting signals with colour-light signals would be a very expensive solution. Radio would also provide a possible safeguard if the equipment were sufficiently sophisticated to enable the signalman to contact the driver in the relatively short time available, yet still leave time for the driver to stop his train before colliding with the train in front — a total of only two or three minutes in the case of the Invergowrie accident. The possibility of another 'Invergowrie' will diminish as the use of radio and colour-light signalling spreads, but it will be around for a long time yet.

This accident has brought into the spotlight a number of important Rules and it would now be appropriate to have a look at them in more detail.

When is a semaphore signal properly 'Off'?
Rule C. 3.2.1. says 'arm raised or lowered 45°', whilst there is a technical tolerance which allows the arm to be anywhere between a minimum of 37½° and maximum of 65°. Where signals are a long way from signalboxes, expansion and contraction of the operating wire in hot and cold weather can make a substantial difference in the extent to which the arm moves when the signal lever is pulled. Wire adjusters are normally provided in the case of signals which are a long way from the signalbox so that the signalman can adjust the tension of the wire to compensate for the effect of temperature variations. Where the signal is out of his sight an electrical indicator, known as a 'repeater', is provided in the signalbox to show the position of the signal arm. It is usually a three-position indicator showing 'On', 'Wrong' and 'Off'. There is a 5° tolerance before 'Wrong' is shown. The signalman is required by Rule to observe the signal arm or its repeater every time he operates a lever, to make sure it responds correctly. If it does not do so, and if he is unable to rectify matters by using his wire adjuster, the signal must be treated as being defective. (At the time of the accident there was neither wire adjuster nor repeater for the Starting signal at Longforgan.)

In practice, however, the driver is presented with a wide variety of signal-arm positions, usually around 45° for signals near the signalbox but occasionally going as low as 25° or 30° for more distant ones, especially on a hot sunny morning after a cold night. What is the driver to do? The Rule Book clearly says 45°. It also clearly says that a signal imperfectly exhibited must be treated as a Danger signal, but this is where theory and practice divide. Drivers know from experience how to judge whether a signal can safely be considered to be 'Off' but there is obviously an area from 30/25° downwards where increasing doubts ought to arise in a driver's mind and where he ought to be querying the

Right:
The white diamond-shaped plate on Settle Junction's Up Starting Signal tells drivers that their trains are on a track circuit at that point and that they do not need to go to the signalbox to remind the signalman of their presence if they are stopped there by the signal being at red. Author

matter with the signalman. However, drivers do not always stop to do so, as is demonstrated perhaps by the Invergowrie accident and certainly by the Winwick Junction accident. It is too easy to assume that anything other than horizontal must have been pulled by the signalman; perhaps because that assumption is usually correct.

When the Starting signal is at danger the Home signal must not be taken 'Off' for an approaching train until the train is close to the Home signal and has been brought nearly to a stand.

This rule, of very ancient lineage (it was in the Rule Book 100 years ago), is designed to avoid a driver overlooking the danger message of the Starting signal. It is well understood by drivers and is applied day in/day out, times without number. However, to be absolutely safe it needs to be applied meticulously by the signalman so that the driver is in no doubt as to its message — you may pass the Home signal but be prepared to stop at the signalbox; the Starting signal is at Danger. Even this procedure was not absolutely safe at Longforgan on 22 October 1979, but we shall never know why. The Rule was certainly correctly applied by the signalman, but there can be an area of doubt in the application of the Rule. If the signalman comes to be in a position to clear all his signals just as the train is

Top:
Britain's worst ever railway disaster occurred at Quintinshill on the Caledonian Railway, near Gretna Green, in 1915, when 227 people were killed, mainly soldiers. The scene is partly obscured in this photograph by smoke rising from the remains of the burnt-out troop train. If the rules had been properly carried out the accident would not have happened.
British Railways (LMR)

Above:
Quintinshill 58 years later, even after all modern safeguards had been applied. Fortunately only freight trains were involved when one ran into the back of another which was standing at the Starting signal. The driver of the second train admitted dozing off after sighting the Distant signal at Caution and agreed that he must have cancelled the AWS warning before falling asleep. G. Kinghorn

approaching the signalbox what is the driver to assume? And how far away does the train have to be before the driver can be sure that the clearance of the Home signal means that the line ahead is now clear? Drivers would normally be specially alert if they were to pass a Distant signal at Caution and then see the Home signal 'Off' some distance away, but if the Home signal is cleared just as they are approaching it, it is giving one of two radically opposing messages:

1 You may pass the Home signal, and the line ahead is clear, or

2 You may pass the Home signal, but the line ahead is *not* clear;

although strictly speaking it is saying 'You may pass me but I'm saying nothing about the state of things ahead. You must look out for yourself'. Hence the need for special care, of which drivers are very well aware. It might be thought that semaphore Stop signals could only give two messages — 'Stop', and 'Go' — but as we have seen they can give a variety of messages depending on how they are operated in relation to the position of the train.

There was an accident involving the operation of the Home signal, which occurred at Kirby Cross, between Colchester and Walton-on-the-Naze on 5 April 1981, when an electric multiple-unit passed the Starting signal at Danger and collided head-on, fortunately at low speed, with an approaching train on the single line ahead. The conclusion of the Public Inquiry was that the signalman had cleared his Home signal too soon and that the driver had overlooked the Starting signal. In passing, it is interesting to note that a co-acting detonator-placer was installed at the Starting signal, but it was ineffective because it was badly worn.

The Rule Book attempts to lay down a code of practice which will enable trains to be worked safely and efficiently in all circumstances, but there are two unofficial customs which have been in widespread use for many years and they concern this particular rule. The first one is designed to help the driver to know whether the section ahead is still blocked when the Home signal is cleared just as he is approaching it. When the section ahead is not clear, the signalman will pull the lever of the Home signal quite slowly and deliberately, causing the signal arm to move slowly. Drivers seeing this understand that the section ahead is not clear, and act accordingly. The second unofficial custom is designed to assist drivers, who have been almost stopped at the Home signal, to know whether the Starting signal is 'Off' or not when it is out of sight. At such places it is often the practice for the signalman to lean out of the signalbox window and give the 'all right' hand signal to the driver, meaning: 'I have cleared the Starting signal'. If there is no hand signal, it can be taken to mean

that the Starting signal is still at Danger. It was a useful practice in the days of heavy, loose-coupled trains because it enabled the driver to control his train more smoothly. These unofficial practices are only safe if everyone knows what they mean, but arms in the air can be misleading, as a tractor driver found to his cost at Catholme level crossing near Wichnor Junction, between Burton-on-Trent and Tamworth, on 15 February 1969, when he misunderstood the signalman's hand signal not to cross the line and drove his tractor and trailer into the path of a three-car diesel multiple-unit which was approaching at 60mph.

When a train is brought to a stand owing to a Stop signal being at Danger, a member of the traincrew must go to the signalbox to remind the signalman of the presence of the train.

This is another link with the early days of railways. It does not apply if the train is standing on a track circuit (indicated by a white diamond plate on the signal post) but it did apply at Longforgan because there was no track circuit between the Home signal and the Starting signal. The train should have been stopped just beyond the level crossing to allow the guard to go back to the signalbox, and the procedure would then have been for the guard to have written details in the signalbox train register book and for the signalman to have placed a metal lever collar on the Home signal lever to physically prevent him from pulling the lever and to remind him of the standing train. With the widespread installation of track circuits, accidents caused by failure to carry out this rule are much less frequent than they once were, but the worst disaster in the history of railways in Great Britain, at Quintinshill, just north of Gretna Junction, in 1915, would have been prevented if this Rule had been properly carried out.

But to return to the question with which this chapter started — how to protect the stranded train. Many of the safeguards already explained were not devised specifically with the safety of a stranded train in mind, but rather with the protection of trains stopped by signals, or otherwise, in the normal course of train operation.

Furthermore they only apply on lines worked in the traditional manner with lineside signalboxes using the Absolute Block Signalling system. On lines equipped with

Left:
Twin built-in electrically-lit tail-lamps seen here on a Swiss Federal Railways coach at Basle. Note the power-operated plug-type sliding doors. Author

Above:
The Bardic tail lamp, operated by a rechargeable electric battery. The lamp is reliable, and a fully-charged lamp will operate for 40 hours. BR have had several hundred in use for quite a few years, but are looking for one that is cheaper and requires less-frequent recharging. Ian Allan Library

Below:
An experimental battery-operated tail lamp, in use as a buffer-stop lamp at Leeds. Author

Below right:
Another type of battery-operated tail lamp, made by the Lamp Manufacturing and Railway Supplies Ltd. It incorporates a light-sensitive cell. Author

modern signalling and continuous track circuiting, as is now the case on most trunk routes, the stranded train protects itself. By occupying a track circuit, it causes the signal in rear to be held at Danger. But even this may not be enough, as was demonstrated on a line that runs through the very heart of peaceful commuter-land from Marylebone to High Wycombe. During a snowstorm on the morning of 11 December 1981 one diesel multiple-unit ran into the back of another which had been brought to a stand by tree branches bending low over the line due to the weight of snow on them. The driver and three passengers were killed. The circumstances of this collision, near Seer Green, are explained in detail in Chapter 6, but the first train had only been standing for a few minutes when the collision occurred — insufficient time for detonator protection by the guard to be effective.

Could anything more be done to protect a standing train? There are two aspects to this — one is to make a standing train more conspicuous to another train approaching it, the driver of which knows it to be somewhere in the vicinity; the other is to give emergency, last minute warning to an approaching driver that he is running into unknown but imminent danger.

There was a long-held belief that it was perfectly satisfactory for trains to sneak about unnoticed like thieves in the night and that there was no need to illuminate the front and rear, other than to tell signalmen what class a train was, and that it had not left part of itself behind in the section. The tail lamp came to be vital, not to warn a following train, but to tell the signalman in the days before continuous track circuiting that it was complete and that the section it had just passed through was clear and safe for another train to pass. The view was firmly held that there was no need for trains to be conspicuous, as the signalling system would ensure that they were kept apart, and that men working on the line should look out for their own safety by keeping their eyes and ears open. Traces of these beliefs still linger on, for how else can one explain the railway's love affair with the oil-lit tail lamp, which is only slowly going out of use, or the miserable little lights on the front of locomotives and multiple-units, which are only gradually being reinforced by the use of penetrating headlights? Having said that, the oil tail lamp has many advantages — it is cheap to make, easy to use, has low running costs, and does not go dim if the train's batteries run down. It is very reliable and gives quite a good light too, being clearly visible at half a mile on a clear night on straight track (and no matter how good a tail light is, it cannot be seen round corners). However, a number of factors are combining to push it into the museum — the rise in the cost of lamp oil, the cost of storage and distribution, fears about future difficulties in obtaining supplies of lamp oil when BR is the only large user, and the heavy labour cost of cleaning, filling and trimming oil lamps. But more than anything it is BR's foresight in equipping nearly all locomotives and multiple-units with twin electrically-operated, built-in tail lamps that is forcing the issue (coupled with the huge reduction in the number of freight trains, which were the heaviest user of oil tail lamps) and the realisation since the Rule was altered to require both to be lit, that twin tail lights present a much more visually arresting and easily recognisable image than a single light. The problem that remains concerns locomotive-hauled trains. It is to be hoped that all new coaches designed for locomotive haulage will have twin built-in tail lamps, but the existing coaches will be in use for many years yet, and freight and parcels trains have to be provided for. The contrast between twin electric tail lights and a single oil-lit tail light is too great to accept and the search is on for an acceptable substitute. Paradoxically, the problem is made more difficult because the numbers required are not huge, therefore they do not benefit from the much lower unit production cost which would apply if larger numbers were required. To put two on each train would not double the

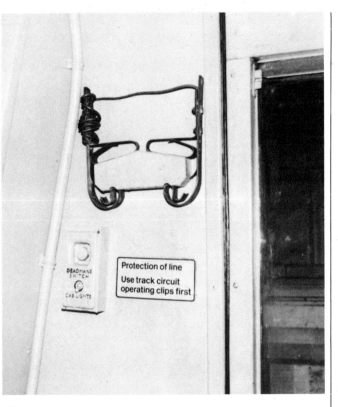

Above:
A track circuit operating clip in position in the driver's cab of a DMU, ready for emergency use. Author

Below:
A track circuit operating clip in use, short-circuiting the electric current of the track circuit and activating automatic safeguards. Ian Allan Library

total cost but it would create difficult handling problems. Battery-lit tail lamps are quite cumbersome and heavy and often have to be handled from ground level and it is unrealistic to suggest that there should be two on each train. It would, however, be reasonable to have two on every passenger train, as is widely practised on continental railways, but for other trains it rather appears that a single tail lamp has to be accepted, with as bright a light as can be realistically achieved. It is often suggested that tail lamps should flash on and off in order to be more visually arresting than a steady light, and this may provide the answer where only one lamp is used, and might help to avoid those rear-end collisions which occasionally occur on lines known as 'permissive' where freight trains are allowed to follow one behind the other. Even on the

continent there is no universal practice — some railways use flashing tail lamps, some do not. BR has been testing a number of types of electric battery-operated tail lamps which emit a flashing light, one of which is extensively used on the Deutsche Bundesbahn (the German Federal Railway). Another type has been developed by the BR Research Department in conjunction with private industry, and has eight LEDs (light-emitting diodes). BR hopes to replace all oil tail lamps by the late 1980s with electric battery-operated lamps.

The guards of the stranded trains at Invergowrie and Seer Green must have wished they had some means of alerting the drivers of the approaching trains that they were running into danger. Radio may seem at first sight to be an answer, but would it have been of practical value with so

Left:
The emergency services at work after the Micheldever accident of 26 January 1985, when Class 33/1 No 33104 running light engine wrong-line from Worting Junction collided with the stranded 03.30 Bournemouth-Woking electric multiple unit which it had been sent to rescue. Simon N. Rowley

use in a lifetime's career? Would it be readily available for use at literally a second's notice? (in other words guards would have to carry it with them at all times). Would it work without fail? Would guards know how it worked? Small distress-flares of the type used by mountaineers and sailors would meet most of the requirements — they are cheap, could be renewed periodically, would be available at a second's notice and would immediately alert the driver of an approaching train, but would guards feel happy to be carrying them around in their pockets? Probably not, but the same objections could be made against detonators, which guards have always carried around, and a dozen detonators are surely more hazardous than one or two small flares. However, railway traditions die very hard and flares are unlikely to be adopted unless there is a sudden spate of 'Invergowries', or unless supplies of detonators dry up — a distinct possibility. Since the use of detonators for fog signalling was discontinued in 1981, BR's requirements for supplies of detonators have declined to such an extent that it is hardly worth a manufacturer's while to produce them. What is more, they do not find favour with the Railway Inspectorate owing to the risk of injury to the user by flying fragments, nor with the police because they are stolen from railway premises in quite large numbers. So one day flares may replace detonators, and another piece of railway history will be consigned to the museum. It is interesting to recall that Col Pringle, reporting on the Ais Gill crash of 1913, discussed at some length the use of flares as a means of protecting a stranded train, in fact he made a firm recommendation that flares should be carried in all guards' vans, but before the railway companies could properly consider this proposal, events were overtaken by the more urgent worries of World War 1.

The best safeguard of all is modern signalling with AWS and continuous track-circuiting. Track circuiting also allows the use of a simple but effective piece of emergency warning equipment, carried in every driving cab and brakevan, consisting of two spring clips connected by a short piece of wire, and known appropriately as a track circuit operating clip. When one of the clips is placed over one rail and the other clip over the other rail the weak electric current of the track circuit is diverted through the wire, resulting in a short-circuit that is detected by the signalling equipment, which in turn switches to Danger the signal in rear (or holds it at Danger if it is already showing a red aspect). It also alerts the signalman to the fact that an emergency may have arisen. Initially it proved quite difficult to get traincrews to use track circuit operating clips as an instinctive reaction in an emergency, a situation commented on in a number of Department of Transport Railway Inspecting Officers' Reports, and the problem was only solved by prominently displaying a notice in every driving cab, alongside the track circuit operating clip, saying 'Protection of line — use track circuit operating clip first'. At first there were doubts as to the effectiveness of the clip, but extensive tests in different parts of the country, at various times of the year, showed an effectiveness of over 99% — better even than detonators.

Detonators may seem old-fashioned, indeed they are old-fashioned, but they have many advantages — they are cheap, quick and easy to use, foolproof, effective, small and easily carried, instantly available for use and have a long

little time available? There may have been time for the signalmen concerned in both accidents to have contacted the drivers with an emergency call, but there was surely insufficient time for the train crews of the stranded trains to have contacted the drivers of the approaching trains — they would have lost vital seconds in getting to their radio equipment and more in making contact; but it is a facility which *could* be valuable if designers of radio equipment could incorporate such a feature.

There are problems in designing emergency warning equipment if it is only to be used on very rare occasions. The circumstances of Invergowrie are comparatively rare, which means that the vast majority of guards are never faced with them. Is it a practical proposition to provide emergency equipment that 19 out of 20 guards may never

Right:
BR's standard oil tail-lamp at the back of the 15.40 (Sundays) Carlisle-Euston.
Author

life. Whilst their use on BR is declining they are still invaluable in some situations where there is at present no obvious alternative. One of their many uses is the secondary protection of a stranded train. The main protection, against the approach of a train which ought not to be there, has already been described. The secondary protection is against the assisting locomotive, which has a right to be approaching, but whose driver may not know exactly where the stranded train is standing, and whose forward view may be limited during fog, or at night, or by the curvature of the line in cuttings or through overbridges, etc. To guard against the possibility of a collision between the assisting locomotive and a stranded train, detonators are placed on the line 300yd from the train in both directions. In addition, the guard or driver of the stranded train is required to travel with the driver of the assisting locomotive to guide him safely towards the train. This procedure should be foolproof but occasionally there are collisions, through carelessness, or because the Rules were not being properly observed or even because the assisting locomotive was being driven at too high a speed. On 23 May 1981 the locomotive of a passenger train ran out of fuel between Neath and Swansea and another locomotive was sent to assist. Both locomotives were damaged when the assisting locomotive collided with the failed one. The driver of the stranded train had failed to put down his secondary detonator protection because he thought the guard had done so. The guard of the stranded train should have preceded the assisting locomotive on foot for the last 300yd (ie from the detonators which ought to have been there but were not) but in the absence of detonators had no warning as to where he should alight, and the assisting locomotive was being driven too fast.

A somewhat similar case occurred near Micheldever on the Waterloo-Basingstoke-Southampton main line during the small hours of 26 January 1985. The 03.30 Bournemouth-Woking, consisting of three four-car electric multiple-units, and conveying a number of railway staff as passengers, struck a minor chalk slip in the cutting between the two Popham Tunnels. Some of the train's current-collector shoes were damaged and it lost power,

finally coming to a stand with the front two coaches outside the tunnel mouth. The guard went to the front of the train to confer with the driver, in accordance with the rules, and it was arranged that the guard would go back to protect his train in the rear and advise the signalman of the situation. This he did, and the signalman told him that he would arrange for a light locomotive to be sent to the front of the train, and that the guard should arrange for someone to go forward and meet it 300yd ahead. The relief locomotive, No 33104, set off from Worting Junction, running in the down direction over the Up line, initially at about 50mph but slowing down to about 25/30mph when about a mile from the disabled train. The driver was keeping a sharp lookout for the red light which should have been shown 300yd from the disabled train, when the train itself suddenly loomed up out of the darkness only a few yards away. There was no time for the driver to brake and he smashed into the stationary train at about 30mph, injuring both himself and his assistant.

The accident resulted from several failures to carry out the rules properly. The driver of the disabled train should have put down detonators 300yd in front of his train and stayed there, showing a red light, but he omitted to do either; the signalman should not have allowed the assisting locomotive to proceed towards the disabled train until he had received an assurance that there was someone at the 300yd protection point — he received no such assurance; and the assisting locomotive was being driven too fast. The fundamental principle of railway safety is that there is more than one line of defence, so that if the first line of defence fails there is a second, to act as a safety net. At Micheldever there were no fewer than three lines of defence, and all failed. Protection by the driver was the first, the signalman was the second, and the driver of the assisting locomotive the third, although he could hardly have avoided a collision in the circumstances but he might have been able to reduce its force. Each man was anxious to get the trains moving as quickly as possible and each man allowed those very worthy considerations to override the needs of safety; by no means an unusual occurrence, as these pages show.

Permanent Speed Limits

People on holiday, in Spain or Italy perhaps, may occasionally wonder, while lazing in the sun, whether everything is all right back home. Their thoughts may turn idly to the possibility of being burgled, or of having a burst water pipe. But whatever horrors they may contemplate it is unlikely that anyone in their wildest dreams would ever visualise returning home to find their house damaged by what can only be described as a low-flying train.

The 19.50 sleeping car express from Aberdeen to King's Cross on Saturday 23 June 1984, the 'Night Aberdonian', consisted of seven almost new Mk 3 sleeping cars, with a parcels van at each end of the train. The locomotive was Class 47/4 diesel-electric No 47452. It left Aberdeen on time and made its usual scheduled stops as far as Edinburgh Waverley, where the traincrew were relieved and a fresh set of men (driver and guard) took over. At 23.05, still on time, it set off on the next leg of its journey, non-stop to Newcastle.

The route from Edinburgh to Newcastle is very picturesque, particularly in its early stages where it closely follows the coast, but it suffers from an unusually large number of speed restrictions round curves, one of the most severe being a 50mph restriction through Morpeth station. Although the locomotive had a maximum permitted speed of 95mph the train was timed somewhat more slowly than this in the interest of the greater comfort of the sleeping car passengers, and it was not really necessary to travel at more than about 80mph in order to keep time, although the train could quite safely have been driven at speeds of up to 95mph on suitable stretches of the line if it had been necessary to regain lost time. However on the night of Saturday 23/Sunday 24 June 1984 it was running on time.

The journey was uneventful until the train was approaching Morpeth just before 00.40. All the speed-restricted curves had been safely negotiated, including the severe one through Berwick-upon-Tweed and over the Royal Border Bridge, but the train did not make its customary slowing as it approached Morpeth station and

Below:
Class 40 No 258 takes a northbound coal train through the curve at Morpeth on 17 July 1970. I. S. Carr

the 50mph curve. On the contrary, it continued unchecked at a speed of probably between 85 and 90mph and hurtled through Morpeth station. For a few seconds the train held the rails but then it started to overturn and left them at a tangent. The first vehicles to overturn were probably the leading two sleeping cars. The locomotive came to rest on its side against a bank, having crossed over the Down line, which it destroyed; and the two vehicles following it, a parcels van and the first sleeping car, jack-knifed behind it and came to rest on their sides across both lines, completely blocking the railway. The second sleeping car led the remainder of the train straight towards a group of bungalows, two of which were actually struck and damaged. All the sleeping cars came to rest on their sides except the last one. The residents of one of the bungalows were on holiday in Spain. The residents of the other had a rather more immediate shock.

Incredibly, not a single passenger was killed, and even more incredibly not one of the 29 who were taken to hospital was detained. It was a spectacular but extremely expensive demonstration of the safety of design of British Rail's modern sleeping cars. Only the driver and two sleeping-car attendants were detained in hospital. There were no fatalities.

But why did the driver fail to reduce speed for the Morpeth curve? Lt-Col A. G. Townsend-Rose, the Inspecting Officer who held a Public Inquiry into the accident, concluded that:

'. . . the driver had clearly failed to properly control his train. There are two possible reasons for this; that he suffered a severe bout of coughing shortly before he should have begun to reduce the train's speed (as had been suggested in the evidence given) and that he remained incapable until the train overturned. It seems that the driver had never reported to the Railway Medical Officers the fact that he suffered from an incapacitating coughing condition. In any case he had only to take his feet off the DSD pedal (the Driver's Safety Device — usually referred to as the "Deadman's Pedal") to stop the train if he had begun to cough uncontrollably and he could also have shut off power and applied the brakes very quickly. Alternatively it is possible that he became drowsy and inattentive because of the drink he had taken. Although he may have failed to reduce the train's speed sufficiently for the 65mph restriction some 13 miles north of Morpeth, he was alert enough to sound his horn . . . seven miles further on. In the last six miles approaching Morpeth at some 80mph or more he may have fallen asleep, or become so drowsy that he completely forgot about the approaching curve. I must say that I am strongly inclined to the possibility that he fell fully or nearly asleep as being the most likely.'

It is not unknown for people to feel drowsy after sitting quietly for some time, whether they have taken drink or not, and irrespective of the hour of day or night. Car drivers sometimes feel drowsy on long journeys, especially on motorways, and occasionally crashes occur as a result. Many people will recognise the feeling of involuntarily 'nodding off', in fact it is such a common experience that one might expect some kind of safeguard to be provided on a locomotive.

Everyone knows about the 'Deadman's handle' or pedal, which has to be kept depressed by the driver. If pressure is released, power is shut off and the brake is automatically applied. It is a powerful safeguard, provided on all locomotives and multiple-units, and generally very effective in case of unconsciousness and death, although these are fortunately rare occurrences. It is not, however, particularly effective in cases of drowsiness or momentary periods of light sleep when the muscles have not had time to relax sufficiently to enable the spring-loaded handle or foot-pedal to overcome the weight of the hand or foot. Whether it would be effective during a severe bout of coughing is not known. It is also susceptible to misuse, highly irregular though that might be.

Automatic Warning Signalling (AWS) is another powerful safeguard against lack of attention caused by drowsiness

Above:
The locomotive and leading vehicle of the Up 'Night Aberdonian', which came to grief on the Morpeth curve shortly after midnight on Sunday 24 June 1984. S. Miller

Top right:
A Mk 3 sleeping car. The strength of the Mk 3 body shell undoubtedly contributed to the remarkably low casualty figures, with no fatalities and not a single passenger seriously injured. British Rail

Above right:
The overturned sleepers of the 'Night Aberdonian' lie in the front garden belonging to one of the houses adjoining the line. S. Miller

Right:
A remarkable aerial photograph showing how the derailed 'Night Aberdonian' headed straight as an arrow towards the two bungalows, and narrowly avoided destroying both of them. London Express News & Feature Services

or 'nodding off'. It too is not foolproof, as we have already seen, but the sound of the warning horn as the driver passes a Caution signal is normally sufficient to bring him back to his senses, and if it does not the automatic brake will stop the train safely. Even at the end of a journey approaching a terminal station the last signal will show at least a Caution aspect, to prevent a drowsy driver from crashing at speed into the buffers. However, there were no special safeguards approaching the Morpeth curve from the north.

To see why this was so, we need to look back over the last 30 years to study the accidents that have had a bearing on this subject, and examine their special features. The first one to be considered occurred at Sutton Coldfield on 23 January 1955 when a Sunday express, the 12.15pm York-Bristol, consisting of 10 coaches hauled by Class 5 4-6-0 No 45274, which was being diverted from its normal

Above:
The scene today, after repairs to both the track and the bungalows. The severity of the curve can clearly be seen in this photograph. Author

route via Tamworth, was derailed when passing over the 30mph speed-restricted curve through the station at between 55 and 60mph. The casualty list was high by today's standards: 14 passengers and 3 railwaymen were killed. A total of 23 were detained in hospital. The salient features of this accident compared with the Morpeth derailment were:

1 Speed was only 25-30mph in excess of the restriction, and restrictions normally had a built-in safety margin to allow for drivers misjudging their speeds on locomotives not equipped with speedometers.
2 There was no 'Deadman's Pedal', as the locomotive involved was a steam locomotive.
3 The locomotive was double-manned.
4 There was no AWS on the line or on the locomotive.
5 The accident occurred at 4.13pm in full daylight on a fine clear day.
6 There were no lineside warning signs about the speed restriction.
7 There was no comfortable stuffy cab to cause the driver to 'nod-off'.

The driver and fireman were both killed and it is impossible to say why the driver overlooked the speed restriction. At that time it was not the practice on lines of the former London Midland & Scottish Railway to erect lineside signs at speed restrictions, there being no apparent need. There had been only one previous serious derailment of this type (in 1931 at Carlisle Canal Junction on the LNER) since before World War 1, and awareness of speed restrictions was considered to be part of a driver's normal route knowledge. A driver was, and still is, required to be completely familiar with a route before he is allowed to drive a train over it. However, as a result of the Sutton Coldfield accident the British Transport Commission (forerunners of British Railways) decided to erect lineside cut-out signs at the beginning of each speed restriction, depicting the speed allowed. They were intended to serve only as markers, and not as safeguards against a driver who had forgotten to reduce speed. Cut-out signs of this type were already provided on lines of the former London & North Eastern Railway. The Great Western Railway had also given some consideration to this problem and had provided illuminated notices of various types at places where speed restrictions required special emphasis, or where there were no distinctive landmarks.

When the railways were nationalised, the Railway Executive, as part of a process of reviewing the former private companies' safety arrangements with a view to standardisation, recommended the provision of indication signs at the commencement of speed restrictions where there were no landmarks or where there was experience of persistent excessive speed. It was felt that whilst illumination of the signs would improve matters, it was not essential. However, no action was taken because the new regime soon found itself faced with financial problems. In any case, the curve at Sutton Coldfield would hardly have qualified for a sign under either condition.

Some time after British Railways had decided to erect cut-out signs at the beginning of speed restrictions they decided to mark the termination point also of permanent speed restrictions on high speed lines (maximum speeds of 90mph or more), so providing an indication of every change of speed, either upwards or downwards.

The extreme rarity of this type of accident at the time (1955) might be thought not to have justified any further action; in fact it is difficult to see what more could effectively and realistically have been done, given the available technology and financial resources, apart from erecting illuminated warning signs at braking distance from speed restrictions. However, this would have been

expensive, and a driver who was sufficiently drowsy to be unaware of an approaching severe curve may well have failed to notice the warning sign. An additional safeguard was needed, of a type that the driver could not overlook, and that was to come later as we shall see.

In the Sutton Coldfield accident neither the fireman nor the guard was effective in braking the train for the curve. We cannot know what, if anything, the fireman did, but the action that the guard took to apply the brake was ineffective. We have noticed before, and we shall notice again, cases where guards were reluctant to intervene; what we do not know, and what there are no means of knowing, is the number of occasions when the guard *has* saved the day. The driver is not likely to report his own failing, and the guard is equally unlikely to report his mate.

Without additional safeguards it was both perfectly obvious and inevitable that sooner or later there would be a repeat of the Sutton Coldfield disaster, although based on experience it was likely to be many years. After all, it had been 24 years since the previous case, but as it happened there wasn't very long to wait. By coincidence, the train concerned, the 10.15pm sleeper from King's Cross to

Above left:
The driving cab of a Class 47 locomotive, the type used in the Morpeth derailment.
1 **AWS visual indicator.**
2 **Brake valve for train and locomotive.**
3 **Air brake for locomotive only.**
4 **Gauges for brake pressure, engine rpm and speed.**
5 **Power controller.**
6 **Forward, idling and reverse controller.**
7 **Warning horn.**
Ian Allan Library

Left:
'Deadman's pedal', on the floor beneath the desk of a Class 86 electric locomotive. Author

Below:
Disaster in a quiet suburb on a Sunday afternoon. The wreckage of the 12.15 York-Bristol express at Sutton Coldfield on 23 June 1955. T. Gladdy

Edinburgh, was also being diverted from its normal route because of engineering works. Approaching Lincoln on the diversionary route there is a very severe curve which is restricted to 15mph, but the train was still travelling at 55mph when it hit the curve. Seven coaches overturned, two passengers and a sleeping car attendant were killed and 49 were injured. The date was Sunday 3 June 1962, the time 12.49. Fortunately in this accident the driver survived to give his evidence. In fact his locomotive, an English Electric Type 4 2,000hp diesel-electric, was not derailed, and came to a stand in the middle of Lincoln station. He was not a regular driver of main line diesels but had taken duty specially that night to conduct the normal driver of the express over the diversionary route, as the normal driver was not acquainted with it. The conductor driver was fully aware of the speed restriction approaching Lincoln but it is thought that he may have misjudged his speed. It is easy to imagine how that could happen; drivers of steam locomotives had always been accustomed to estimating their speed by the feel of the locomotive, and by the noise and vibration. A driver who had spent perhaps 40 years on steam locomotives, and then found himself on a diesel, and who then estimated his speed in the traditional way instead of by glancing at his speedometer, could so easily overspeed in the dark, given the smoothness and quietness of a nearly new diesel locomotive with power shut off and the engine just ticking over.

However, there was clearly an element of doubt in Col Reed's mind, when he reported on the accident after holding a Public Inquiry. He concluded:

'. . . after making all possible allowances, it is difficult to accept that he had firmly intended to reduce speed to the required limit of 15mph at the junction, and that the actual speed of about 55mph was wholly due to misjudgement.'

Col Reed did not speculate what else it might have been due to. It is interesting to note from the evidence in the Report that the signalman at Sincil Bank signalbox, almost opposite the point where the derailment occurred, had not

Above:
The magical 100mph. The cut-out sign being erected for the first stretch on the East Coast main line between Stoke Summit and Lolham, which started with the summer timetable of 1964. Cloth caps were *de rigueur* in the days before high-visibility vests.
British Railways (ER)

Left:
The '125' era arrives.
The Scotsman

Right & far right:
The 60mph permanent speed restriction warning sign on the Up main line at Carlisle Kingmoor, together with its warning magnet. Author

placed his level crossing gates across the road and cleared his Home signal until the train was almost at it, yet the train passed him at about 55mph. It is obvious that the driver could not have stopped at the Home signal if it had remained at Danger. There was a lineside cut-out sign at the commencement of the curve, and one can only speculate whether a warning indicator at braking distance from the curve would have been effective, with or without an AWS magnet to remind the driver. If the overspeeding was entirely due to misjudgement it would not have been effective, but if there was some other cause, eg inattention, it might well have prevented the accident.

The guard of the express was also not the regular guard, but like the driver had come on duty specially to conduct the train over the diversion between Peterborough and Doncaster. He was travelling in the ninth vehicle and began to get worried about the speed of the train as it approached Lincoln. He rose from his seat to apply the brake but before he could do so he felt the lurch caused by the derailment. Col Reed felt that in the particular circumstances he was not to blame for not having applied the brake.

The inability to form any real conclusions about the true cause of the Lincoln derailment naturally made it more difficult to propose any remedial action. The provision of an advanced warning indicator at braking distance from the curve might have been effective but it was also felt that the element of risk would diminish as drivers became more accustomed to diesel locomotives, and that the circumstances of the Lincoln derailment were unlikely to recur. There was no real evidence to justify substantial expenditure on warning indicators all over the railway system, yet, without any further precautions, and with entire reliance upon the driver's knowledge of a route, and on his constant alertness, there remained a loophole in the railway's safety defences which, sooner or later, was bound to lead to tragedy. How long it would take was impossible to say, given the dates of previous derailments on curves — 1931, 1955 and now 1962.

When it did finally happen, on 7 May 1969, the face of British Railways had changed completely. Steam loco-motives had disappeared, colour-light signalling and AWS were widespread, and Dr Beeching had departed, leaving his shadow across the land. The circumstances of the accident were uncannily like those of the 1984 derailment at Morpeth. The train concerned, the Down 'Aberdonian' 19.40 sleeping car express from King's Cross to Aberdeen, was the sister of the one involved in 1984. The driver entered a 40mph speed-restricted curve at slightly over 80mph (85-90mph in the 1984 accident), at 01.31 (00.40 in 1984). And finally the wrecked train came to rest at the identical location — just south of Morpeth station. Truth is indeed stranger than fiction. But similarities cease there because in 1969 six people were killed and 19 seriously injured.

The Down 'Aberdonian' on 7 May 1969 left Newcastle at 01.06, seven minutes late. It consisted of 11 vehicles marshalled as follows:

1 Guard's van
2 Sleeping cars
4 Coaches
1 Guard's van
2 Sleeping cars
1 Brake coach.

All the vehicles were of Mk 1 design and they were all buckeye-coupled. The oldest was built in 1957. The locomotive was Class 55 diesel-electric 'Deltic' No 9011 *The Royal Northumberland Fusiliers*, and was double-manned by a driver and secondman who had taken over at Newcastle at the start of their turn of duty. The journey from Newcastle to the Morpeth curve was perfectly normal. The driver said in his evidence at the Public Inquiry that the night was dark but very clear. He observed all speed restrictions including one at Cramlington, and then, with all signals at Green he opened the controller fully and accelerated to 80mph. He closed the controller at the usual place for the Morpeth curve and thought that he must then have begun to think about an official letter that he had been handed when signing-on, asking for an explanation of four

minutes lost on a previous journey. He thought that he had allowed his attention to wander, and he was brought round, and made a full brake application, just as he hit the curve. The locomotive rode the curve very well (as at Lincoln in 1962) and he thought that the train had also done so safely until he looked back when the locomotive stopped, and saw the wreckage behind him. How his heart must have sunk! One cannot help but sympathise with him in his awful predicament. A few moments inattention, and a wrecked train. A heavy price for a simple human failing and an illustration yet again of the heavy responsibilities carried at that time by drivers day in and day out.

And what of the secondman? By the time he realised that the train was going too fast for the curve, and that the brakes were not being applied, they were closely approaching it. Despite an understandable unwillingness to appear to be interfering, that may be thought natural in a secondman in such conditions, he started to move across the cab of the locomotive to warn the driver, when he was thrown to the floor by the lurch of the locomotive entering the curve. He had acted too late, but the Inspecting Officer, Col J. R. H. Robertson, found that he was not to blame for that. Anyone who might be tempted to think otherwise should put himself in the secondman's shoes and ask himself whether he would have acted differently *without the benefit of hindsight*. At 84mph there were only a few seconds for him to reach a positive decision. The practice of carrying a secondman on night trains was later abandoned. It proved to be of no practical value. Accidents happened with two men in the cab and it was not unknown for both to 'nod-off', the one relying on the other to keep alert. Two men are carried in the cabs of trains travelling at over 100mph at any time, but they are both drivers and the circumstances are somewhat different, as will be discussed in a later chapter.

Morpeth 1969 proved to be a landmark in the long history of railway safety. As had happened so often before, a serious accident provided the necessary impetus for remedial action. No sensible man could any longer doubt that safety at speed-restricted curves ought to be improved if suitable means could be found of doing so. It was no longer enough just to be sure that drivers were well aware of such curves. Something was needed to guard against a moment's inattention; and by good fortune the means had become readily available. The installation of AWS was by this time proceeding rapidly and nearly all locomotives had been equipped with receiver apparatus. What could be easier than to install an AWS permanent magnet in the track just at the place where a driver would normally start to brake? Then, if the driver was inattentive the sound of the warning horn would alert him. If the driver were temporarily insensible, as may have happened in the 1984 Morpeth derailment, the train would be stopped safely by the automatic application of the brake. Either way, safety would be provided for. So why did the second Morpeth accident occur?

It is one thing to decide to install a permanent magnet on the approach to curves. Nothing easier. But Britain's railway lines are full of curves, and the approaches to major stations are often a mass of speed restrictions. To put a magnet at every one, at braking distance, would need many thousands of magnets. Acknowledgement of the warning by drivers might become routine. It might even, as some feared, become subconscious. The value of the warning might become degraded and as it is the same warning as the one received at a Caution signal, that would be an unacceptable risk. In closely-signalled areas with many speed restrictions drivers would be passing over magnets, sometimes for signals, sometimes for speed restrictions, every few hundred yards, and that could cause confusion. So it was necessary to decide which speed restrictions should be treated and which should not. And thus, the seeds of the second Morpeth accident were sown.

With the Morpeth curve very much in mind, it was felt that there were two factors in the reckoning — the speed of an approaching train and the severity of the speed

restriction. Col Robertson felt that permanent magnets should be installed on all lines where trains were allowed to travel at 75mph or more, wherever a speed restriction demanded a reduction in speed of one-third or more, eg from 90 to 60mph, or 75 to 50mph. In addition an illuminated advanced warning board should be provided 200yd beyond the magnet, braking distance being measured from the board to the start of the restriction.

There were many details of principle to be settled but by November 1972 a total of 47 installations had been completed. Year by year the figure increased until by the end of 1977 there were 318 installations in all, and the programme was complete. The precautions taken, whilst appropriate to the Down line situation at Morpeth, would not have prevented the derailments at either Sutton Coldfield or Lincoln, because in both those cases the approach speeds were limited to 60mph, yet they showed just how destructive derailments can be at that speed. It might be thought therefore that the speed conditions to be satisfied before warning equipment was installed approaching a curve were not sufficiently all-embracing, as many dangerous locations would continue to be unprotected. This was emphasised by another serious high-speed derailment on a curve near Eltham (Well Hall) station on the Southern Region on Sunday 11 June 1972, when a return excursion train from Margate entered a 20mph curve at about 65mph. The train was wrecked, five passengers and the driver were killed, and many people were seriously injured. Col Robertson, who also took this Public Inquiry, concluded that the driver had grossly impaired his ability to drive safely by drinking a considerable quantity of alcohol both before and after booking on duty ... The secondman did not know the route and could not have realised that the driver was not braking for the curve when he should have been.

The curve at Eltham would not have qualified for an Advanced Warning Indicator and permanent magnet, because the approach speed was less than 75mph, and although other safeguards were subsequently applied there, that disaster showed tragically yet again that curves on lines below 75mph could also constitute a hazard. However, at that time BR had only just started to equip high-speed lines. Nevertheless, three out of the last four accidents (Sutton Coldfield 1955, Lincoln 1962 and Eltham 1972) had occurred on relatively low-speed lines (60mph), yet in all three cases the trains were severely damaged and passengers had been killed. It might therefore have been prudent to have started planning for an extension, a second stage, for the installation of Warning Indicators and magnets, to follow completion of the first stage in 1977, but it was not done. Perhaps attention was distracted by the prominence of the drink factor in the Eltham crash, and the need to take immediate and firm measures to deal with it, but in the event it was some years before a second stage began to be considered; and before it could become effective further accidents had happened.

It may seem strange that the Down line at Morpeth was equipped, but not the Up. After all it is the same curve, with the same 50mph restriction, approached at high speed in both directions. But whereas in the Down direction in 1969 the speed limit suddenly dropped by half from 80mph to 40mph (now 50mph), in the Up direction the speed limits fall in stages, from 100mph to 80mph (for ¼ mile), and then to 70mph for ¾ mile, before the 50mph curve is reached. By the Rules of the time none of these changes in speed justified an Advanced Warning Indicator because none of them was more severe than a one-third reduction, therefore no Indicator was provided, other than the standard cut-out. There are many examples of such staged reductions on BR, known as cascades, but when the 'Morpeth Rules' were being drawn up after the 1969 derailment it was felt to be more important to deal with the straightforward cases. The original 'Morpeth Rules' did not deal with all speed restrictions, only the most vulnerable ones, and the Rules have now been amended to take account of severe restrictions of speed where speed is reduced in a series of stages. In general, each stage must be

Left & right:
The sad result of attempting to go round a 20mph curve at 65mph at Eltham (SR) on 11 June 1972. Gary Merrin

considered as if it were from the initial approach speed, and where this is 75mph or more and the total reduction required is one-third or more an Advanced Warning Indicator and permanent magnet must be provided. At Morpeth in the Up direction the total reduction is from 100mph to 50mph and warning equipment has now been installed there.

The new arrangements might well have prevented a serious derailment at Paddington on 23 November 1983, when yet another sleeping car express came to grief. The train was the 21.35 from Penzance, and consisted of 14 coaches and vans, including four sleeping cars, hauled by a Class 50 diesel-electric locomotive No 50041 *Bulwark*. At 06.11 it was approaching Paddington when, instead of slowing down for the crossovers outside the terminus, it continued at speed. It was still travelling at more than 65mph when it entered a 25mph crossover; the locomotive dashed into the sharp curves, with wheel flanges and rails screeching loudly in protest. For a few seconds it clung tenaciously to the rails, rocking violently, but momentum was too strong and it finally lost its grip and became derailed, running on the sleepers for some distance before overturning on to its side. Behind it the train rushed onwards into almost complete derailment — only the last coach stayed on the rails. Incredibly there were no serious injuries and only three passengers were taken to hospital suffering from minor injuries and shock, but the scene outside Paddington station was one of devastation. Many days were to pass before everything was back to normal.

The driver was unhurt and he climbed out of his

locomotive cab unaided. His feelings at that moment can be imagined; the terror he had gone through hurtling forward in his derailed locomotive wondering whether he would survive; his intense relief when he found that he was uninjured, followed by a dreadful apprehension that behind him in the train may lie dead and injured passengers and fellow railwaymen, and finally, perhaps, a frantic search in his mind for the cause of such a disaster.

In his evidence at the Public Inquiry, held by the Chief Inspecting Officer of Railways, Maj C. F. Rose, the driver said that he started to apply the air brake when he was still about 2½ miles from the terminus. As the train did not appear to be slowing he made a full service brake application and finally an emergency application. The gauges in his cab showed maximum brake force but there was still no discernible reduction in speed before the point of derailment.

The most detailed investigations, lasting for many weeks, were carried out into the train's braking system, but nothing could be found to account for the failure. The brakes had worked perfectly at all the station stops between Penzance and Reading, and worked again seconds before the train became derailed. Maj Rose concluded that it was most probable that the driver lost concentration, either through drowsiness or by allowing his mind to wander, and failed to realise how closely and how quickly he was approaching the terminus. If that is what really happened, the 'deadman's pedal' was ineffective, for the same reason as we have seen before in a short period of drowsiness.

Left:
The scene of the Paddington accident on 23 November 1983. The strength and safety of modern coaches and sleepers are clearly shown in this photograph. Although the passengers had a rude awakening, none of them was badly hurt.
Mick Roberts

Top:
The Old Oak Common breakdown crane re-rails one end of Mk 3 sleeping car No 10563 under the glare of floodlights on 23 November. Mick Roberts

Above:
The much-battered *Bulwark* back on the rails on Saturday 26 November. Mick Roberts

An example of the sinuous curves between Edinburgh and Newcastle. No 40032 is seen near Houndwood, between Berwick and Dunbar, in 1980. Peter J. Robinson

The particular significance of the Paddington accident was its disclosure of a situation which was dramatically highlighted by the subsequent accident at Morpeth. HSTs may travel at their maximum speed of 125mph until they are 4½ miles from Paddington. For the next three miles the speed limit is 85mph, then 60mph for a mile, until the station throat is approached, where a 25mph restriction applies through to the platforms. According to the 'Morpeth Rules' then in force, the arrangement of this cascade of speed limits just avoided the need to provide an Advanced Warning Indicator and a permanent magnet — the reduction from 125mph to 85mph is just less than a third (32%), and so is the reduction from 85mph to 60mph (30%). If these speeds were chosen deliberately to avoid the need to provide warning equipment, it was an unfortunate and expensive decision. Approaching Paddington under clear signals, as did the driver of the 21.35 from Penzance, the first AWS warning was at a signal almost at the fatal crossover — effective enough to prevent the train from crashing into the buffers at full speed but not intended to ensure a safe speed through the crossover. The revised 'Morpeth Rules' will do that now.

We have already seen that it is not practicable to extend the 'Morpeth Rules' to cover every restriction of speed. When the original Rules were drawn up after the 1969 accident they were thought to be sufficient at the time, and a great step forward in improving safety, which they were. The new Rules, which also cater for approach speeds between 75 and 60mph, extend the safeguards, but there will always be vulnerable areas just beyond the margin. The question now is whether enough was done after 1969 to prevent further high-speed derailments. Should the circumstances of the Paddington and the second Morpeth derailments have been foreseen and guarded against? Of the four accidents on which a judgement might have been based — Sutton Coldfield 1955, Lincoln 1962, Morpeth 1969 and Eltham 1972 — three occurred on lines with a maximum speed of 60mph, which might be taken as an indication that those were the lines most at risk. There was certainly nothing to indicate an unusual danger at sharp curves approached by a cascade of speed restrictions, and nothing to suggest that the approaches to large stations and terminals, usually approached by cascades, ought to be dealt with specially, Nevertheless, an impartial observer might have detected the illogicality of safeguarding the Morpeth curve in the Down direction and not in the Up, just because there happened to be a cascade in the Up direction. Whilst the original Morpeth Rules did not provide for cascades, might it not have been common sense to have made an exception at Morpeth? Where was the logic in safeguarding a drowsy or inattentive (or incapacitated) driver in the Down direction but not in the Up? The existence of a cascade in one direction was irrelevant in such circumstances.

Whether the Paddington accident could have been forecast is a different matter. There had been no case, certainly this century, of a train failing to slow down when approaching a major terminus, and such an eventuality was thought to be so unlikely that there was no justification for expenditure to guard against it. And if the brakes *had* failed, as the driver consistently maintained, warning equipment would have provided no safeguard. Most efforts to help the driver have so far been directed towards guarding against the effects of drowsiness or inattention, by providing safeguards such as AWS at signals or speed restrictions, or by double-manning. AWS, though invaluable, has been shown to be less than 100% perfect. Double-manning has been shown to be ineffective (Morpeth 1969, Eltham 1972). Should efforts now be concentrated on methods of maintaining the driver in a state of alertness? Equipment to achieve this, known as a Vigilance Device, is provided in the cabs of HSTs[1]. A warning bleep sounds every minute, and if the driver does not respond by releasing and then depressing the 'deadman's pedal' the brakes are automatically applied. Although even this is not entirely foolproof (as demonstrated at Hayes & Harlington), and does not ensure that a driver observes and reacts correctly to every signal, it is a step in the right direction and worthy of development, which indeed BR are doing. doing.

In another respect drivers' responsibilities are being increased. The relentless marketing pressures to reduce end-to-end journey times, and the increased speeds at which trains can travel, may have the effect of increasing the number of occasions on which speed has to be reduced for intermediate speed restrictions. Between Berwick-upon-Tweed and Morpeth, a distance of 50 miles, there are no fewer than 25 changes in the maximum speed allowed, following a similar number between Edinburgh and Berwick, and a driver travelling in places at a speed of two miles a minute is having to adjust his speed (and, more important, having to remember to do so) once a minute on average.

Further north, on the East Coast main line to Edinburgh and Aberdeen, those same pressures to reduce journey times have led the Scottish Region to draw up a separate maximum-speed profile for HSTs, so that full advantage can be taken of their superior riding qualities and lower axle-weights. But in consequence drivers on that route now have to contend with a separate set of speed restrictions for HSTs, superimposed on the existing speed profile. No additional assistance is given to the driver. It has also to be remembered that an express train is normally travelling at, or near, the maximum safe speed, and the only assistance the driver is given, apart from locations with Advanced Warning Indicators, is the lineside cut-out, suitable only for route-learning, and useless otherwise. He has to rely on his route knowledge, as he has always had to do, but with many of his location markers, such as wayside stations and signalboxes, gone. Even the replacement of semaphore signals by colour-light signals, excellent though they are, is not exclusively an improvement; semaphore signals are often distinctive and individually styled, helping a driver to know exactly where he is on a dark night. Colour lights are anonymous. Technology now exists to give the driver a continuous in-cab indication of the speed limit for the section of track he is on, together with advance warning of any reduction required. It might be difficult to justify the cost, especially as the Morpeth-type loophole has been plugged, but speeds are still rising and location-finding is becoming no easier. It might also be a means of withdrawing the second driver from the cab of trains travelling at over 100mph.

How will posterity judge the events described in this chapter? Will it say that BR took responsible action at the appropriate time, or will it say that it took action too late and on too small a scale, giving the impression that it did not really believe in what it was doing? One cannot help feeling that it may be the latter.

---

[1] Class 50 locomotives were fitted with an electronic vigilance device when first introduced into service, but it proved troublesome and unreliable and was removed.

Temporary Speed Restrictions

In the previous chapter we were concerned with speed restrictions of a permanent nature, mainly, but not always, round curves, and it is now time to turn our attention to those of a temporary nature, usually imposed for a few weeks only, on track awaiting renewal or repair, or after such work whilst it settles. Such locations are signposted at the lineside at the beginning and end of the restriction, and there is an advance indicator, called a warning board, at braking distance, showing the speed restriction in miles per hour, with a permanent magnet in the track for additional safety, working in conjunction with the locomotive's AWS equipment. All the signs are illuminated at night and drivers are provided each week with booklets (known as 'Weekly Engineering Notices') giving details of restrictions on all routes over which they work. If a restriction has to be applied at short notice a handsignalman is stationed at the warning board and he gives a Caution indication to drivers, supplemented by a warning detonator. In addition a special notice is posted at drivers' depots in the 'Late Notice' case. It all sounds very safe, and it is, but it was not always so.

Is there some malign fate that makes sleeping car expresses appear so often in these pages? If so, it was at work on the night of 5/6 June 1975. The 23.30 sleeper from Euston to Glasgow left on time, with Class 86 electric locomotive No 86242 hauling 12 sleeping cars, a buffet car and two vans. Just beyond King's Langley the locomotive broke down and another one, No 86006, was put on the front, the whole train starting off again 75min late. Despite the trailing weight of the train and the failed locomotive — 667 tons — No 86006 reached full speed and was running at about 80mph as it approached Nuneaton at 01.54. Just south of the station there was a 20mph temporary speed restriction (called a 'slack' in railway parlance) whilst the track layout was being altered. The express hit the slack at unchecked speed and rushed headlong into disaster. No 86006 left the rails almost at once and smashed its way into the station, for several hundred yards. No 86242 actually mounted the platform and came to rest touching the station awning. The coaches at the front of the train were scattered in all directions, some on their sides, whilst those at the rear remained upright and fairly well in line. The last vehicle, a van, came to rest exactly at the spot where No 86006 had first become derailed. Four passengers and two sleeping car attendants died. Altogether 38 people were taken to hospital and 10 were detained with serious injuries.

Right:
Temporary speed restriction warning signs, showing:
1 **The warning board, with twin flashing white lights. The battery is in the box at the base of the sign. In the bottom right-hand corner of the picture can be seen a hot axlebox detector.**
2 **The '20' sign, which marks the beginning of the restriction. This is at Long Preston (North Yorks).**
3 **The 'T' sign, which marks the end (the termination) of the restriction.** Author

At the time of the accident it was not the practice to provide a permanent magnet at the warning board but both the driver and his secondman had the printed notice and knew of the slack at Nuneaton, indeed the driver had been over it, at the slow speed required, the night before on a similar train. Regrettably, the lights at the warning board were out on the night of the accident and although both the driver and the secondman said that they were looking for them they did not see them. At the Public Inquiry both men said they then assumed that the restriction had been removed, although they said no word to each other. They were not entitled to make such an assumption, because if the restriction really had been removed the warning board would have remained in position, illuminated, and the figures showing the speed allowed in miles per hour would have been altered to show the normal speed. Such alterations occur frequently, and are provided for in the Rules.

The Inquiry revealed a disturbing state of affairs and there was evidence that the lights at warning and indicator boards often went out, or that the equipment was stolen or vandalised. Drivers were supposed to report such failures, stopping specially in some circumstances, but were not always doing so. On the night in question quite a number of trains passed the warning board when it was defective. Between 22.30 and 00.58 the drivers of six out of 15 trains passing were prepared to say that the speed indication light

at the warning board was out. All admitted that they had not reported the fact at the first convenient opportunity as they were required to do by the Rules. The day might then still have been saved. The driver of the next train that passed, at about 01.10, said that the speed indication light was out but that the two horizontal warning lights were lit, although they were dimmer than he had seen them on previous occasions. On the next train at about 01.40 neither driver nor secondman saw any lights on the warning board. They should have stopped and told the signalman so that he could warn all other drivers, but they did not do so. Even at this late stage the accident could have been prevented. The driver of the last train before the accident claimed at first to have seen all the lights but later altered his evidence to say that he had not been in a position to see the warning board at all as his train passed by. It seems therefore that sometime between 01.10 and 01.40 the remaining lights at the warning board went out, and from then on the board was not illuminated in any way.

What is one to make of all these drivers, responsible, experienced men, failing to carry out the Rules properly? The Rules provided a safe method of working. There are three possible conclusions — the first one being that drivers' knowledge of the Rules may be unsatisfactory. They are not re-examined at intervals on their knowledge of the Rules, and are relied upon to keep themselves up to date. The second conclusion is that drivers knew full well what they ought to do but had become tired over many years of stopping to report failures which were still occurring. Drivers as a body dislike making out reports; they dislike even more making out reports and seeing no effective remedial action. This is a natural human reaction, not confined to drivers. But to understand is not to condone. It is only remarkable that this sorry state of affairs did not lead to more accidents, but in fact it had been many years since faulty lights at warning boards had caused one. Accidents at speed restrictions in previous years had been caused mainly by the drivers missing the warning board in daylight. The third possible conclusion is touched upon in the Inquiry Report. The driver of the train involved in the accident agreed that his mind had been very much occupied with regaining as much as possible of the lost time. He had been using his driving skill to the maximum to make up lost time and he agreed that this preoccupation might have prevented his giving full consideration to the possible implications of the 'missing' warning board. Perhaps this concern about punctuality, very proper in normal circumstances, also affects the actions of other drivers and makes them reluctant to stop out of course to report what might appear to be minor failures.

Although it had been many years since the warning arrangements for temporary speed restrictions had last featured as a contributory factor in an accident it was necessary to consider whether additional safeguards should be provided. An examination of Continental practice revealed that several railway systems used the automatic warning part of the signalling system, in conjunction with the AWS equipment on the locomotive, at warning boards for temporary speed restrictions, and it was decided to adopt the practice on BR by placing a permanent magnet between the rails just before the warning board so that the driver would always receive a warning on his AWS equipment, which would alert him if he had missed the warning board and would automatically apply the brakes if he failed to react. It seems such an obvious solution that one may wonder why it had not been adopted sooner. One reason was that there was no apparent need, even though the possibility of an accident was always there and could so easily have been guarded against. Another reason was the reluctance to allow what was a part of the signalling apparatus to be used for non-signalling purposes, based on fears about possible unsafe side-effects. A third reason, and possibly the most important, concerned the problem of the complications that could arise if the proposed location for a magnet for a temporary speed restriction should fall near that of an AWS magnet for a signal or a permanent speed restriction, or near a signal itself, or in a junction layout. There were many such practical problems to be

2

3

overcome in the application of the new arrangements, and the instructions to staff on the precise positioning of the warning board and the magnet run to many pages to cover all the different circumstances.

The decision to use permanent magnets at warning boards was very popular with drivers and removed those nagging doubts which they had had from time to time that they may have missed a warning board or misunderstood an entry in the Weekly Engineering Notice, or that the warning board may have been stolen by vandals. Only in one respect are the new arrangements considered by many drivers to be less than satisfactory. Previously the warning board was located at a fixed distance from the slack (eg 1¼ miles where trains run at 100mph or more) and drivers knew exactly how much room they had in which to reduce their speed to the required level. They could then make whatever adjustments were necessary for gradients, dry or wet rail, type of brake, approach speed, etc. However, to help in overcoming the problems which arose in drawing up the new principles to be adopted in deciding precisely where the magnet and warning board should be located, it was thought to be better to change from a fixed distance to a calculated one, based on the braking distance needed to reduce speed to the required level. But it overlooked the fact that each individual train's braking capacity and requirements are different, depending on a multitude of factors, and it puts drivers in a state of uncertainty. They will always have enough braking distance, but frequently too much, without knowing how much. Drivers then have to 'feel' for the lineside indicator at the start of the slack and may sometimes be worried that they have missed it, especially in the dark. It also leads to unnecessary loss of time in running and is an unpopular change with drivers. Both they and their Union, the Associated Society of Locomotive Engineers and Firemen (ASLEF), tried to persuade BR to change back to a fixed distance but they were unsuccessful. BR's view was that the complications which sometimes arise in finding a suitable location for the warning board and magnet make a system based on a fixed distance unsuitable for the very reason that the fixed distance would have to be increased to an extent unknown to the driver in those cases where the warning board has to be put further away from the speed restriction in order to find a suitable location for it. The same anomaly arises, of course, with the system adopted by BR, which is based on braking distance.

The lineside equipment used for indicating the beginning and end of speed restrictions, and the warning boards, together with their illumination, came under some criticism at the Nuneaton Inquiry. Change often comes slowly on Britain's railways. The design of the equipment had altered very little since before World War 1, but trials had been carried out with bottled gas rather than paraffin oil for the lights at the warning board, and this method was coming into widespread use. It gave a brighter light. Bottled gas was used in the Nuneaton lineside boards, and the lights went out because the bottle was exhausted. The correct procedures had not been followed by the staff responsible, which illustrates the hidden perils of change. Ironically, the change from oil to bottled gas had been made to help the driver, but if the lamps at Nuneaton had been oil-lit it is unlikely that they would all have run dry at the same time.

The equipment and its illumination may seem archaic and primitive for such a vital function, but it worked, at least until the Nuneaton accident. It worked because drivers knew they had to be specially alert to pick out the flickering oil lamps. The use of gas-lit bull's-eye lamps at the warning board was really quite a step forward in improving their conspicuousness. But what more could have been done? Let us itemise the requirements:

1 The equipment must be capable of being manhandled to site along the railway line. The three individual items may be up to two miles or more apart.
2 It must be sufficiently robust to withstand all weathers, plus the turbulence caused by passing trains.

Right:
The awful results of human error at Nuneaton on 6 June 1975. The scattered coaches and sleepers of the 23.30 Euston-Glasgow train lie in the wake of the train locomotive, which has mounted the platform. R. J. Lowe

56

3 It must be capable of being erected on site and stand firmly.

4 It must be as visually arresting as possible, both by day and by night.

5 Thousands are required, so the purchase or manufacturing cost must be kept down.

6 The method of illumination must be as reliable as possible.

7 The equipment, and means of illumination, should require as little attention as possible whilst in use.

BR's Civil Engineering Department set to work to improve the equipment, adopting space-age technology with the use of electric battery-operated light-emitting diodes (LEDs) as the basis of illumination. The new equipment is reliable, being mostly solid-state, the batteries have a very long life, an indicator shows when they are running down, and energy is conserved in two ways — the lights flash on and off rhythmically, and a light-sensitive cell switches them off in good daylight. The new designs are not the perfect answer, but within the constraints listed above they are an improvement. However, they still depend on the human element — they need to be erected firmly in the correctly calculated location; focussed accurately and monitored properly.

Two other improvements followed to help to remove doubts from drivers' minds. The first concerned the removal of a speed restriction earlier than planned and

published, or the non-imposition of a speed restriction which had already been published (owing, for example, to the cancellation of the planned work). In such cases a warning board would still be erected, but instead of the 'speed' panel showing a number (signifying miles per hour) it would carry a special sign to indicate without question that there was no speed restriction in force.

The second improvement concerned a situation which arose from time to time at junctions where a speed restriction applied on only one leg of the junction, but where the warning board had to be erected before the junction in order to give sufficient braking distance. In such cases drivers proceeding on to the unrestricted route also passed the warning board even though it did not apply to their train. Therefore in order to remove any doubt in the driver's mind the warning board now carries an arrow pointing left or right to whichever leg of the junction the speed restriction applies, so that drivers proceeding towards the other leg can continue at the appropriate speed without worry but, more importantly, drivers proceeding on to the speed-restricted leg will be in no doubt that the restriction applies to them.

One last problem remains on those lines where speeds are high — the indicator at the start of the speed restriction is not always sufficiently conspicuous to enable the driver to pick it out with certainty from confusing backgrounds up to a quarter of a mile away, as he needs to do to be able to

reduce his speed safely on the one hand and avoid the loss of time by premature braking on the other. This factor becomes particularly noticeable when the warning board has had to be moved further out to find a suitable location for it. Motorway-style count-down markers, reflectorised but not illuminated, would be of great assistance to the driver but would place increased demands on the Civil Engineer's staff, although only one marker would be needed at, say, a quarter of a mile from the speed restriction, and the additional workload on the platelayers (or trackmen, as they are now called) might be well worth it in the context of the improved train running which would result. The indicator at the start of the restriction itself cannot really be made much larger because it would then be liable to be blown over by high winds or by the draught of a passing train. Furthermore, its size has to be limited so that it can be located safely between adjoining tracks on multi-track sections.

The best solution of all on high-speed lines would be the ability to superimpose the temporary speed restriction warning arrangements on to the in-cab system designed for permanent speed restrictions mentioned in the previous chapter (although lineside marker posts would still be required at the beginning of the restriction to give the driver an aiming point). Primitive warning boards, no matter how improved, hardly fit in with ultra-modern, multi-million pound signalling. It is incongruous to say the least to have a HST costing millions running smoothly on track costing millions, guided safely by signalling costing millions, yet having to rely for the safe reduction of speed at a temporary restriction on rudimentary equipment costing a few pounds.

Below:
Nuneaton — the early hours of 6 June 1975 and BR recovery crews attempt to sort out the tangle of broken rails and de-railed sleepers. Ian Allan Library

Procedures at Stations

Easter Monday 1979. The 19.40 electric passenger train from Glasgow to Wemyss Bay was approaching Gilmour Street station, Paisley, under clear signals. To the driver at the controls it was just another routine day, another familiar journey. Neither he nor his passengers had the remotest idea that tragedy and death lay immediately ahead.

At the same moment the 18.58 special passenger train from Ayr to Glasgow was standing in the station waiting for departure time, the passengers tired but happy, returning to Glasgow after a day out at the seaside. Some were dozing, some were reading, while others were just relaxing after the day's exertions. None had any inkling of impending disaster. The guard was standing at the doorway of his van waiting for passengers to finish getting in and out. The driver was sitting quietly at the controls waiting for the 'rightaway' signal. On the platform the leading railman was getting ready to signal to the guard that station duties were complete. The last few moments of absolute normality were slipping by.

Finally the leading railman raised his arm to signal to the guard that all the carriage doors were closed. The guard rang the bell to the driver, and the train moved off. The final, fatal events had been acted out. A few seconds later the two trains met violently head-on and seven people were killed.

What happened was quite simple. According to the Department of Transport Accident Report the driver of the train from Ayr to Glasgow had unwittingly driven his train past a Danger signal at the end of the platform. After that it was purely a matter of fate that the paths of both trains should cross at the same precise instant. If either train had been a few seconds earlier or later it would have been a near miss instead of a collision. That is the way with accidents. Trains had been driven past platform starting signals at Danger on many occasions (there were 36 known cases in 1977/78 alone), and although such errors did not often result in a collision it was clearly only a matter of

Below:
A 1986 view showing the scene of the accident which took place on Easter Monday 1979. Signal P31, seen above, was wrongly passed at Danger by the Ayr-Glasgow DMU, which then collided head-on with a Glasgow-Wemyss Bay EMU just as it was taking the route shown in this photograph. At the time of the accident there were four tracks east of Paisley but they have since been reduced to two. Author

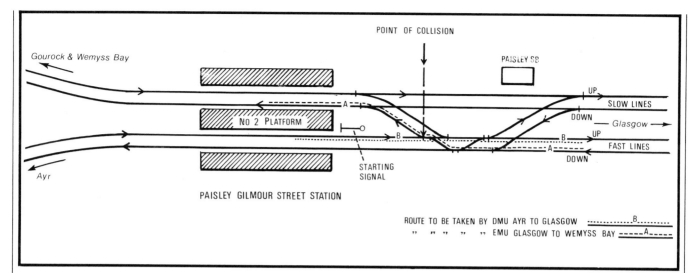

POINT OF COLLISION

Gourock & Wemyss Bay

PAISLEY SB

UP
SLOW LINES
DOWN
— Glasgow —
UP
FAST LINES
DOWN

A

B

B

A

NO 2 PLATFORM

Ayr

STARTING
SIGNAL

PAISLEY GILMOUR STREET STATION

ROUTE TO BE TAKEN BY DMU AYR TO GLASGOW ·············· B ···········
" " " " " EMU GLASGOW TO WEMYSS BAY ----- A -----

time before there would be another crash in which people would be killed.

However, before going further it would be useful to examine the procedures for starting trains from stations, as laid down in the British Railways Rule Book. There are three people involved in the operation — the person in charge of the platform, the guard and the driver — and their duties at the time of the Paisley accident were as follows:

Person in charge of the platform
He must see that passengers have joined and alighted, that all parcels traffic has been dealt with, that all doors are closed, that everything is in order and that it is time for the train to leave. He must then indicate this to the guard by giving him the 'All right' signal (either arm held above the head, or at night a white light held above the head).

The Guard
He must satisfy himself that everything is in order so far as he is concerned, and then give a signal to the driver that the train is ready to start. By day he waves a green flag, and by night he shows a steady green light. On multiple-unit trains, instead of using a flag or lamp, the guard presses a button which sounds a bell or buzzer in the driving cab. (To simplify matters the term 'bell' will be used throughout.)

The Driver
His job is specifically to observe and obey signals. He normally takes no part in station activities and merely waits for the indication from the guard that the train is ready to go.

All this sounds very simple and straightforward, and it often is, but what happens on curved platforms where the driver cannot see the guard, or where the station is unstaffed, as many are these days? Or at busy stations with crowded platforms?

Curved Platforms
If the driver cannot see the guard's signal, the person-in-charge of the platform must pass on to the driver the guard's signal, using a green light at night, but by day he has to give the 'All right' signal (one arm above the head) because he doesn't have a green flag.

Unstaffed Stations
The guard has to carry out all platform duties, although most trains stopping at unstaffed stations are fairly short ones. Platform staff are usually on duty where long trains are dealt with.

At busy Stations
To overcome the difficulty of the driver not being able positively and correctly to identify the 'ready to start' signal from the guard or station staff when the platform is crowded or when his line of sight is obstructed by structures or barrow loads of parcels, an electrical indicator, known as a 'Ready to start' indicator, is installed near the locomotive, usually next to the platform starting signal and acting in conjunction with it. When the train is ready to start and the guard has given his signal, the person in charge of the platform operates the 'Ready to start' button which causes the indicator to show an illuminated 'R' to the driver when the signal is clear. If the signal is at Danger no 'R' can be shown and this neatly avoids the Paisley problem. With multiple-units the bell is used instead of the indicator.

The cause of accidents of the Paisley type is known in railway circles as 'Ding-ding, and away' and has a long, long history. As long ago as 1957 Brig Langley of the Railway Inspectorate, Department of Transport, had said in his Report following a Public Inquiry into the collision at Staines Central on 9 August of that year that there had been a number of accidents caused by drivers unwittingly setting off against platform starting signals at Danger after receiving the guard's 'rightaway' signal and that from time to time consideration had been given to altering the Rules so as to require the guard not to give the driver the signal to start if the platform starting signal was at Danger, but he thought that this would imply a measure of dual responsibility for the observance of signals which might cut across the long-established Rule that it is the fundamental responsibility of the driver. He did not recommend any change to the Rules but he did point out the great psychological effect of the guard's 'rightaway' signal, shown by the way drivers had on occasion allowed themselves to be misled by it. However, he thought it desirable that guards and station staff should *where practicable* wait until the platform starting signal had been cleared before giving 'rightaway', and, where they couldn't see the signal, conditions should be reviewed to see whether they could be improved, especially at busy junctions. The railway's response to this was lukewarm but after pressure from Brig Langley they agreed to see what could be done, if only minor expenditure was involved in such improvements.

The question continued to crop up. In 1967 following a similar collision between a Manchester-Bury electric train and a freight train there was some support within railway circles for a change to the Rules, yet even though there were

Above:
Barrier Bell, Right Away, and Train Ready to Start plungers on platforms 4/5 at King's Cross. Author

Above right:
'Off' indicator at King's Cross, which shows that the platform Starting signal has been cleared. Author

Right:
'Off' indicator on the footbridge at Carlisle. This photo graphically demonstrates the problems on crowded, curved platforms. Author

Right:
Where detonator-placing machines are provided to work in conjunction with Danger Signals, the detonators are slid on to the rail-head when the signal is at Danger. G. Clarke

two other accidents that year of the 'Ding-ding, and away' type — at Birmingham Snow Hill and at Bournemouth — no change was made. Five years later Maj Rose of the Department of Transport held a Public Inquiry into a derailment at Clapham Junction on 7 September 1972 and concluded that the driver had unwittingly gone past the platform starting signal at Danger on receipt of the 'rightaway', which incidentally was given by platform staff rather than by bell from the guard. He reiterated Brig Langley's observation that if the driver were not paying strict attention to the signals he could react subconsciously to the 'ready to start' indication. He went on to say that at the time of drafting a new Rule Book in 1966 (which was finally published in 1972 and is the one now in use) the Railway Inspectorate had suggested to the British Railways Board that the new Rules should place a definite duty on guards to observe starting signals where it was physically possible to do so, and not to signal to the driver to start if the platform starting signal was at Danger. The Board had considered this suggestion but had concluded that such a change would weaken the clear and

undivided responsibility placed on drivers to observe signals, and might lead to dangerous misunderstandings between drivers and guards. It was agreed, however, that the wording of the revised Rule should make it quite clear that the guard's signal to the driver meant only that the train was *ready* to start, and that it was then up to the driver to make sure that the platform starting signal was clear before actually moving off. This might be thought to be a mere tinkering with words and it is doubtful if many people noticed the different wording, let alone understood the implications of the change. It is no use the writer of the Rule understanding the subtleties of his wording if the staff who have to carry out the Rules do not understand such subtle changes.

There were 17 cases in 1972 in which drivers passed platform starting signals at Danger after receiving the 'rightaway' and Maj Rose discussed yet again with the Board the question of a Rule change, but he was eventually persuaded that it was in the interests of safety to preserve the unequivocal responsibility placed on drivers to observe and comply with signals. More accidents followed — at

Right:
A prewar scheme which was postponed. Mr Alfred Barnes, the Minister of Transport, at the controls of the first electric train from Liverpool Street to Shenfield in 1949. The LNER provided sliding-door stock for this busy suburban route.
Ian Allan Library

Staines on 4 April 1974, at Pollokshields East, Glasgow, on 11 June 1974, at Inverness on 5 September 1975 and at Wimbledon on 11 December 1976. Finally there was the crash at Paisley on Easter Monday 1979, the cause being yet again 'Ding-ding, and away'. Once more the question of what to do arose. There was still a majority within railway circles strongly opposed to changing the Rules for the reasons already given, but there was also a strong minority who felt something had to be done and that the theory that divided responsibility for the observation of signals may cause additional dangers had to be tested. What perhaps clinched the issue was the realisation during widespread investigations, of the extent to which train crews in many parts of the country (but not the Glasgow area) were already carrying out their own version of the proposed Rule change because to them it made sense not to give 'rightaway' if the platform starting signal was at Danger. In fact one driver when asked what he would do if his guard gave 'ding-ding' when the signal was still at Danger said, 'I'd ask him what the *** he thought he was playing at'. BR took the plunge and changed the Rule. The argument against the Rule change, although based on the theoretical dangers of divided responsibility, was in practice the problem of the guard not being able to see the platform starting signal in all cases. If drivers were to start relying to any extent at all on the guard not giving 'rightaway' with the signal at Danger, then a deadly trap was being laid at those places where guards could not see the signal, and it was necessary to get rid of the anomaly. A policy was therefore adopted of providing electrical indicators on platforms where they could be seen by guards and station staff and which showed when the platform starting signal was Clear by displaying an illuminated 'Off' indication. Such indicators already existed but their use was not widespread. The Rule Book alteration was a simple one — it merely told guards and station staff not to give the 'Ready to start' signal if they could see that the platform starting signal was at Danger — and it came into force on 2 February 1980. There were one or two more accidents before staff got used to the change, but it appears to have been a complete success. The fears held so strongly and for so long turned out to be groundless after all, although matters have been helped by the substantial investment in 'Off' indicators.

That the problem was mainly one of multiple-units and colour-light signals is shown by the figures for 1977 and 1978. In those two years there were 36 reported cases of platform starting signals being passed at Danger, involving 20 electric multiple-units, 11 diesel multiple-units, and only five locomotive-hauled trains. 31 cases occurred at colour-light signals and only five at semaphore signals. It is very easy to visualise the driver of a multiple-unit sitting quietly at his controls waiting for two rings on the bell, and allowing his concentration to wander, then reacting subconsciously when the rings come and setting off, forgetting about the Red signal. Indeed, drivers as a whole recognised this possibility and had a variety of home-made reminders to use in such circumstances. One driver's favourite was to put his cap on the brake handle to remind him that the signal was at Red. The fact that colour-light signals were involved in so many cases may merely reflect the statistical frequency with which they are met, although because they merely differ in colour, rather than in shape as in the case of a semaphore, they may perhaps not make such an impact on a driver's mind.

Other solutions considered all involved the use of equipment at platform starting signals. The one most favoured was the installation, on the track, of an automatic warning magnet of the type used in the signalling system, a few yards beyond the signal so that the driver would be alerted by it if he were unwittingly to pass the signal at Danger, and which would have its magnetic effect suppressed when the signal was cleared. Given unlimited funds it might have been a good solution, although it might have caused problems at places where long trains had to stop with the locomotive ahead of the signal, or where the signal was placed almost at the fouling point of switch and crossing areas. Trip-stops as provided on London Transport were also considered but in addition to the considerable cost there would have been a heavy maintenance burden of equipment both at the signal and on the train. The possible use of detonator-placers, acting in conjunction with the signal, was also dismissed for similar reasons. These place a detonator on the rail when the signal is at Danger in order to alert a driver should he unwittingly pass it.

The arrangements for starting passenger trains at stations have already been shown to be less simple and more hazardous than might be supposed, but there are other dangers besides those experienced at Paisley, and they mainly concern carriage doors. The devotion shown by BR to slam-doors has long been a matter of irritation to those who have to operate the railway day by day and who would prefer sliding doors. The technology of power-operated sliding doors has been around for many years, indeed London Transport could hardly operate without it, but BR has continued to put new carriages into service with slam-doors on main-line trains, despite having experience of sliding doors over many years. For example the pre-war Southport stock of the London Midland & Scottish Railway had sliding doors, as had the postwar London & North Eastern Railway suburban stock in the Manchester area and on services from Liverpool Street. The Glasgow suburban electrification of the 1960 period was also provided with sliding door stock. All these trains were electric multiple-units, but despite that the London Midland Region reverted to slam-doors for its suburban electrification schemes introduced in the 1960s. The Southern Region too remained firmly wedded to slam-doors for many years. However, sliding doors have now been adopted as standard for suburban trains, both diesel and electric, and the new Mk 4 main-line coaches will have power-operated sliding plug-doors.

Power-operated doors make station operations much safer and help to achieve punctual departures. They are much to be preferred where there are no ticket barriers to prevent passengers from joining at the last moment just as the train is about to depart, and the trend towards 'open' stations reinforces the need for sliding doors. Fewer platform staff are required — indeed none at all in many cases. The greater safety of sliding doors is an important factor — in 1985 six passengers were killed and 25 seriously injured whilst entering or leaving trains. 16 were killed and eight seriously injured by falling out of carriage doors during the journey. Even when there are no casualties, open doors on trains during a journey cause delays and may damage other trains passing. But another important factor is the ability to run sliding-door suburban trains without guards and without platform staff.

So far as main-line coaches are concerned, BR's adherence to slam-doors is odd when one sees the extent to which power-operated doors are used on the continent, for instance on the superb SNCF Corail stock. On BR, passengers have to lower the windows to reach outside for the door handles, and then they often leave the windows open, wasting heating and air-conditioning. Frequently, even in the coldest weather, express trains are to be seen leaving stations with half their windows open, causing a gale to blow through the vestibules when the trains gain speed. BR's Mk 3 main-line coaches are so good that it is a pity they are spoilt by archaic door design, but there are signs that a more enlightened attitude is prevailing as power-operated doors are to be provided on new main-line coaches, and one hopes that retrospective action may one day be taken on High Speed Trains (HSTs).

After the 'ready to start' signal has been given to the driver there remains one problem with slam door trains — that of the passenger who attempts to join, or alight from, the train as it starts to move.

Attempting to join
The passenger who arrives on the platform just as the train is about to depart:
1 May not be aware that the 'ready to start' signal has been given. He may think that he has plenty of time to join the train and be caught unawares when it starts to move.
2 May already be aware that the 'ready to start' has been given and take a chance on being able to get safely aboard the train before it starts to move.
3 May arrive just as the train starts to move, and attempt to join it, risking the obvious dangers.

Attempting to alight
Most passengers are already standing at the carriage door as the train comes to a stop, often with the door already slightly open, and occasionally with it wide open (a thoughtless action which endangers passengers waiting on the platform if they are near the edge and not keeping a lookout). Danger often arises when passengers find they are unable to open a door for some reason — perhaps the window is stiff, or the spring of the inside handle is too strong, or the door is slightly jammed (a recurring problem on older stock) — and they then have to move down the carriage to another door, possibly encumbered with luggage and small children whilst doing so. By the time they reach it the driver may already have received the 'ready to start' signal and be preparing to move off, whereupon the situation becomes fraught with danger.

Guards and platform staff need to be aware of, and on the alert for, any of these happenings so that they can call out to anyone attempting to join or alight when it is not safe to do so, and to stop the train if necessary. Reductions in

Above right:
Incredibly the London Midland Region reverted to slam-doors on the suburban stock for their West Coast main line electrification. Here Class 304 Unit No 003 is seen on introduction to service. British Railways

Right:
It is a pity that the great Sir Herbert Walker did not specify sliding door stock on the Southern Railway. The slam-door tradition persisted long after it should have done. Here a train of 10 coaches (a 2-SAP unit leading a 4-VEP and a 4-CIG) and countless doors leaves Weybridge on a Waterloo-Haslemere train in 1979. Les Bertram

platform staff have reduced such surveillance and made it even more essential for the guard to keep a sharp lookout as the train is leaving a station, so that he can apply the brake if necessary. Where platforms are closed off by ticket barriers there is a control over late-arriving passengers but the trend now is towards open platforms. There are very good marketing reasons for removing ticket barriers — stations have a much pleasanter environment without them, and queues, congestion and delay become things of the past, but there are obvious operating and safety penalties. King's Cross has long been an example of this, where platforms 1-7 have barriers but platform 8 is open. Starting a train from platform 8 needs much more care but the environment is pleasanter for passengers. Sliding doors under the control of the driver or guard solve all these problems.

Having examined some of the many and varied aspects of safety at passenger stations, there remains the question of whether the actions of BR after the Paisley accident were appropriate and effective and, if so, why were they not implemented before the accident instead of after it? That they were effective has been proved by experience, so why were they not adopted *before* the accident? It is sad but true that it so often takes a major accident to force a change that has been resisted up to then following minor accidents or infrequent ones. Many examples could be quoted from the

Right:
A pair of Class 313 EMUs leaves Hadley Wood on a Moorgate-Welwyn Garden City train in 1979.
Brian Morrison

Below:
Modernisation at last on the Southern. Although there were problems with the Class 508s, the doors at least were an improvement. A Waterloo-Dorking train is seen leaving Wimbledon in July 1984. David Brown

long years of the history of railway accidents going back to Armagh and beyond. The Armagh accident in 1889 assisted the passage of legislation compelling railways to adopt continuous brakes on passenger trains and the block signalling system on passenger lines, in the Regulation of Railways Act of the same year. It is interesting to note in passing that the 1889 Act marked a rare example of railway safety being enforced by legislation. Practically all the advances in the safety of train operation made before and since by Government agency have been achieved by persuasion. The Hawes Junction and Ais Gill collisions of Christmas Eve 1910 and September 1913 respectively hastened the end of gas-lit coaches and brought about the more widespread use of track circuits (an electrical device which detects the presence of a train or vehicle). And the fearful double collision at Harrow & Wealdstone on 8 October 1952 led to the British Transport Commission adopting the Automatic Warning System more quickly than would otherwise have been the case. If it seems like closing the stable door after the horse has bolted one can only point to the same situation arising not only in all forms of transport, but in industry in general. It takes a serious accident or a spate of accidents to mould opinion, both public and professional, and provide a mood, an impetus, and a pressure to seek improvements and to spend money on them. Without such backing it is much more difficult to achieve improvements by persuasion.

But to return to the Paisley accident; over the many years in which a change in the Rules had been resisted there had been a gradual change in circumstances. Semaphore signals had been replaced by colour-lights at some stations, the 'sighting' of signals by guards and platform staff had been gradually improving whilst 'R' and 'Off' indicators had been installed in large numbers. The change when it came was more acceptable, but it might also be argued that it was only the railway's built-in resistance to change that prevented it from being made earlier, and that the Paisley accident was really the result of BR's refusal to act sooner, and the Railway Inspectorate's failure to press home its views more forcibly over a period of 20 years and more.

Above:
Door (and window) problems on an HST before departure at King's Cross. Author

Left:
No door problems on these superb SNCF coaches. They have power-operated fold-back doors, which can be controlled throughout the train from any door.
Ian Allan Library

Block Sections and Track Circuits

The early part of December 1981 was very wintry in the south of England. There were exceptionally low temperatures and almost a foot of snow fell. Trees hung low under its weight and the Home Counties looked more like Switzerland than England. It was all very picturesque.

On the morning of Friday 11 December 1981 the driver of the 06.03 stopping passenger train from Marylebone to High Wycombe was passing through the cutting between Gerrards Cross and Seer Green stations when he noticed that trees weighed down with snow were leaning towards the track, and he thought that the train had struck one of them. He reported the facts to the signalman at the next signalbox, High Wycombe, and advised the signalman that he should warn drivers of following trains to proceed cautiously on the line he had just travelled over. The signalman at High Wycombe telephoned his colleague at West Ruislip, which was the next signalbox open towards Marylebone, and passed on the information he had received from the driver.

After a number of trains had travelled through to High Wycombe at caution, the next train to travel over the affected line was an empty DMU and, in accordance with the Rules, the driver was stopped by the signalman at West Ruislip. Here, the signalman told the driver what had happened and that he was to proceed with extreme caution. However, approaching Gerrards Cross station, between West Ruislip and High Wycombe, the train was signalled into the platform loop line and was brought to a stand by the Home signal being at Danger. The signalman there had just arrived on duty, having been delayed by the snow; he cleared the Home signal for the train to pass it, then held a red flag out of the signalbox window as an indication to the driver that the signalman wanted to speak to him. The driver stopped his train opposite the signalbox window, and the signalman told him that the driver of the previous train through the section had reported striking a tree, and

that he was to proceed at extreme caution, to examine the track, and to report any obstruction.

The train set off slowly into the driving snow, but when it reached the cutting the driver saw the top four or five feet of a tree lying across the track. He stopped the train safely and went to a nearby railway telephone to tell the signalman at High Wycombe about the tree. He said he would be able to move it within about five minutes and went to the Guard's compartment to get an axe and a saw from the emergency toolbox.

Meanwhile the signalman at Gerrards Cross signalbox, after sending the empty DMU into the section at caution, accepted the following train, the 07.31 Marylebone-Banbury DMU, from West Ruislip signalbox, and it arrived at Gerrards Cross station within a few minutes. The signalman repeated his procedure. He kept the Home signal at Danger until the driver stopped there and sounded his horn, then he cleared the signal and stopped the train at his signalbox by holding out a red flag. As with the previous train he told the driver that there had been reports of trees down near Seer Green station and that he was to proceed cautiously. The signalman told the driver that he would clear the Starting signal (No 27) but when he tried to do so the lever would not move. The signalling arrangements between Gerrards Cross and High Wycombe signalboxes are rather unusual. There are several track circuits, and additional signals, details of which will be explained later in this chapter, but suffice it for the moment to say that if a train was standing on the track circuit in Seer Green cutting, as the empty DMU was, it would electrically lock the Starting signal at Danger. The signalman at Gerrards Cross would not have been able to clear his Starting signal for another train until the previous one had passed well clear of Seer Green cutting and the station.

The signalman looked at his track indication panel (a large diagrammatic representation of the track and signals

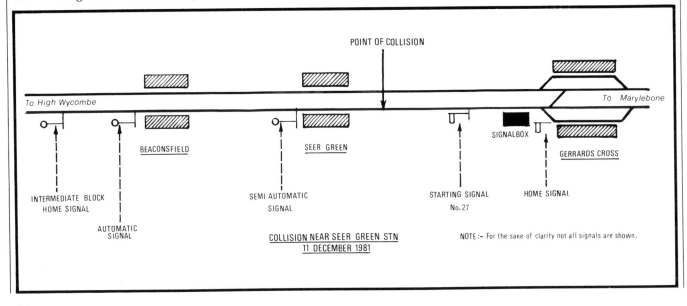

POINT OF COLLISION

To High Wycombe

To Marylebone

SIGNALBOX

BEACONSFIELD

SEER GREEN

GERRARDS CROSS

INTERMEDIATE BLOCK
HOME SIGNAL

AUTOMATIC
SIGNAL

SEMI AUTOMATIC
SIGNAL

STARTING SIGNAL
No. 27

HOME SIGNAL

COLLISION NEAR SEER GREEN STN
11 DECEMBER 1981

NOTE:- For the sake of clarity not all signals are shown.

in his area). The track circuit lights at or near Seer Green station were illuminated (denoting occupied), but in addition he thought that one of the pairs of lights indicating a track circuit towards Beaconsfield (further towards High Wycombe) was also lit. It did not occur to him that the Starting signal lever might be held by the electric lock and he assumed it must be frozen. At the same time he concluded that the continuing illumination of the track circuit in Seer Green cutting must be due to a failure of the track circuit to clear behind the empty DMU, possibly due to branches brought down by it which were now lying across the rails.

Thus was the scene set for tragedy. The track circuit was correctly showing 'Occupied' because the empty DMU was standing on it in the cutting. However, the signalman told the driver that he had a track circuit failure and that he would authorise him to pass signal No 27 (the Starting signal) at Danger. He mentioned the empty DMU and the driver asked where this train was, receiving the reply that it was running down towards Beaconsfield. The signalman, in view of what he thought was a track circuit failure, and the possibility that it was due to some obstruction, advised the driver to proceed at extreme caution, and suggested a speed of between 10 and 20mph. It seemed to the signalman that the driver was anxious to get on as he had made remarks about running late and not wanting to mess around any longer.

The train then started. The signalman closed the window and looked at his track circuit indicators. The track circuit near Beaconsfield that he had thought had been illuminated was out, and only the indicator for the track circuit at Seer Green cutting was showing 'Occupied'. Realising in a flash that something was wrong he rushed back to the window just as the second of the four coaches in the train was passing, and tried to attract attention by shouting, but no one heard him and the train disappeared into the swirling snow. The feelings of the signalman can be imagined as the full horror of what he had done came home to him. What could he do but wait helplessly, and hope. All need not be lost, he must have told himself; after all, he had told the

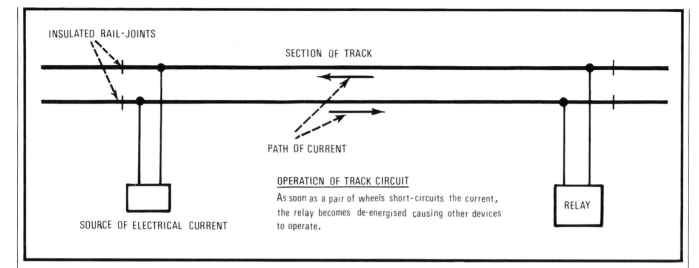

INSULATED RAIL-JOINTS

SECTION OF TRACK

PATH OF CURRENT

OPERATION OF TRACK CIRCUIT

As soon as a pair of wheels short-circuits the current, the relay becomes de-energised causing other devices to operate.

SOURCE OF ELECTRICAL CURRENT

RELAY

driver to proceed at extreme caution, so surely he would stop before running into the stationary DMU. Or maybe the driver of the stationary DMU would have removed whatever it was that was delaying him, and would have set off out of harm's way.

The signalman had not long to wait. Within a very few minutes he heard the telephone ring. With heart pounding, he answered it. His worst fears were realised — the two trains had crashed. The leading coach of the second train had partly telescoped underneath the last coach of the standing train, killing the driver, two schoolboys and a young man of 17. Five people were injured and taken to hospital.

Below:
An insulated rail-joint, as used at the end of a track circuit, or separating two adjoining track circuits.
Author/Ian Allan Library

It might be appropriate at this stage to say a few words about track circuits. They perform their allotted task not merely by telling the signalman whether there is a train on a particular piece of line, but in other ways also. When a track circuit shows 'Occupied' on the signalbox indicator, it can also:

1 put a signal to Caution or Danger behind the train,
2 electrically lock at Danger the Stop signal behind the train,
3 electrically lock a pair of facing points that the train is just approaching, so that the points cannot move dangerously. (NB facing points are those which can alter the route of an approaching train. When a train passes through them in the opposite direction they become known as trailing points),
4 indicate that a length of rail has broken (by the interruption of the current passing through it),
5 be caused by an obstruction (provided that the obstruction short-circuits the electric current),
6 indicate that a track-circuit operating clip may have been used in an emergency.

Items **1-3** are routine, and operate for every train that passes. Items **4-6** may happen without a train being present.

What is the signalman to do if a track-circuit indicator in his box continues to show 'Occupied' after a train is thought to have gone, or suddenly shows 'Occupied' when there is no train on that line? Either the track circuit is doing its proper job and is warning the signalman that there is something amiss, or else there is a fault in the equipment itself, which, being designed to fail-safe, causes the indicator to show 'Occupied'. The signalman is not to know which it is, but for safety's sake he must assume the worst. If a signalman sees a track-circuit indicator showing 'Occupied' when he would not expect it to be, he must not assume that there is a fault in the equipment but must send someone to see if there is a train or obstruction on the track. This is normally done by asking the driver of the next train requiring to go through the section to do so cautiously to see what, if anything, is amiss. If nothing is found, it can then be assumed that there is a fault, but trains must still be 'cautioned through' because the signalman will have lost the assurance given by a working track circuit. Signalling equipment is complex and varied, and the instructions to signalmen and others as to what to do in various circumstances including failure and repairs are correspondingly complex. This is particularly the case with track circuits, because of their many vital control functions.

The signalling arrangements at Gerrards Cross signalbox were more complicated than usual, and in order to appreciate this it is necessary to describe the signalling systems between Gerrards Cross and High Wycombe in some detail.

The normal signalling system between two signalboxes, the Absolute Block system, is described in an earlier chapter, but between Gerrards Cross and High Wycombe signalboxes there were two more systems, known as an automatic section and an intermediate block section respectively. These arrangements increase the number of trains that can be run over a particular line between two signalboxes (the line capacity) by, in effect, creating artificial sections without having to go to the expense of building new signalboxes and paying signalmen to operate them. More frequently they result from economy schemes where it is desired to do away with a signalbox which is no longer needed to work points leading to sidings or a branch line, the sidings or branch line having closed. If the abolition of a signalbox in such circumstances would result in such a long block section that line capacity would be reduced to an unacceptable level, it is necessary to have some means of splitting the section. There are two ways of doing this:

1 Automatic Section

Take three signalboxes, namely A, B and C. Suppose that signalbox B is to be abolished. The line between A and C could then be track-circuited throughout, and be supervised by the signalman at A, who will have track circuit indicators or a diagrammatic panel to tell him if there are any trains in the section, and roughly whereabouts. An electrically-operated signal, probably a colour-light, will be erected about half-way and will work automatically. It will clear to green when all the track circuits beyond it are clear, and will go to red as soon as a train passes it. The signal will have its own Distant signal. The signalman at A will not offer trains to C; he will merely tell him that a train is coming, and what type (or class) it is. Where traffic density demands it, additional automatic sections may be created; there were two between Gerrards Cross and High Wycombe. In a large power signalbox area there may be dozens, or even hundreds of automatic sections, all supervised from the same signalbox.

2 Intermediate Block Sections

The cost of installing track circuits is high, and where the potential savings or other benefits of a scheme do not justify the cost of an automatic section, the Intermediate Block system provides a cheaper alternative. Take the three signalboxes A, B and C again. B is to be abolished. An additional signal will then be erected roughly mid-way between A and C, and track circuits will be installed from signalbox A to the new signal (plus an overlap for safety). As soon as a train proceeding from A to C has cleared all those track circuits the signalman at A will be able to clear his Starting signal to allow a second train to proceed towards the new signal (known as an Intermediate Block Home signal). This signal will have its own Distant signal. Any new signals of this type erected today are likely to be of the colour-light type, but existing ones may be semaphore, with the signal arm being worked by an electric motor. The section between the Intermediate Block Home signal and signalbox C will be worked in the conventional way by the offering and acceptance of trains, because it is not track-circuited. Track circuits are necessary to prove that a train has passed safely through a section, and in addition has not accidentally left part of itself behind (not an uncommon occurrence at one time with loose-coupled trains which were not braked throughout the length of the

Below & below right:
All done by magic. A means of separating track circuits from each other in continuously welded rails, known as 'Aster' track circuits. British Railways

Right:
Track-circuit indicator in signalbox. When the track is occupied the black bar rotates to reveal the words 'Track Occupied'. Author

train, and not totally unknown with supposedly fully-braked trains).

Gerrards Cross had two Automatic sections and an Intermediate Block section between that signalbox and High Wycombe, a most unusual arrangement, and it might be supposed that signalmen appointed to be in charge there would have a fair degree of seniority and experience. That would certainly have been the case in years gone by, but it was not so at the time of the accident. When a vacancy arose at Gerrards Cross it was advertised internally to those railway staff eligible to apply for it but no one applied. Consequently approaches were made to Job Centres, because the vacancy had to be filled somehow. The man recruited in this way had only taken charge in the signalbox on his own on 10 November, less than five weeks before the accident. Maj Rose, who held a Public Inquiry into this accident, considered that:

'Even with additional training, I doubt whether a new signalman, even one as intelligent as this signalman, and however competent he appeared to be, would have gained sufficient experience to take charge of a signalbox such as Gerrards Cross after only some 20 weeks of railway service. "Experience" is difficult to define but it includes the kind of general knowledge of and feel for the railway environment. . . '.

The railways are in a quandary in this matter, and have been ever since the last war. They have never been able to obtain enough recruits from within their own ranks for such responsible jobs as signalmen and guards; consequently they had to have recourse to Job Centres. From 1945 until the late 1970s, when the labour market was overheated, it was often very difficult to obtain suitable recruits and the turnover was high. Standards inevitably slipped a little, although rarely sufficiently to imperil safety.

In the hierarchy of railway seniority, signalmen's posts are well above the normal starting grade of railman, so why has it been so difficult to fill vacancies from among existing railwaymen? The reasons are mainly pay (or, more accurately, 'earnings potential'), and conditions of work. Gerrards Cross signalbox was closed on nights and at weekends, therefore its earnings potential was low and it was consequently unpopular. Stability of employment was

another factor. Signalling was, at one time, regarded as a long-term career, but the closure of lines, sidings, stations, etc, coupled with the modernisation of signalling which puts large areas under the control of one modern power signalbox, has led to the closure of thousands of signalboxes. A young man contemplating a career as a signalman is bound to wonder just how secure his future is, because the process of abolishing old signalboxes will continue.

It will be recalled that the driver of the 07.31 Marylebone-Banbury DMU was told by the signalman at Gerrards Cross to pass signal No 27, his Starting signal, at Danger. This is obviously a vital matter and firm instructions are given in the Rule Book to both signalmen and drivers as to the circumstances in which such signals may be passed at Danger, to allow the train to enter what, in effect, then becomes No Man's Land. The main instances are:

1 A locomotive (or train) going to the assistance of a disabled train.
2 When the signal is out of order.
3 When a failure of other equipment locks the signal at Danger.
4 When single-line working is in operation (a method of working both Up and Down trains over one line, while the other line is being repaired or is obstructed).
5 During a failure of Block Instruments.
6 When a locomotive (or train) has to be used to enable the line to be examined.
7 In connection with trains which have become divided in running, or have run away.
8 When an intermediate signalbox fails to open when it should.
9 In connection with work on the line by the Engineering departments.

The philosophy of keeping the Starting signal at Danger, and instructing drivers to pass it, is to instil in them the seriousness of the situation and to remind them that there is no guarantee that the section ahead is clear, also of the need to travel very cautiously; but in most cases nowadays the signal would be electrically locked anyway and could not be cleared by the signalman. One of the most common causes of signals having to be passed at Danger is a failure

Left:
Settle Junction Up Intermediate Block Home Signal, identified as such by the white plate bearing a vertical black band halfway up the signal post. Note the telephone near the foot of the post (see close-up), enabling the driver to speak to the signalman. If the signal is at Danger and the telephone has failed, the driver is allowed to take his train forward cautiously. Author

of equipment, which is why it is understandable that a signalman might assume that a failure has happened when he finds he cannot clear a signal, although in reality the equipment is doing its proper job.

We are now left with the conundrum of why the driver of the 07.31 Marylebone-Banbury travelled so fast that he was unable to stop in time to avoid a collision with the stationary empty DMU. He may have been led to believe that the empty DMU was further away than it actually was, but according to the signalman's evidence the driver had been instructed by him to proceed at extreme caution. However, it seems that his speed in the driving snow was not less than 35mph, which, in the view of the Inspecting officer, was excessive. Had he been driving his train with the required degree of caution in the particular circumstances of reduced visibility the collision might have been avoided or its effects much reduced.

Through the years there have been several cases of accidents caused by drivers travelling too fast after having been cautioned by the signalman. On Friday 2 January 1976 high winds swept the Midlands with considerable force and many lines were blocked by fallen trees. On the line between Droitwich Spa and Worcester the winds had also brought down the telegraph poles, severing all communication between the signalboxes at Droitwich Spa and Worcester Tunnel Junction. When this happens, trains have to be worked over the line by a Time-Interval system, the instructions for which at the time were as follows:

1 To the Signalman
A train must not be allowed to pass a signalbox into the section where the failure exists without having been previously brought to a stand and the driver advised of the failure. He must also be told that Time Interval working is in operation, and then instructed by the signalman to pass

at Danger the section signal (another name for the Starting signal) and to proceed cautiously.

A train must not be allowed to proceed until the time usually taken by the preceding train to clear the section, plus an allowance for the train having been stopped and having run at caution, has elapsed. In no case, however, must a train be allowed to proceed with a lesser interval than six minutes unless the signalman can clearly see that the block section concerned is clear throughout. Where there is a tunnel in the section, an interval of not less than 10 minutes must be allowed between two trains unless the signalman can satisfy himself that the tunnel is clear.

2 To the Driver
When informed by the signalman that the block apparatus has failed, the driver will be verbally instructed to pass the section signal at Danger and he must then proceed cautiously as there may be an obstruction on the line or the section may be occupied. If, having proceeded into a section where the block apparatus has failed, the driver finds the signals for the signalbox ahead in the Clear position, he must not assume that the line is clear for his train. (Note this last requirement — it is significant.)

The section between Droitwich Spa and Worcester Tunnel Junction signalboxes is nearly 5½ miles long. A number of trains had passed in both directions under the Time Interval system on Saturday 3 January 1976, when the 05.30 train from Birmingham Curzon Street to Worcester Shrub Hill, consisting of a diesel-electric locomotive No 31241 and one parcels van, arrived at Droitwich Spa signalbox at 09.04. The signalman gave appropriate instructions to the driver, including permission to pass the Starting signal at Danger, and the train set off at 09.08. It passed through the section and arrived at the Home signal for Worcester Tunnel Junction signalbox at 09.23. There is a short tunnel between the Home signal and the signalbox and there is a telephone at the signal so that the driver and signalman can speak to each other if necessary. The signalman already knew that there was a train in the section because he had seen the track circuit showing Occupied, but as he did not know what train it was he had to wait until the driver announced himself on the telephone before he could set the appropriate route at the junction.

Meanwhile, back at Droitwich Spa a light locomotive (ie a locomotive without a train), Class 52 'Western' diesel-hydraulic No 1055 *Western Advocate*, travelling from Bescot to Gloucester, had arrived at the signalbox at 09.13. In his evidence at the Public Inquiry held by Maj King, the signalman said that he thought he had told the driver: 'The block instruments and the bells are out of order between Droitwich and Tunnel Junction. There is no telephone communication: all the telephones are out of order. We are working on the Time Interval system, and will you proceed cautiously through the section, and pass Signal 70 [the Starting signal] at Danger . . . I shall have to keep you for a minute or two until a suitable time has elapsed'.

The light locomotive departed at 09.18, 10 minutes after the parcels train, which was still in the section. Normally, to have two trains in a section at the same time is a situation that signalmen dread — the first words in the Absolute Block Signalling Regulations say that the object of the system is to prevent more than one train being in a block section on the same line at the same time. Nevertheless there should have been no danger — the weather was fine and clear, it was daylight, and the driver of the light engine had been well appraised of the circumstances. He was fully experienced with many years' service, and knew that he had to keep a sharp lookout as there was no guarantee that the section was clear. Indeed,

the special Time Interval method of working implicitly assumes that a second train might enter a section before the train in front has passed completely through it. More than that, it assumes that as individual drivers may drive at different speeds while passing through the section (one train may have a better brake, another a heavier load) a second train might catch up with the one in front whilst they are both still on the move. It also assumes the possibility that the first train might have stopped out of course for some reason (eg a breakdown) anywhere in mid-section. There should be no danger, provided that the second driver is travelling with the necessary degree of care, and can stop within the distance ahead that he can see the line to be clear.

Meanwhile, at the parcels train standing at the Home signal at Worcester Tunnel Junction the driver walked back from the telephone and climbed aboard his locomotive, little knowing that approaching him at fairly high speed, and getting closer all the time, was the light locomotive. Seeing the signal at Clear, he sat down and released the brake valve and was waiting for the brakes to come off when he suddenly felt a tremendous thump. No 1055 had crashed into the back of him at about 45mph, killing its driver, and the guard who was riding with him. The time was 09.25.

We shall never know why the light locomotive was going so fast. It had come through the 5½-mile section in approximately seven minutes, and Maj King concluded that it was not being driven with the caution that the circumstances demanded. The Home signal at Tunnel Junction (but not the Distant) was cleared as No 1055 approached it; in fact the driver may have seen the signal arm move from Danger to Clear, but the Rule warned him that he should not assume that the line was clear for *his* train. Did the Clear signal lead him into a trap? We shall never know. It is a warning which was inserted in the Rules as long ago as 1924 specifically to draw drivers' attention to the possibility of such a trap.

This accident demonstrates how great a part that fate sometimes plays. If No 1055 had approached Worcester Tunnel Junction a minute earlier the Home signal might still have been at Danger and the driver would, unless something very unusual had happened, have slowed down in time to stop at it (and avoided colliding with the very short train in front). A minute later, and the signal might already have been put back to Danger behind the parcels train before it was seen by the driver of No 1055.

An accident similar in some ways to the one at Seer Green occurred at Hyndland on the North Glasgow electrified line, on 5 June 1980. Fortunately there were no fatalities, although 35 passengers and three members of the traincrews had to be taken to hospital. The line concerned is track-circuited throughout, and has colour-light signals and AWS. There had been an earlier failure of signalling equipment and the train service had been disrupted. During the morning the signalman noticed a track circuit showing 'Occupied' although he could not remember a train being there, so he asked the driver on the opposite line to have a look as he went past. Unfortunately there was a misunderstanding between them and the driver reported that the line was clear. Satisfied that the occupation of the track circuit was due to a fault in the equipment and not to the presence of a train, the signalman authorised the driver of the 09.27 Dalmuir-Motherwell passenger train, a three-coach electric multiple-unit, to pass the protecting colour-light signal at Danger. In his evidence at the Public Inquiry the signalman said that he had told the driver that there was a track circuit failure ahead and that he was to proceed with caution, although this was disputed by the driver, who said that he was not instructed to proceed with

Above:
The wrecked cab of Class 52 'Western' No 1055 after the collision at Worcester Tunnel Junction. The driver has very little protection in such a crash. Graham F. Scott-Lowe

caution nor was he told why it was necessary for the signal to be passed at Danger. The driver accelerated his train to between 25 and 30mph even though his forward visibility was severely limited by the curvature of the line, and he was thus unable to prevent his train from colliding violently with a train that was standing on the track circuit, another three-coach electric multiple-unit which was empty and which was waiting to set back into the maintenance depot. Maj Rose, who held a Public Inquiry into the collision, concluded that the driver had failed to drive his train with the necessary caution after being told to pass a signal at Danger and that the signalman had too readily assumed that the 'Occupied' indication of the track circuit was due to a failure of the equipment rather than the presence of a train. Maj Rose also commented on a general laxity in passing verbal messages concerning train movements and the safety of the line.

We have met the 22.15 sleeping car express from King's Cross to Edinburgh before, when it was derailed at Lincoln in 1961, and we are about to meet it again. During the night of Saturday 7 November 1981, trains which normally ran on the East Coast main line from King's Cross were having a lengthy diversion over the Midland main line north of Sheffield because of engineering work. At Altofts Junction, between Normanton and Leeds, the routes diverge, the Midland main line continuing to Leeds, and the other line proceeding to York. The diverted trains were using the latter to regain their booked route. The 21.00 King's Cross-Edinburgh express had been sent to the Starting signal at Altofts Junction and was held there for some time by the signalman who then apparently forgot about it and assumed that the track circuit, which was indicating the presence of the train, had failed. When the 22.15 sleeper from King's Cross arrived at his signalbox he authorised the driver to pass his Home signal at Danger, as it was electrically locked and he could not clear it. The driver of the sleeping car express took his train forward and collided at a speed of between 10 and 15mph with the rear of the express standing at the Starting signal, slightly injuring seven passengers. The young signalman had worked at

Altofts Junction signalbox for only 2½ months. This accident contained a number of familiar features:

1 The signalman assumed that a track circuit had failed when in reality it was doing its proper job.
2 Was the driver of the second train misled into thinking the line was clear?
3 The rear of the first train was not sufficiently conspicuous to prevent the second train from crashing into it.
4 The relative inexperience of the signalman.

As a result of these accidents and others of a similar nature BR considered what more could be done. The problem was not becoming less frequent, and is not likely to become so in the future. As more and more equipment which has a safety function is provided in signalboxes and in the signalling system, it is only to be expected that the total number of failures might increase, even if the failure rate per item of equipment remains constant. In order to be able to keep trains running during a failure the signalman has to resort to special alternative measures and these very often require drivers to pass signals at Danger. It is very easy for the signalman to assume that, when something unforeseen occurs, it is due to technical failure, rather than the particular piece of equipment doing the job for which it was designed, which is guarding the safety of trains and protecting passengers against the possible effects of failure of the human element.

The importance of avoiding delays to trains, and of maintaining high standards of punctuality and reliability, are constantly being drummed into signalmen, and these are indeed very important issues, but there is a risk, no matter how slight, that constant emphasis on standards of service to the customer may assume an importance greater than it ought to vis-à-vis safety. Safety must always be paramount, but at the same time the conscientious signalman or driver is always anxious to minimise delays, hence the occasional lapse, which is often not the result of recklessness or carelessness, but is the result of a genuine concern to do one's best for the customer, part of the railway tradition of service.

BR's considerations were based on two possibilities — (1) the issuing of a printed notice to a driver by the signalman whenever a signal has to be passed at Danger, and (2) the laying down of a maximum speed at which a driver may travel after passing a signal at Danger. The advantages of the printed notice, or ticket, were thought to be as follows:

1 The completion of a ticket would give the signalman a breathing space in which to collect his thoughts.
2 The ticket would specify which signal was to be passed at Danger, and the reason, eg signal locked at Danger by track circuit showing Occupied.
3 The ticket could carry a warning to the driver reminding him of the need to travel cautiously, prepared to stop short of any obstruction, and pointing out that there may well be a train or other obstruction anywhere on the line ahead.
4 If it were decided to impose maximum speeds this could be shown on the ticket.
5 It would reduce the risk of misunderstanding which is always present with messages passed by word of mouth, especially on the telephone.
6 It would provide the driver with a record of being authorised to pass a signal at Danger, in case of subsequent dispute.

Both drivers and signalmen would be supplied with tear-off booklets of tickets. Where the message is given verbally, the signalman would complete a ticket and hand it to the driver; where the message is given over the telephone the driver would complete the ticket. This procedure is followed on some Continental railways but it was finally concluded by BR that the situation was not sufficiently serious to justify such a change. However, the idea is available should the position deteriorate. It was argued that the driver might find it difficult to complete a ticket standing at a lineside telephone in the dark and in pouring rain, but the answer to that objection is that if the driver can't remember what he has been told when he gets back to the warmth and light of his cab, to complete the ticket there, he isn't in a position to take his train forward safely. What is certain is that some drivers would have welcomed the ticket system. They are often uneasy about passing signals at Danger in case of dispute or argument afterwards, and the existence of a ticket would be documentary proof in their favour.

The second consideration concerned the laying down of a maximum speed. It would obviously be inappropriate to lay down one specific speed, because it would have to be low enough to be safe in the worst conditions of darkness, fog, etc without imposing unnecessary delay in conditions of bright sunshine — an impracticability. There are so many factors to be taken into account:

1 Daylight or darkness.
2 Clear or foggy.
3 Curvature of the line.
4 Obstruction to the forward view caused by overbridges, station buildings, etc.
5 Tunnels and their length.
6 Severity of gradient, rising or falling.
7 Effectiveness of available brake-power.

Many of the factors may not be constant throughout a long section. Eventually, after much debate, two alternatives emerged; to lay down maximum speeds of 30mph for clear weather in daylight and 15/20mph in darkness or poor visibility, leaving the driver to use his judgement to run at a lower speed if conditions required it. The other alternative was not to quote specific maximum speeds in case they came to be regarded as the norm, but to leave it to drivers' judgement, whilst at the same time drawing their attention to the problem. The second alternative was chosen and a notice to drivers was issued to be kept at the front of one of the books of Rules and Regulations known as the *General Appendix to Working Timetables and Books of Rules and Regulations*. It is a sort of all-purpose volume for those instructions which do not naturally fit into any of the other publications, so as a result it is quite a thick book, although vigorously weeded from time to time. The difference between the Rule Book and the General Appendix is basically that the Rule Book sets out safe procedures for running trains under varying circumstances, but without explanation; it says 'Do this' or 'Do that' and wisely leaves no room for debate or argument. The Rules, as far as possible, are clear and concise; at least that is the aim, although the complexities of modern equipment sometimes make it difficult to achieve. The *General Appendix*, on the other hand, can allow itself the luxury of explanation and amplification. The notice to drivers referred to reads as follows:

When a signalman instructs a driver to pass a signal at Danger and travel cautiously through a section . . . the Driver must travel at such a reduced speed as will enable him to stop safely and well clear of any train or other obstruction which may be on the line ahead. In determining the safe speed at which he may travel the Driver must be guided by the braking capability of his train and his view of the line ahead, due regard being paid to darkness, fog or falling snow, or where curvature of the line restricts the view of the line ahead, or any other adverse circumstances. THE DRIVER MUST ALWAYS BE ABLE TO STOP WITHIN THE DISTANCE HE CAN SEE THE LINE TO BE CLEAR.

Whether this will be sufficiently effective remains to be seen, but so far it appears to be. If events prove otherwise, BR has two shots in its locker.

There remains one more question to consider — the passing of messages by word of mouth. As we have seen, such messages can quite literally be a matter of life and death, therefore the importance of passing them accurately and understanding them fully cannot be over-emphasised, but if safety is to be assured the content of the message being passed must be right too. This means that the giver of the message must have accurately assessed the situation, avoided jumping to any wrong conclusions or making false assumptions, chosen his words carefully and phrased his message clearly, unambiguously, concisely and in accordance with the Rules. Should the message contain explanation or merely instructions? Explanations might make the message easier to understand, but they can also distract and mislead, despite the best of intentions. Speculation must be avoided, in case the seeds of a wrong assumption are planted in the recipient's mind. The environment in which messages are passed is often very unhelpful, as for example in the case of the signalman having to lean out of his signalbox window to shout a message to a driver, possibly in a dialect which is not the driver's, using local terminology, in a howling wind against the throb of a diesel engine. It is not likely to be a model of grammatical elegance, and bitter experience teaches that it may not be correctly understood. Or picture a driver speaking to a signalman from a lineside telephone; one which is located between two tracks with other trains whistling by at 100mph or more, and with rain water trickling down his neck. One can only wonder that there are not more errors.

Radio helps to overcome the environmental problems mentioned in passing messages, and by its very nature causes messages to be passed in a more disciplined manner, partly because mistakes can be made so easily if the laid-down procedures for identification, etc are not properly followed. It might also be added that if radio had been available to the signalman at Gerrards Cross he might have been able to tell the driver of the DMU to stop his train, in time to avoid the crash (see also the discussion on the Invergowrie collision in Chapter 2). It is clear that the provision of radio on a wide scale could greatly assist the cause of safety but its use on BR for communication between signalmen and drivers is coming very slowly, although early in 1986 BR ordered sufficient sets of train radio equipment from Storno Ltd to equip 525 locomotives and multiple-units, at a cost of £1 million. The cab-mounted radio-telephones will have emergency buttons to alert controllers to any hazard. Progress could be quicker, but once again it is a question of money, with the British Railways Board being increasingly squeezed year by year by the government of the day to reduce its financial support from public funds. Continental railways do not suffer from such financial hardships — the French, the Germans and the Dutch, for example, have already equipped most of their trains with radio, whilst British Rail have only just started with the suburban lines from St Pancras and King's Cross and on lines in parts of Scotland and Wales.

The attitude of the railway Trade Unions to radio on trains is interesting. Individual drivers would welcome it because they can see its advantages, and their Union, ASLEF, adopted a not unhelpful attitude. The National Union of Railwaymen on the other hand was more cautious in its approach because it could see that radio would help BR to run trains without guards, and unfortunately the two issues became linked, culminating in industrial action. The introduction of radio was delayed for several years.

The Seer Green accident was a classic of its kind because it raised so many questions. We have ranged far and wide in this chapter discussing the many issues, the most important of which were:

1 Safe procedures for authorising drivers to pass signals at Danger.
2 What to do when track circuits unexpectedly show Occupied.
3 The speed of trains after the driver has been cautioned and sent past a signal at Danger.
4 Passing verbal messages.
5 Recruiting experienced signalmen for complex signal-boxes.
6 Avoiding jumping to conclusions.
7 Radio communication between drivers and signalmen.

Could an accident of the Seer Green type happen again? The answer must be that the possibility still exists, although the likelihood is remote. Most of the remedial action has consisted of amending the Rules and Regulations yet again. That is fine if every driver and every signalman reads the amendments, understands them and the reasoning behind them, and is then sufficiently well-informed and experienced to apply them correctly at a time of pressure. It is a lot to expect of the system.

What else could BR have done? It could have:

1 Made the rear of trains more conspicuous by providing two bright tail lamps on all passenger trains.
2 Provided guards with emergency flares.
3 Provided radio communication between signalmen and drivers.
4 Introduced a ticket system for passing signals at Danger.
5 Laid down maximum speeds at which trains may travel after being cautioned and passing signals at Danger.
6 Avoided having inexperienced signalmen in complicated signalboxes.
7 Provided 'refreshers' for drivers, to ensure that their Rules knowledge was always up-to-date and that, as far as possible, they understood the implications of, and the reasons for, changes in the Rules.

BR has already made considerable progress with item **1** (tail lamps), whilst item **3** (radio) is being introduced as fast as BR feel that it can be afforded. None of the other measures is particularly expensive so why has BR not adopted them? The reason can only be that the situation was judged not to be sufficiently serious to justify the changes in operating procedures involved. Would those changes prevent another accident of the Seer Green type? The answer must be that they could not be guaranteed to do so, but only that they would make another accident less likely. But let the last word rest with Maj Rose, in his report dated 31 January 1983: '(The Seer Green accident) was made more poignant by the fact that such accidents are rare events . . . In four out of the past seven years not a single passenger died in a train accident. Rail travel is now safer than it has ever been . . . I do not believe that (this accident) has indicated any area, other than the continued replacement of outworn semaphore signalling by centralised colour-light signalling, where large additional investment in safety measures would be justified or cost effective.'

In the Signalbox

No trains run, except in sidings, without the full knowledge and consent of the signalman. He is vitally involved in every case. One false step on his part, a wrong assumption, a hasty conclusion or just plain human forgetfulness, could lead to disaster; and has often done so in the past. Yet, of the eight Public Inquiries held by Inspecting Officers of the Department of Transport into serious accidents in 1984, none involved the signalman. Three of the accidents were caused by driver's error, three had a technical cause, one was caused by the light in a tail lamp going out and one was caused when a train ran into cattle which had strayed on to the line. In 1983 a signalman was involved in just one accident (at Wrawby Junction, Eastern Region) out of six which were the subject of Public Inquiries, and in 1982 one out of five (at Clayton Bridge level crossing, near Manchester). There has been only one case of an accident being caused by irregularities in the working of the Absolute Block Signalling system since 1977.

It is a matter of interest that both the accidents mentioned in which signalmen were involved (Wrawby Junction and Clayton Bridge) occurred during failures of signalling equipment. At Wrawby Junction the signalman overlooked the need to put a clamp on some points worked by an electric motor during a failure. The points then moved unbeknown to him and caused two trains to collide. In the case of the Clayton Bridge accident, the level crossing there is operated remotely by the signalman at Baguley Fold Junction, some distance away, and monitored by him by means of closed-circuit television equipment. A track circuit had developed a technical fault and was locking a Stop signal at Danger to prevent it being cleared. This signal protected the level crossing, and the signalman authorised the driver to pass the signal at Danger. The barriers at the level crossing were already lowered across the road for a train travelling in the opposite direction and as soon as that train had cleared the crossing the barriers started to rise whilst the other train was just about to go over it. A car set off over the crossing and was hit by the train. The signalman had overlooked the fact that he had left the operating switch for the barriers in the 'automatic-raise' position, and he should have placed it in the 'manual' position before authorising the driver to pass the signal at Danger. We have noticed before how new or unfamiliar equipment can contain its own hidden hazards, especially during a failure.

When one considers the total number of trains which signalmen deal with each day, and the ever-present possibility of error, BR has a magnificent safety record, and one of which signalmen, and British Rail as a whole, can be, and are, rightly proud. Yet how has it come about?

This chapter is not intended to be a history of signalling, except perhaps for the last few years. There are other books available which cover that fascinating story. Suffice it to say that safety in signalboxes has always been the subject of close managerial and technical study ever since the

Below:
The wreckage of the leading coach of the DMU involved in the collision at Wrawby Junction between the 17.32 passenger train from Cleethorpes to Sheffield and an oil-tank train on 9 December 1983. One passenger was killed. John Wright

Above:
Clayton Bridge level crossing, before its conversion to remotely-controlled lifting barriers, showing '8F' 2-8-0 No 48652 on an enthusiasts' railtour on 27 May 1968. D. A. Idle

operation of points and signals was collected together locally in one signalbox in the early days of railways. Every accident is studied to see what lessons there are to be learnt, so that remedies can be applied, and although by now there is little new to discover about safety in signalboxes, changes in methods or equipment may bring new hidden dangers.

Let us look in one of the thousands of traditional manual signalboxes which still remain today to see how safety is provided for, and consider separately the signalman, the signalling equipment, the method of working, and the operating of trains. To take the signalman first. What are the qualities needed? He needs self-reliance, because he has to act on his own with very little supervision; self-discipline, to be able to accept and apply the rigid disciplines of the signalling system and the Rules; resourcefulness to cope with emergencies; self-confidence to deal with the pressures of train working and failures of equipment; and steadiness both to accept periods of inactivity between trains and to cope safely with the urgent demands of failures and emergencies. It is no mere coincidence that these are the qualities which might describe a policeman; the original railway signalmen were policemen employed by the early railways, and signalmen are still known as 'Bobbies'.

Signalmen receive very little direct supervision, nor do the better ones require it. A visit once or twice a week by the local Manager or Area Inspector is the norm, the purpose being to see that the working is strictly in accordance with the Rules and Regulations; that the equipment is in proper working order; and that the emergency equipment is in its proper place and readily available. The supervisor will also examine the train register book, in which the signalman records the time at which all bell signals are sent or received and any unusual events. The signalman is required to enter these times immediately so that he always has an up-to-the-minute record of the state of train-working. But the most important aspect of the supervision of signalmen, as with any supervision, is to know the quality of the men concerned, how reliable and dependable they are, how conscientious, how good their knowledge is and how good they are at applying it. It is important to recognise their strengths and weaknesses, so that supervision, help and guidance can be directed where it is most needed and where it will be most effective. It is particularly important to be able to spot the man who is unreliable or careless so that he can be specially watched and dealt with as necessary. It is also necessary to keep a fatherly eye on those keen young signalmen who, without the benefit of maturity gained from years of experience, may act impetuously in their anxiety to minimise delay during failures or emergencies.

Moving on now to an examination of the equipment in the traditional signalbox; the most striking feature is the row of levers which operate the points and signals. They are

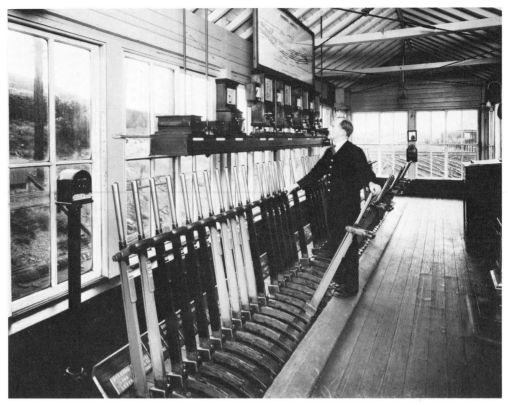

Right:
The austere and functional interior of an LNWR signalbox is well portrayed in this view of Marsden signalbox on the Huddersfield-Manchester route, taken at least 40 years ago. Although this was a busy four-track route the signalman had only the basic equipment to help him. On the 'block shelf' above the row of levers can be seen the block instruments and bells. There appears to have been no electrical control on the starting signals, which would therefore have been free to be pulled at any time. LNWR lever frames were very solidly built. British Railways

painted in different colours for the different functions and are interlocked so that they cannot be operated in confliction with each other. On a shelf above the frame of levers are the block signalling instruments, the bells for receiving signalling messages from the next signalbox and the tappers for sending them. As mentioned in Chapter 2 there are electrically-operated safety controls governing the operation of the block instruments and signals. There are also indicators of various types showing the operation of track circuits, the position of signal arms which are out of sight and whether signal lamps are lit or not. Above the shelf there is a large diagram giving the track layout of the area under the control of the signalman, with points, signals, gradients, distances, etc shown on it. In busier signalboxes some of the indicators just mentioned may be electrically incorporated in the diagram so that the signalmen can see at a glance where trains are. There will also be a supply of detonators for use in an emergency and there may be detonator-placing equipment, usually operated by a lever in the frame, which places detonators on the line opposite the signalbox to warn drivers in a last-minute emergency. Finally there will be a red flag, a green flag and a handlamp which can show separately red, green, and white.

The method of working depends on the type of line, but it is usually the Absolute Block System for double lines outside modern power-signalled areas. The use of the Block system on lines used by passenger trains represents one of the very few cases where Parliament has actually intervened to compel railway companies to adopt safety measures. Section 1 of the Regulation of Railways Act 1889 enacts that:

'The Board of Trade may from time to time order a railway company . . . to adopt the Block system on all or any of their railways open for the public conveyance of passengers.'

The system has already been described on page 29. On some lines used only by freight trains (usually known as goods lines), and often at busy passenger stations, a form of working is adopted, known as Permissive Block, which allows more than one train to be in a section at once. Speeds on such lines are low and if a train is being allowed into a section which is already occupied by another train, the driver is made aware of this by the signalman using a special signal, known as a Calling-on signal, which takes the form of a miniature arm located below the Stop signal. This type of working used to be extremely common and it was a frequent sight 20 or 30 years ago to have freight trains queuing up one behind the other on the approaches to marshalling yards, etc. Now, with changes in the pattern of freight working it is becoming much rarer.

It will readily be appreciated that allowing trains to follow each other in such a manner is not without a degree of danger, and requires the driver to keep a sharp lookout, especially during darkness. Accidents are still occurring on such lines — on 7 November 1980 the 12.10 freight train from Guide Bridge to Bayston Hill, hauled by Class 47 diesel-electric locomotive No 47190, crashed into the rear of another freight train at 25mph in daylight and good visibility on the Up Salop Goods Line at Crewe. The driver, who together with the guard was killed, was considered by the Inspecting Officer at the Public Inquiry not to have kept a good lookout, as the train in front could be seen for 200yd, yet the driver did not start to brake until he was only 60yd from it.

On 3 February 1984, at 02.14, a particularly unfortunate set of circumstances led to the death of a driver and guard at Wigan North Western station. A points failure was causing some delays, and trains were being detained at signals. A Freightliner train was standing just beyond the station at a colour-light signal worked from Warrington power signalbox. Standing at the next signal behind was Speedlink freight train 6M79, the 21.05 Mossend (Glasgow)-Bescot (Birmingham), hauled by an electric locomotive No 86032. The line through the station was authorised for permissive working when necessary, but only for passenger trains. However, the signalman, anxious to move 6M79 forward so that he could divert an express round the two freight trains, gave the driver permissive authority to draw

forward. Whilst the signalman was not specifically authorised to do this, it was not unsafe as all the signalling equipment necessary to allow it to be done safely was provided; it was merely that, due to changes in the pattern of freight train working, it was no longer necessary for freight trains to follow each other in a permissive manner at Wigan, therefore the authority to do so had been cancelled. The driver of 6M79 received the appropriate permissive signal (two small white lights, one diagonally above the other), which was located on the same post as the main line signal and a few feet below it, the main line signal remaining correctly at Red. The rear wagon of the Freightliner train was empty and its low flat profile was almost invisible. The tail lamp, which might have saved the day, was out. In the darkness and rain 6M79 ran into the back of the Freightliner train and both driver and guard were killed. No blame could be attached to the driver; what was needed was a more reliable tail lamp. This was the third collision in five years where a second train had run into the back of a Freightliner train whose tail lamp had failed.

To return to our story, however. We have looked at the signalman, his equipment and his rules. He is now ready to start signalling trains. But he needs something else if he is to do his job properly. He needs a timetable so that he knows what trains to expect, where they go to, and when. He also needs to know how to recognise them and how they rank for priority in running. All trains have an individual four-character number, the first digit being the train classification, the second a letter indicating a geographical area or destination region. The third and fourth numbers give the individual train number. All trains are grouped in classes 1-9, and 0; the classes being:

Class 1:   Express passenger train
Postal train
Newspaper train
Breakdown van train going to clear the line or returning therefrom
Light locomotive going to assist disabled train or snow plough going to clear the line
Motorail train not conveying passengers

Class 2:   Ordinary passenger train
Breakdown van train or snow plough not going to clear the line
Officers' special train

Class 3:   Parcels train permitted to run at 90mph or over

Class 4:   Freight train permitted to run at more than 60mph

Class 5:   Empty coaching stock train

Class 6:   Freight train not permitted to run at more than 60mph

Class 7:   Freight train not permitted to run at more than 45mph

Class 8:   Freight train timed at 35mph or below or conveying wagons with maximum permitted speed of 35mph

Class 9a: Freight train not fully fitted but with brake force not less than shown in Working Manual for Rail Staff

Class 9b: Unfitted freight train

Class 0:   Light locomotive(s)

Notes 1   The term 'Freight Train' includes parcel trains
2   All trains except Class 9 must be continuously braked
3   Engineers' trains and machines will be classified by their speed
4   The term 'Breakdown van train' includes an overhead wiring train.

Trains used to be recognisable by the arrangement of one or two white lights at the front, and every schoolboy eventually found out what the different arrangements meant, in fact every book on railways, intended for boys, contained a full set of diagrams; one lamp at each side of the buffer beam was the most exciting, because that denoted an express passenger train. This system continued until the end of the steam era, in fact the early diesels were equipped appropriately with small electric lights, and hinged white discs for daytime use.

Trains have always had their own individual numbers for identification purposes but these are only shown in the working timetables issued to the staff, and not in the public timetables. Continental railway administrations however, make widespread use of train numbers in their advertising literature and passenger information systems. When the four-character system was introduced on BR, locomotives were equipped with illuminated boxes or panels at each end so that the number could be exhibited on roller blinds for the benefit of operating staff. This was a very useful operating facility, which was particularly valuable when the service was disrupted, but the Mechanical Engineer found the blinds expensive to maintain, so the indicator boxes were blanked out. From an operating point of view it was a great pity, but it was a victim of the incessant financial pressures on BR.

Signalmen at junctions obviously need to be aware of the identity of approaching trains, and there are a number of ways of achieving this:

1 By using special 'Is line clear?' bell signals for trains going on to the branch line.

2 By using special 'train entering section' bell signals for trains going on to the branch line.

3 By the use of a special telegraph needle, deflected one way for the branch, the other way for the main line.

4 By telephone-circuiting, in which the identity of the train is either given to a number of signalboxes simultaneously; or individually after the 'Is line clear?' bell signal has been sent.

At large stations signalmen do not usually clear their signals for a train which has stopped there, until they are told that it is ready to leave, in case it is delayed for reasons unknown to the signalman. The advice to the signalman that a train is ready to leave is usually given electrically by the platform supervisor pressing a plunger or button known as a 'Train Ready to Start' button, which operates an indicator in the signalbox.

By a process of gradual improvement over many years, by the application of technical skills and ingenuity, the use of the latest techniques and much capital investment, signalling has been brought to a very high level of safety indeed. One accident which might be taken as a landmark

deliberately adopting an irregular method of operating the Block System, by using a short-cut procedure. This saved them work; in particular it saved them from having to get up from their seats so often to answer the bells. The standard of supervision was too low, despite regular visits to the signalbox by a variety of Inspectors and Managers. To supervise effectively the supervisor needs to know the signalman's job thoroughly. He also needs to be aware of, and keep a sharp lookout for, the tell-tale signs that everything is not as it should be. However, Area Managers, their assistants and Inspectors cover large areas nowadays, which may contain many signalboxes. Some signalboxes may only be visited by a supervisor once or twice a week which means, taking the effects of shift work into account, that individual signalmen may only be seen once or twice a month, and then only for a short time. The amount of supervision that can be given in such circumstances is clearly very small. It is fortunate therefore that the great majority of signalmen work perfectly well (and safely) with such minimal supervision, but it is all the more important to be able to identify the few who do not.

In years gone by, all stations of any size had their own station master, whilst smaller stations were paired. There was, therefore, regular on-the-spot supervision of a type that cannot be given today: indeed, the situation is getting worse, as British Rail continue to amalgamate areas, making local supervision even more remote. There is a strong case, not only on safety grounds but on commercial grounds too, for restoring station masters to the larger stations. It makes no sense at all to have such stations as Lancaster, Durham and Taunton without a resident 'Mr Railway', with the dignity and status, or what one might call the 'recognisable presence', of the former station master. The young traffic managers of today may be good at management, but 'presence' requires a certain maturity which they have not yet had time to acquire. The young signalmen at Gerrards Cross and Altofts Junction (and at Chinley, where a driver was killed in a collision in March 1986) would all have benefitted from closer and more frequent supervision. Whether the accidents would then not have happened is impossible to say, but there is at least a chance that they would not have done.

Although the Liverpool-Southport line is a busy suburban route, with trains every few minutes in the peak, the signalling equipment lacked many of the controls which one would have expected to find there, indeed there were virtually none between Hall Road signalbox and the next two signalboxes towards Southport, ie Hightown and Eccles Crossing. Yet, there had been a previous collision at Hall Road in 1961, after which Col McMullen, the Inspecting Officer, had recommended that a number of specific controls be provided to safeguard against human error or forgetfulness; whether from simple failure of the human element or arising from slack working. What Col McMullen actually said was: 'The signalmen at Hall Road . . . are required to deal with over 100 trains per day in each direction. There are, however, no block controls on the Starting signals and there is no Welwyn Control[1] . . . For traffic of this nature full track-circuiting and train

because it led to a decision to increase over BR as a whole the extent to which particular safeguards were applied, occurred on 4 July 1977 near Hall Road station on the suburban electrified line between Southport and Liverpool.

The 20.15 three-car electric train from Southport to Liverpool had been stopped for about 5min at the Home signal at Hall Road signalbox because the signal was at Danger. The signal was then cleared and the train had just started to move off when it was run into in the rear at about 20mph by a five-car electric train, the 20.30 Southport-Liverpool. All the vehicles of both trains were damaged but fortunately no one was killed, although 35 people were taken to hospital, two of whom were detained overnight.

This was a classic case of 'Two in a section', the signalman's nightmare, and it arose from irregularities in the working of the Block System by the signalman at the next signalbox open on the Southport side of Hall Road, ie Eccles Crossing, who wrongly allowed the second train to proceed, having concluded that the section was clear. The Public Inquiry, held by Maj Olver, an Inspecting Officer, brought to light a number of unsatisfactory features.

There was evidence that some signalmen were at times

describers are desirable, but this equipment is expensive. I do, however, think that at least a block release on the Starting signals and the Welwyn Control should be provided . . . and I recommend that consideration should be given to their provision.' Unfortunately BR had not implemented this recommendation, although they had already programmed the work for 1978 when the second Hall Road accident occurred.

After the second Hall Road accident BR determined to make some amends, not only on the Southport line but anywhere else where similar conditions existed[2]. They adopted the following new standards:

1 On important lines, ie main trunk routes and/or routes with 10 or more trains in the same direction in any one peak hour

(i) The Home signal lever and the Distant signal arm must be proved to be in the Normal Position (ie lever back in its frame, signal arm at Caution) before the Block Instrument can be placed at 'Line Clear'.

(ii) There must be a berth track circuit on the approach side of the Home signal which, when occupied, would place the Block Indicator to 'Train in Section', or hold it in that position. Welwyn Control must be provided.

(iii) There must be sequential interlocking between the Home and Starting signals.

(iv) The Starting signal must be electrically locked at Danger until released by the Block Indicator for the next signalbox being placed to 'Line Clear' for one operation of the signal only. A second operation must require a second 'Line Clear'.

2 On less important lines of a more local nature

The controls and equipment mentioned in 1(i) and 1(iv) must be provided.

The work was staged over a number of years because of its cost and the demands on technical manpower at a time when staff numbers were being reduced to allow BR to meet its government-imposed financial targets. Actually the capital cost of the additional equipment was not great, and could easily have been met out of one year's budget, but the work was labour-intensive and to have concentrated the limited technical resources on it would have delayed other worthwhile projects.

The term 'Welwyn Control' has been used a number of times. It denotes a piece of equipment designed after a particularly serious accident at Welwyn Garden City in 1935 and is provided in conjunction with the equipment and controls mentioned in 1(ii) above. After the Block Indicator has been placed in the 'Train in Section' position it cannot be turned to any other position until the train has

1

Contrasting Architectural Styles in Power Signalboxes

1 **Manchester Piccadilly, opened in 1960.** British Railways

2 **Coventry, dating from 1962. Light and airy, the design gives the signalmen an all-round view, a feature lacking from more recent designs.** British Railways

3 **The nadir of signalbox design? The wooden hut on the roof is not a pigeon loft but the signalling operations room. This signalbox — Reading — covers a very wide area.** British Railways

4 **An original design, to say the least. Birmingham New Street. The signalling operations room is on the top floor.** British Railways

5 **Into the 1970s. Designed to confuse a potential saboteur into thinking that it is a crematorium, or a modern waste-disposal plant? Motherwell.** British Rail

6 **The most unlikely-looking signalbox ever? This building, at Westbury, has a distinctly central-European look about it.** D. E. Conway

2

3

been proved to have passed through the section by its occupation of the berth track circuit at the Home signal. The question then arises of what is to be done if for some reason the train is cancelled after the Block Indicator has been placed in the 'Train in Section' position, or has been put there by the signalman in error. How can it then be released? Welwyn Control provides such a release, requiring the signalman to turn a small wheel about 100 times whilst a disc revolves to tell him when he has done enough. The idea behind the monotonous turning of the wheel is that it gives the signalman time to reconsider whether he ought to be obtaining a release, or whether there might really be a train somewhere in the section. It guards against the dangers of misdirected impetuous action. It also gives the train time to arrive at the Home signal. It is an ingenious idea and it seems to have been effective. Long before 1935 several railway companies had devised similar systems but the releases could be obtained quickly and easily and several accidents resulted from over-hasty action by signalmen. The Midland Railway's Rotary Block was an example of this; it was a very safe system normally, but to obtain a release from 'Train in Section' all the signalman had to do was break a small piece of glass and press a button (similar to a fire-alarm). It was not something to be done lightly, because there was a lot of explaining to be done afterwards and reports to be written,

but it *could* be done hastily and without sufficient thought if the signalman was under pressure and anxious to avoid delay. Sykes Lock and Block system, widely used on several pre-Grouping companies, particularly those which formed the Southern Railway, and very highly regarded, had shortcomings of a similar nature.

So far as the signalman is concerned, the ultimate in safety must be the modern power signalbox, or Signalling Centre as it is sometimes called. It is a far cry from the early days of signalling when safety depended on the signalman faithfully carrying out his Rules and Regulations, with an accident being the likely result of any error. The science of signal engineering subsequently developed to provide a very high level of safety in manual signalboxes equipped with all the latest safety devices and controls, but it was still possible for signalmen to make potentially dangerous mistakes, or to operate the signals in such a way that the message they gave to drivers was less than completely unambiguous. Power signalboxes overcame those problems, although they were not designed primarily to improve safety levels, which were already very high, but rather to provide a more efficient means of planning and organising train movements in busy, complex or congested areas, an activity which goes under the title of train regulating. The power box signalman is now a train regulator, not employed to exercise his brawny muscles on pulling heavy

4 **5**

BIRMINGHAM NEW STREET SIGNAL BOX

6

Above:
The work of dozens of old manual signalboxes is combined in one modern power signalbox. This is Carlisle. British Railways

Right:
A close-up of the station area on the Carlisle panel. The signalman appears to be about to cancel a route from platform 4 to the Up LNWR, shown by the white lights.
British Railways

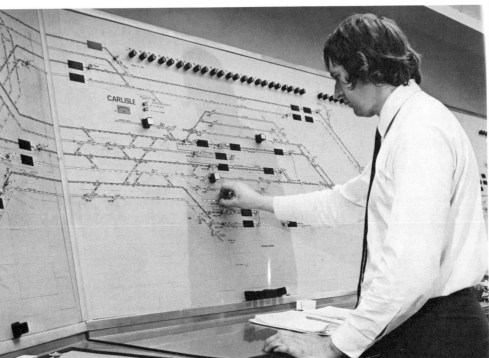

levers, with his brain power concentrated on the discipline and routine of the signalling Rules and Regulations, but rather to exercise his skill and judgement to achieve the best possible level of train regulation, optimising the use of the track, and keeping delays to a minimum. The job description has changed somewhat; the man description even more, and it is to the credit of so many signalmen that they have successfully adapted to the major change of environment, especially the change from being king of their own little castle to being members of a possibly quite large team in highly-technical surroundings, and not even seeing more than a fraction of the trains they deal with.

The most arresting features of the operating room in a modern power signalbox are the operating and indications panels. In some boxes they are combined, in others separate. The indications panel carries a diagrammatic representation of all the lines under the signalman's control. The signalman sets a route for a train by simply pressing two buttons — one at the start of the route and one at the end of it. If the route is available (ie if it has not already been promised to another train) the electrical equipment will do the rest. It will check if the route is available; if it is, it will move the points, lock them, guard them against other train movements and not clear the signals until all safety requirements have been satisfied. The signalman will know when this has happened (sometimes almost in a split second) because the route he has selected will light up, showing a row of white lights. He will know when the train comes along because red lights will appear along the route. He will know which train it is

because its identification number will be displayed on the panel by the train describer equipment, and the signals, which will all be of the colour-light type, will revert to Danger behind it. The whole area will be track-circuited and very safe. There will be no bells (except emergency ones) and no block instruments.

It will probably have occurred to the reader by now that the process of setting routes and regulating trains is tailor-made for computerised operation, without the intervention of signalmen. This is already the normal practice on modern Metro systems with a fairly simple repetitive timetable, a limited network of lines and a high degree of punctuality. If sufficient capital is available it seems certain to be adopted on BR where similar conditions prevail, eg on large parts of the Southern Region and in suburban areas around London and other major cities, in fact there are already several small-scale installations on the Southern Region, and a major system is planned for the new Yoker signalbox to deal with the north-Glasgow electrified service. It will be no less safe.

The verdict on the standard of safety in signalboxes must be that it is now very high indeed despite occasional lapses; but that is only half the story. Safety will only be assured if the message given by the signalman through the lineside signals is correctly received, interpreted, and acted upon by the driver; and that is the subject of the next chapter.

[1] See description on page 84.
[2] Studies had already been taking place following the collision near Whitehaven on 27 November 1973.

From the Driver's Cab

On 16 December 1971 at Lenton South Junction, Nottingham, there was a collision which not only aroused a great deal of interest among drivers, but also caused them some uneasiness. A heavy coal train, hauled by two Class 20 diesel-electric locomotives Nos 8115 and 8142, was proceeding slowly off the branch line on to the main Nottingham to Derby line at about 06.15 when it was run into head-on by the 01.30 parcels train from Liverpool to Nottingham, pulled by a Class 25 diesel-electric locomotive No 7605. The combined speed of the two trains at the moment of impact was something in the region of 40mph, and both drivers were killed by the force of the collision, together with the guard of the parcels train who was riding in the front cab of the locomotive.

The signalling in the area was of the modern multiple-aspect colour-light type, equipped with the Automatic Warning System, and was operated from Trent power signalbox, which had been opened only two years previously. According to the evidence of the guard of the coal train, and the signalman at Trent, the route had been set for the coal train to proceed from the branch line on to the Up main line to Trent and Derby, and the signal protecting the junction had been cleared to Green for it. The particular route along which the coal train had to traverse the junction required it to proceed for about 100yd in the 'facing' direction along the Down main line in order to reach a crossover which would take it on to the Up main line, and it was whilst travelling along the short section of Down main line that the collision occurred (the term 'facing direction' indicates a train movement in a direction opposite to the normal one for that section of line, eg an Up direction movement on a Down line). However, it should have been perfectly safe because the signals and signalling equipment (track circuits, interlocking, etc) were designed to cater for such movements.

The signalling equipment was exhaustively examined and tested after the accident, and no fault could be found which might have accounted for it. In the absence of any fault the main line signal protecting the movement off the branch would have been showing Red, with the signals in rear of it showing double Yellow and single Yellow respectively as they were approached by the driver of the parcels train. All three signals were provided with AWS and each one would have sounded a warning in the driving cab. If for any reason the driver had failed to react to those warnings and had not pressed his AWS acknowledgement button, the brakes would automatically have been applied. The train would then have been brought safely to a halt, at least from the double Yellow and single Yellow signals; and even from the Red signal the severity of the collision would have been reduced, as the distance from the AWS magnet serving the Red signal to the point of collision was 480yd, and the braking distance for the parcels train travelling at its maximum permitted speed of 45mph was only 500yd.

Lt-Col McNaughton held a Public Inquiry into this accident and concluded from the evidence that the driver of the parcels train had cancelled, in an automatic or subconscious manner, the AWS warnings he had received. No other conclusion was possible from the evidence, but drivers both in the Nottingham area and beyond found it difficult to comprehend how an experienced driver could have acted in such a manner. However, we now know from the driver's evidence at the Public Inquiry into the collision at Wembley on 11 October 1984 and from earlier accidents, that this can occur. One difficulty from a driver's point of view in such cases is that he cannot subsequently prove whether a signal was Green for him or not, even if he were to survive a crash (which is often not the case). If the evidence of the signalling equipment indicates that he has wrongly passed a signal at Danger he cannot prove otherwise, but neither can one prove absolutely that the signal was at Red when he passed it. The most that can be said is that no fault could afterwards be found in the signalling system, nor could anything be found to account for any failure. In effect the driver is left high and dry and some drivers would welcome a form of tachograph on the locomotive, to record both speed and adverse signals, and remove the element of doubt.

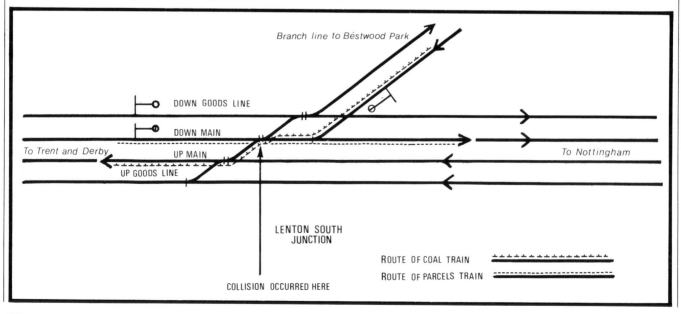

Below:
The destructive power of
head-on collisions.
Locomotives Nos 7605, 8115
and 8142 at Lenton South
Junction near Nottingham
after the accident on
16 December 1971.
Jack Hooke

Left:
The rear cab of Class 25
locomotive No 7605 was
completely destroyed by the
vehicles of its own parcels
train. Jack Hooks

Bottom:
A Class 150/1 Sprinter unit,
heading towards
Nottingham, passes over the
precise spot of the 1971 crash
at Lenton South Junction.
This is the view in 1986
looking westwards towards
Trent and Derby. Author

The driver is similarly exposed where speed checks are concerned. These are carried out regularly using a variety of methods, including radar speed meters. The preferred system is the 'measured track circuit', the length of which is known. The speed is calculated by taking the amount of time which elapses between the initial occupation of that particular track circuit and the initial occupation of the next one. The procedure can be carried out manually but it is preferable, and easier in modern power signalboxes, for it to be done automatically by the signalling equipment, with the results being printed out. If a train is then noticed to have been exceeding its maximum allowed speed the driver is seen and challenged. In the case of manual speed checks there is always a possibility of observer error, but with an automatic system there is practically none.

To return to the Lenton South Junction accident, the possibility was explored as to whether it would have been possible for the signalman to have changed his mind and altered the route which he had set, thus creating a potentially dangerous situation. The supposition is as follows:

Above:
No 37107 takes its train through the crossover at Haughley Junction after coming off the Cambridge line with the 12.55 Peterborough-Parkeston Quay, a few weeks after the collision between two mail trains, whose wreckage is still sheeted-up on site. John C. Baker

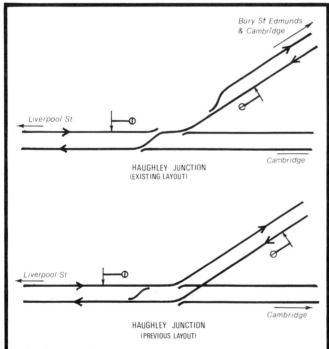

Flank Protection

With the existing layout, if a train from Liverpool Street wrongly runs past the junction signal at Danger it can collide head-on with a train coming on to the main line from the Cambridge direction. This could not have happened on the previous layout because the train from Liverpool Street would have been diverted on to the Branch towards Cambridge out of harm's way; the interlocking of the junction points would have ensured this.

'If the signalman had decided to run the parcels train over the junction first, and had cleared all his signals for it, and had then changed his mind and decided to let the coal train go first, he could have put his signals to Danger against the parcels train just as it was approaching the junction and too late for it to stop in time, and cleared his signals for the coal train. The coal train would then have moved off on to the junction to be met head-on by the approaching parcels train whose driver had been unable to stop.'

It sounds possible although most unlikely, but in fact the signalling equipment has been designed to make it not only unlikely but impossible. This is achieved by a process known as approach-locking. Once the signalman has set a route for a train, that route cannot be cancelled and a conflicting route set, until the train has passed over it or until a release mechanism has timed itself out. This release generally takes two minutes, sometimes more, and is designed to ensure that there is sufficient time, after the junction signal has been put back to Danger, for a train to come safely to a halt at it before the points can be moved, or alternatively if it is too close to the signal to be able to stop there it will have time to pass safely through the junction before another route can be set. At some locations approach-locking becomes operative as soon as the junction signal is cleared from Red; at others, where circumstances might require re-routeing to be done fairly frequenttly, approach-locking does not become operative until the junction signal has been cleared from Red *and* an approaching train has reached the sighting point of the furthest signal approaching the junction which would change from Green to Caution in the event of the junction signal being replaced to Danger.

We have noticed before how new technologies create new hazards. It is a paradox that despite the signalling in the Nottingham area as a whole being safer after the opening of Trent power signalbox than before, this accident might not have happened with the old signalling because of what is known as 'flank protection'. With a traditionally-signalled junction the trailing points leading from the branch line cannot be moved to allow a train to travel from the branch on to the main line until the parallel facing points have been set *towards* the branch. This ensures that if a train approaching the junction in the facing direction accidentally runs past the junction signal at Danger it will be diverted on to the branch out of harm's way instead of crashing headlong into a train coming off the branch. There was an accident, similar in some respects to the one at Lenton South Junction, which occurred on 22 June 1982 at Haughley Junction where the former Great Eastern main line from Liverpool Street goes forward to Norwich and a line to Cambridge via Bury St Edmunds turns off. The former double junction had been re-modelled by the Civil Engineer to reduce costs and simplify maintenance, but it also had the effect of removing flank protection. At 01.18 the 01.01 mail train from Ipswich to Peterborough accidentally overran the junction signal which was at Danger and collided with its opposite number, the 23.10 mail from Peterborough to Ipswich, which was just coming off the Cambridge branch on to the main line under Clear signals. Four members of the two train crews and two Post Office staff were injured and taken to hospital, but fortunately no one was killed.

Modern signalling controls should make such simplified layouts perfectly safe, but to be absolutely sure there must be 100% certainty of obedience to signals by drivers. It is not without significance that AWS was provided at both Lenton South Junction and Haughley Junction, and at both it was ineffective. At the former it is assumed that the driver cancelled the AWS warning subconsciously without

Left:
Switch diamonds in the Up main/Down Grimsby line at Werrington Junction, a few miles north of Peterborough. This photograph was taken about 30 years ago after the junction had been remodelled to allow high speeds to and from the branch. Ian Allan Library

Above:
A close-up of switch diamonds at Gretna Junction, looking north. The route is set for a train from the Dumfries direction. The complicated locking and detection apparatus can clearly be seen. This photograph was taken before the junction was remodelled under the Carlisle resignalling scheme.
British Railways

reacting to it; at the latter the train crew mismanaged the braking to such an extent that not only were they unable to stop at the junction signal but carried on for a further 230yd before hitting the other mail train. The benefit to the Civil Engineer of such simplified layouts is the elimination of the diamond-shaped crossing where the two tracks cross each other, saving both capital outlay and maintenance costs. It also eliminates a possible source of derailment if the crossing is not maintained to a sufficiently high standard. The debit to the Operator is the inability to run trains on to and off the branch simultaneously, and the creation of an additional potential hazard; on the other hand, it may allow higher speeds through the junction.

Signalling equipment is designed to 'fail safe'. A failure will have the effect of either replacing a Clear signal to Danger, or preventing a Danger signal from being cleared. This is known as a 'right-side' failure and is not at all uncommon given the tens of thousands of signals, points and track circuits on Britain's railways. On the other hand it can be very disconcerting to a driver who has passed a Green signal, suddenly to find himself confronted with a Red. He has no means of knowing immediately whether it has been caused by an equipment fault or whether the signal has been put to Red in an emergency; and he may easily have a few anxious moments if he passes the signal

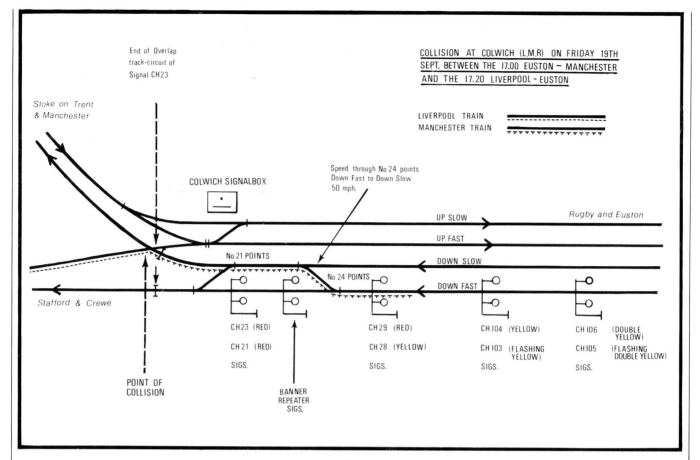

COLLISION AT COLWICH (LM.R) ON FRIDAY 19TH
SEPT. BETWEEN THE 17.00 EUSTON – MANCHESTER
AND THE 17.20 LIVERPOOL – EUSTON

LIVERPOOL TRAIN
MANCHESTER TRAIN

Stoke on Trent
& Manchester

COLWICH SIGNALBOX

Speed through No 24 points
Down Fast to Down Slow
50 mph.

UP SLOW   Rugby and Euston

UP FAST

No 21 POINTS

DOWN SLOW

No 24 POINTS

DOWN FAST

Stafford & Crewe

CH23 (RED)   CH29 (RED)   CH104 (YELLOW)   CH106   (DOUBLE
                                                                 YELLOW)
CH21 (RED)   CH28 (YELLOW)   CH103 (FLASHING   CH105   (FLASHING
                                          YELLOW)   DOUBLE YELLOW)
SIGS.   SIGS.   SIGS.   SIGS.

POINT OF
COLLISION

BANNER
REPEATER
SIGS.

before he can stop his train. To him, a Green signal followed by a Red is irregular and a wrong-side failure, but in fact it is very unlikely to be so; the signalling system is carrying out its designed function of failing-safe, ie a right-side failure. It is sometimes difficult to convince drivers that it is so, especially if failures occur frequently in particular areas due perhaps to equipment which is nearing the end of its life, or where high standards of equipment reliability may be difficult to achieve for technical or other reasons, such as unsatisfactory ground conditions affecting the operation of track circuits.

Signalling equipment nowadays is extremely complex, and the finer points of design and operation may be outside the knowledge and experience of many drivers. It is fortunate, and safe, that drivers customarily obey implicitly and with complete confidence the message given by signals without pondering too deeply on the reasons why a signal may be giving a particular message, or changing its message. Accidents caused by wrong-side failures are extremely rare, although one occurred at Bushbury Junction on the line from Stafford to Birmingham on 13 August 1979 when the 13.29 express from Manchester to Birmingham was derailed at about 35mph. No passengers were hurt but the driver was badly injured. Part of the junction layout known as a 'switch diamond' was not properly closed and this should have locked the junction signal at Danger, but it did not do so. A bearing screw in the point-operating machine had become disengaged and allowed the equipment which detects the position of the switch diamond to register that they were properly closed, when in fact they were standing slightly open. The irregular detection allowed the junction signal to be cleared from Red, and the train was derailed as it passed through the slightly-open switch diamond. The very rare wrong-side failures which occur are sometimes caused by irregular point detection incorrectly allowing a signal to show Clear

when it ought to be held at Red. It is almost unknown for a wrong-side failure to allow a signal to show Clear and lead a train into the danger of collision with another train.

It may seem at first sight that the messages given by railway signals are essentially simple. Red means stop; Green means go, and Yellow or Double Yellow means slow down because you are approaching a Red. In semaphore signalling a Distant signal (which is a yellow arm) in the horizontal position means 'Caution, the Home signal is at Danger'. If the arm is raised or lowered 45° it means 'Clear, and all the Stop signals worked from the same signalbox are also Clear'. A Stop signal has a red arm, and may be called the Home signal or the Starting signal (or the Outer Home signal, or the Advanced Starting signal). When the arm is horizontal it means 'Danger, Stop'. When the arm is raised or lowered 45° it means 'Proceed'. Every schoolboy knows that, or ought to. But things are not quite so simple, as we have already seen in Chapter 2 when we discussed the working of the signals at Longforgan signalbox, and some of it may not be evident to drivers, or even known by them. Let us consider a few examples in the field of multiple-aspect colour-light signalling.

There is a safety margin known as an overlap, usually 200yd long, beyond most signals that can show a Red aspect, and it affects the working of signals in the following way. A signal (call it signal A) will not clear from Red until the previous train to pass it has proceeded through the signal section beyond, has passed clear of the next signal (B) and has passed completely clear of the overlap track circuit beyond Signal B. Where speeds are low the length of the overlap may be reduced, and in some station areas where speeds are very low, say 10 to 15mph, there may be no overlaps at all. Overlaps are an important part of the safety of junction working; after a route has been set up to a signal at a junction, the overlap of that signal is assumed to be part of the route; in other words it has been 'promised' to that train and cannot at the same time be promised to another train approaching from a different direction. In many cases, signals at a junction are located at overlap distance from the fouling point (ie the place where trains may cross each other's route or collide with each other) and this allows trains to approach close to the junction to wait their turn whilst other trains are using it. The concept of a safety overlap comes from the early days of Block Signalling, and for semaphore signals it is 440yd. Its purpose now is really to allow for the possibility of the driver mismanaging his brake and accidentally running past a Danger signal; it does not provide much of a safeguard against a driver who has failed to see the Distant signal and has only just applied his brakes when close to the signal at Danger, nor is it intended to act as a safeguard in such circumstances.

The majority of cases where drivers accidentally overrun a signal at Danger result from mismanagement of the brake, or from anticipating that the signal will clear when it does not; and not from the driver missing a signal altogether or misunderstanding its message. Usually the train stops with the locomotive only a few yards beyond the signal, and the driver reports to the signalman by means of the telephone at the signal (nearly all colour-light signals have a telephone) that he has 'just slipped by an engine-length'. The signalman will probably already know because he may have seen the overlap track circuit become illuminated on his indication panel. Drivers may not know how long (or short) an overlap track circuit is, but they can sometimes tell by the insulated rail joint at the end of it. They are unlikely to know in a station area but will be used to seeing fouling movements taking place a short distance ahead of them which they would not see out on the main line. At some stations such as Birmingham New Street, a restricted approach arrangement is in operation, whereby the signal controlling entry to the station will not clear from Red if the platform Starting signal is a Red, until the train is very close to it.

At junctions where drivers have to reduce speed in order to turn off the main line safely, or for example where they cross from a Fast line to a Slow line, the junction signal may be held at Red even though the route beyond it may have been set, until the train is assumed (through track circuit occupation) to have reduced its speed to a safe level. This process is known as 'approach control' and is very, very common. At high-speed junctions flashing-yellow aspects may be used to give the driver plenty of warning and avoid his having to reduce speed unduly. Drivers are accustomed to approach-control without necessarily knowing how it is achieved technically.

Drivers are vulnerable in their driving cabs if an accident occurs, and several of them are killed or seriously injured every year as we have already seen. However, if a driver causes an accident and survives, he may be charged with manslaughter if fatalities occur, or with endangering life if no one is killed. Such prosecutions have followed a number of the accidents mentioned in this book but have rarely been successful. For the prosecution to succeed, a high degree of negligence or recklessness has to be proved, and juries have been very reluctant to convict. Perhaps both they and the judge feel that the driver has already suffered

Below:
A view of Colwich Junction looking north after being relaid following the collision between two expresses on 19 September 1986, showing the Crewe line to the left and the Manchester via Stoke line to the right. The impact took place on the diamond crossing (top centre). Author

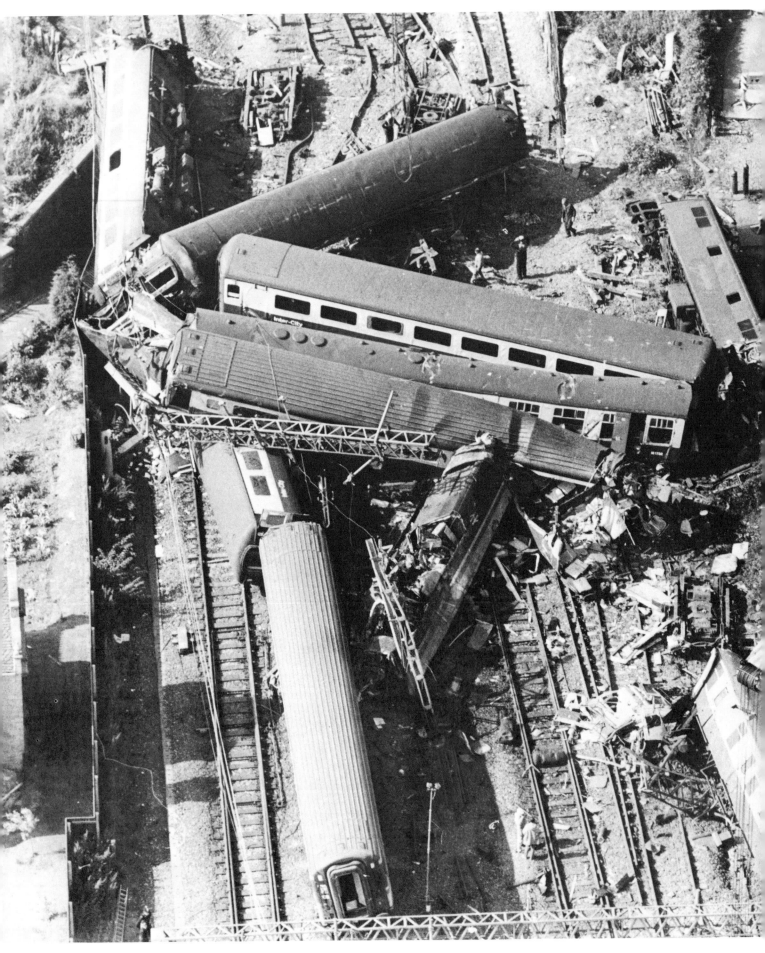

enough, with death and destruction on his conscience for the rest of his life as a result of some understandable human failing, without having to undergo further punishment and disgrace. It is interesting to note that these matters had come to prominence as long ago as 1840, when Section 13 of the Railway Regulation Act provided penalties for railway servants guilty of misconduct or neglect, or who were drunk when on duty. These powers are still in force today, although contained in later Acts. The most recent prosecutions followed the accidents at Nuneaton in June 1975 and Morpeth in June 1984. In the earlier case the driver was indicted on six counts of manslaughter but was acquitted by the jury on all charges. In the latter case the driver was found 'not guilty' by the jury of endangering the lives of 71 passengers through wilful omission or negligence. It ought perhaps to be pointed out here that the conclusions of an Inspecting Officer of the Department of Transport following a Public Inquiry into an accident are his personal conclusions based on the weight of evidence. His task is to establish the cause of an accident and he is not concerned with criminal negligence, nor with civil liability. He will always reach a conclusion, which may be firm or less so depending on the nature of the evidence. It is sometimes not possible to be 100% sure, especially if the driver is killed and his cab is wrecked, thus destroying a lot of the evidence. Evidence may allow a particular conclusion to be drawn, but it may not be sufficiently strong to result in a successful prosecution, or a successful charge under the railway's own internal disciplinary scheme. It might also be added that every serious accident is formally investigated by a team of railway experts before any Public Inquiry is held, and the team are required to reach a conclusion, based on the evidence, as to the probable cause. They are not required to make recommendations as to remedial measures — that is done separately by accident experts — unlike the Department of Transport Inspecting Officers, who do both. The railway's own accident reports are not published although copies are made available to the Inspecting Officers, whose reports *are* published.

A driver's job, in essence, is to run his train to time, to brake safely, and to obey all signals and speed limits, and to do this he needs to be thoroughly acquainted with the routes over which he works. Every six months he will 'sign' for such routes. Once a driver has passed his initial rigorous examination it is left almost entirely to his own sense of responsibility to keep himself fully acquainted with the Rules, and up to date. He will not be examined again, and the most he will have to do is to produce his Rule Book annually for inspection and satisfy an Inspector who will ride with him once a year for a few hours that he is still driving properly. The Inspector may ask questions about driving techniques, but not about the Rules. That is taboo; the Unions will not agree to it. These arrangements are not entirely satisfactory and it would be more effective if drivers were given periodic refresher courses not only to keep their knowledge up to date but also to ensure that they were aware of changes and understood them.

It is interesting to note that following two recent accidents in France caused by drivers failing to observe temporary speed restrictions, the French National Rail-

Left:
Locomotives and coaches lie scattered in all directions after the high-speed head-on crash at Colwich Junction on 19 September 1986. Looking at the mass of tangled wreckage, it is hard to believe that not a single passenger was killed, even through both trains were full. In the centre can be seen No 86429 *The Times*, which had been at the head of the Liverpool-Euston train, whilst to the right of the tracks is the locomotive of the Euston-Manchester service, No 86211 *City of Milton Keynes*. Times Newspapers Ltd

ways (SNCF) ordered oral Rule examinations for all staff responsible for safety. Drivers, who are examined on their route knowledge and safety procedures every three months, came out on strike. The proposal was dropped.

As we have seen from the accidents discussed and reviewed so far, no good case can be made out for having an additional man in the driving cab to help the driver, at least at speeds up to 100mph. When maximum speeds rose from 100mph to 125mph it was in some ways a leap into the unknown, and there was no sure way of knowing how drivers would react to the stress of signals coming at them 25% faster, but in fact modern signalling is so good, and so easy for drivers to understand, that there seems to be no case for an extra driver solely from the point of view of obedience to signals. Multiple-aspect colour-light signalling with AWS has considerably improved the driver's lot and removed much of the stress. There are, however, other factors, and these will now be discussed.

It is necessary to have a firm policy regarding the technical aids to be provided in the driving cab to guard against the effects of inattention, sleepiness or incapacity of the driver. AWS is provided to guard against all three but may be over-ridden involuntarily. The driver's safety device (the 'deadman's pedal') has been shown in this book to have been ineffective on several critical occasions, and modifications have been carried out to improve its efficiency. A centrally-pivoted design was introduced which required the driver to maintain it in a centrally-balanced position, and later a vigilance device was introduced which caused a bleeper to sound every minute and required the driver to release and reset the DSD. Whilst fairly effective, it was found to be cumbersome and intrusive, and modifications were planned which had the effect of postponing the bleep for a minute every time the driver proved that he was alert by operating any of the controls, such as brake, horn, power controller, etc. A great deal of thought, research and experimentation have gone into this subject, not only on BR but also abroad. It is a worldwide problem, but so far as BR is concerned it is clear that in order to increase safety something better is needed which concentrates *directly* on ensuring that the brake is applied at the right time rather than *indirectly* on ensuring that the driver stays alert. The latter does not in itself automatically guarantee that the brake will be applied when required.

There appear to be three alternatives:

1 An automatic system, whereby any necessity to brake, either for adverse signals, or for speed restrictions, is taken out of the driver's hands and done for him automatically. Metro systems nowadays often employ this method of working but it may be unsuitable for main-line working on two counts — expense, and the effect on the driver of having too little to do.
2 A monitoring system, which continuously checks the train's speed but only interposes when it detects that the train is going too fast. The speed and braking of the train would be left entirely in the driver's hands provided that he handled his train correctly. If he failed to do so for any reason the back-up system would over-ride him and take charge. By this means the dangers of drowsiness, inattention, incapacity or errors of judgement would be guarded against. Vigilance devices would not be needed, at least for safety; at the worst a train might pass through a station where it is booked to stop, without doing so, but it could not do so at an unsafe speed.
3 An advisory system such as the present BR standard AWS which has served the cause of safety well over the years, but which is now showing its age. The driver is expected to keep sufficiently alert at all times in order to use the advice he receives from the system, but in practical human terms it requires a standard of performance which is not consistently achievable across the length and breadth of the country all day and every day, and vigilance devices have had to be developed to fill the gap. They do so reasonably well but are a cumbersome addition; if the driver is running past a series of Caution signals and speed restrictions his AWS horn will sound at every one, and the warning it gives has to be acknowledged and acted upon. On top of that his vigilance device will bleep every minute, requiring him to re-set his DSD pedal. Furthermore the horn and bleep may coincide. Altogether it is an untidy arrangement and hardly appropriate for high-speed running.

What BR needs to do now if it wishes to enhance its already high safety standards and avoid more 'Wembleys' is to advance from an advisory system to a monitoring system, one that recognises when a driver ought to be braking for a Red signal or a speed restriction, and automatically applies the brake without the possibility of being over-ridden if the train is going too fast. A highly sophisticated and expensive automatic system is not necessary, nor is cab signalling. Even at 125mph the driver is perfectly capable of observing, interpreting and reacting to signals in plenty of time, and probably would be at speeds of up to 140mph. The basic requirement of a monitoring system is that it should continuously detect the state of the signals ahead, by interrogating equipment laid in the 'four-foot' (the space between the two rails), so that when the train came within braking distance of a Red signal or speed restriction the appropriate speed calculated from the braking curve could be displayed on the driver's instrument panel. If the driver did not keep his speed below the level indicated, the brakes would automatically be applied. For the purpose of calculating braking distance, the track-borne equipment would indicate distance and gradient; the train-borne equipment would monitor the speed. A train-borne computer, programmed with details of the train's braking capability, would continuously calculate the braking curve and display the required safe speed to the driver. It would also monitor the train's actual speed and interpose if it exceeded the safe speed. The track-borne equipment would also provide details of the maximum line speed, together with any speed restrictions, and the train-borne equipment would calculate the associated braking curve. There would be no need for the driver to acknowledge a warning at a Caution signal; for it would be the degree of the driver's reaction to the approaching Red that would determine whether the automatic safety back-up intervened. In normal circumstances the safety back-up would *not* intervene; it would merely watch and guard. The driver would drive and brake his train in an entirely normal manner. He would have no need to look at the 'Safe-speed' indicator, because it goes without saying that if he drove his train correctly he would never travel at more than the safe speed. The danger of subconscious cancellation of an AWS warning would disappear. The driver would still look ahead, and observe and react to signals exactly as now. He would not need an AWS warning at a Caution signal, merely a location reminder for him to observe the signal. Inattention or drowsiness approaching a Red signal would always result in the brakes being applied, because there would be no override button which could be operated subconsciously. This system would leave the driver firmly in control, an important feature to avoid the 'zombie' effect of taking too much control and initiative out of the driver's hands. Double-manning of the driving cab would be unnecessary at any speed.

One of the disadvantages inherent in such a monitoring system is that the braking curve has to be calculated on the

Above:
A railway breakdown crane prepares to lift an overturned BR Mk 3 coach into the fields behind following the Colwich disaster. Gary S. Smith

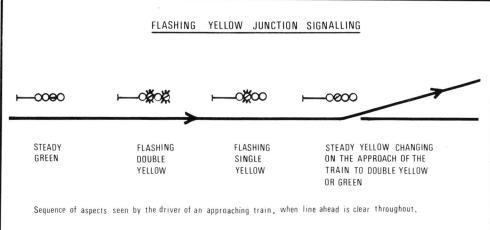

FLASHING YELLOW JUNCTION SIGNALLING

| STEADY GREEN | FLASHING DOUBLE YELLOW | FLASHING SINGLE YELLOW | STEADY YELLOW CHANGING ON THE APPROACH OF THE TRAIN TO DOUBLE YELLOW OR GREEN |

Sequence of aspects seen by the driver of an approaching train, when line ahead is clear throughout.

basis of 'worst performance', that is to say it must be based on a poor brake, a wet or greasy rail, heavy loads, etc. The resulting calculated braking curve will therefore be too restrictive in almost every case. The driver, on the other hand, takes all these factors into account in deciding how to operate the brake and cannot only be infinitely variable in deciding where to commence braking but can also adjust his level of braking throughout the duration of the operation if he wishes to give different weight to any particular factor. The machine cannot reproduce this human flexibility but it would be too restrictive to accept a 'worst performance' braking curve all the time. What is proposed, therefore, is that the system should incorporate a brake performance selector, which the driver would pre-set according to his judgement of conditions, ranging from worst performance at one extreme to best performance at the other. This would then allow the system to calculate the braking curve to correspond as closely as possible with the way in which the driver actually brakes, and so avoid an over-restrictive indication of the required speed, or premature intervention of the automatic braking.

What are the advantages of such a system?

1 It leaves the driving of the train in the driver's hands. Does not impair his skill, or his pride in his job. Avoids the zombie effect.
2 It provides an infallible safety back-up. No more 'Wembleys' or 'Morpeths'.
3 Double-manning is unnecessary.
4 The driver will continue to look ahead for signals and warning signs. It is important that he should not spend time looking at his control panel or try to do both.
5 It incorporates both signals and speed restrictions/limits in one system.
6 It avoids the need for the driver to press the AWS acknowledgement button at Caution or Red signals.
7 When a driver is braking for a Red signal which is out of sight he will know immediately if it clears, because the advisory speed indicated will rise. He will then be able to accelerate sooner than he can at present.
8 Approach control of signals at junctions would no longer be necessary. The junction signal for the low-speed route could be cleared to Green as soon as the points were set (provided the line ahead was clear). The track-borne apparatus approaching the junction would announce which way the junction was set and the appropriate speed restriction. This information would be received by the locomotive computer, which would calculate the braking curve required. The computer would also tell the

driver of the speed required at the junction, leaving him to brake to that speed but monitoring that he was doing so.

In case this proposal should be thought to be too revolutionary, it might be mentioned that the French and Italian Railways have had something similar for 20 years or more. Even BR were experimenting with the idea, but it was killed by the lack of a settled and established political, organisational and economic framework. Long-term development and research and the long-term investment required, indeed faith in the long-term future, are all needed for a project of this nature but are very difficult to achieve in all the many upheavals, both internal and external, that have plagued BR in the last 30 years. There is little doubt that if during those 30 years BR had enjoyed the same happy, progressive and supportive relationship with, and generous treatment from, its political masters as its continental railway colleagues have had from theirs, we too would have a more effective train-protection system by now. But even if work were to start at once it would be the turn of the century before real benefits began to be felt, given 5-10 years for development, design and proving, and a further five to 10 years for installation on high-speed routes. There is no time to be lost.

If proof were needed that the present AWS is inadequate, it was provided in full measure at Colwich on the West Coast main line of the London Midland Region between Lichfield and Stafford on the evening of Friday 19 September 1986. At Colwich, proceeding northwards, the line divides, the main line continuing towards Stafford and Crewe, with the line to Stoke-on-Trent and Manchester turning off towards the right. Nearly 900 passengers had a miraculous escape from death when a Down Manchester express wrongly passed a signal at Danger and stopped with its electric locomotive plumb in the path of an Up express from Liverpool to Euston closely approaching at about 100mph under Clear signals.

This accident, which astonishingly resulted in only one death, that of the unfortunate and innocent driver of the express from Liverpool, was a classic case, and neatly encapsulates five of the perennial hazards which we have discussed so far: Inadequate AWS (as at Wembley 1984); lack of flank protection (as at Lenton South Junction 1971); the perils of change; jumping to conclusions (as at Nuneaton 1975); adequacy, or otherwise, of refresher training for drivers.

The railway at Colwich is electrified at 25kV ac. Modern multiple-aspect colour-light signalling is provided, and

AWS is installed at every signal. The signalling system in force is the Track Circuit Block system. Shortly before the accident a relatively new system of junction signalling had been installed in the route of the Manchester express, which incorporated Flashing-Yellow signals to give the driver a positive advance indication that the facing points ahead were set for a diverging route over which speed must be reduced (see sketch of this arrangement). Prior to its introduction, a safe speed at the diverging junction had been achieved by the normal procedure of maintaining the junction signal at Danger for the lower speed route until the train was close to it, thus causing the speed of the train to be reduced. However, at junctions laid out to permit higher speeds of up to 70mph or more on the diverging route the normal procedure, known as approach control, was found to be too restrictive and caused the speed of an approaching train to be reduced unnecessarily early and sometimes too severely, therefore the 'Flashing-Yellow' system was devised to allow trains to travel through diverging junctions at the designed speed without any unnecessary loss of time. The first example was installed at Didcot in March 1979, since when they have become increasingly widespread and common.

On the evening of the accident the signalman at Colwich observed from his illuminated panel that both expresses were approaching at more or less the same time and he decided to give priority to the Liverpool-Euston train, as he was fully entitled to do. This meant that the Manchester train would have to wait its turn over the junction and might have to stop at signal CH 23 protecting the junction. The Manchester train was approaching on the Down Fast line (see drawing) and the signalman had set No 24 points to divert the train to the Down Slow line to bring it up to No 23 signal. This caused the following sequence of signals to be presented to the Manchester driver:

CH 105 Flashing Double-Yellow (Advance indication of diverging route ahead of next signal but one)
CH 103 One Flashing-Yellow. (Preliminary Caution and indication of diverging route ahead of next signal)
CH 28 Steady Single Yellow, with route indicator. (Route ahead set for a diverging direction. Next signal at Danger)
Banner Repeater for CH 23 Erected because a new road bridge had obscured the driver's approach view of signal CH 23. Its function is to give the driver an advance indication of the aspect shown at signal CH 23. It showed Danger, but as it is merely a Repeater signal the Driver was not required to stop at it.
CH 23 Red (Danger-Stop)

According to the driver's evidence at the Department of Transport Public Inquiry at Crewe on 23 October 1986, held by Maj Olver, he saw the signal aspects exactly as described and braked from 100mph to about 80mph at the Flashing Double-Yellow, then to 60mph at the Flashing Single Yellow, reducing speed further to 45mph at the crossover from Down Fast to Down Slow. Here he made the fatal error. He said that he was surprised to see signal CH 23 at Red and expected it to clear; then when he could see it wasn't going to clear he made an emergency brake application. At this awful moment he saw the Liverpool-Euston express approaching at full speed on a collision course. He still hoped that he would be able to stop in time, but when he realised a collision was inevitable he jumped clear at the last moment. His train had almost stopped. 'I thought I was going to be killed', he said.

What was the nature of the driver's error? He thought that Flashing Yellows meant that the line ahead was clear through the junction to the Stoke line past signal No 23, hence his bewilderment when that signal was at Red. He then assumed that the signal must be Approach-Controlled and would clear as he approached. His fundamental error was almost one of nomenclature. He did not regard the Down Fast to Down Slow route at No 24 points as a junction, whereas the signalling system did. It was as simple as that. Having interpreted the signalling aspects that he received to mean that he had the road right through to the Stoke line, his mind became programmed to that effect. When he realised that something was wrong it was just a few seconds too late to recover the situation and save the day.

So what of our five principles?

Inadequate AWS. The BR system warned the driver that CH 23 signal was not Clear, but he already knew that. Its failure was that it did not enforce its warning, indeed it was not designed to do so in such circumstances. The improved system proposed earlier in this chapter would have ensured that the train stopped at CH 23 signal despite anything the driver did, or any mistake or misunderstanding on his part. It does not require Flashing Yellows or approach control.

Lack of flank protection. In a conventional layout the driver of the Manchester train would have been diverted out of harm's way. At Colwich he only had a bare 200yd overrun margin. Without an AWS which *guarantees* that a train will stop at a Danger signal, such lack of flank protection can be deadly.

The perils of change. The flashing yellows had only just been introduced at Colwich and the driver misunderstood them.

Jumping to conclusions. When the driver saw signal CH 23 at Red he was surprised, but thought that it must be at Red because it was approach-controlled and would clear as he got near to it. In reality it was at Red because another train was going to cross that line 200yds head.

Adequacy or otherwise of refresher training for drivers. This speaks for itself. The system should have ensured that the driver knew.

But in the ultimate reckoning, whatever we may say about the cause of the accident, and who did what and why, the railway organisation should have ensured either that the mistake didn't take place, or that there was an infallible safety back-up if it did. It did neither.

Left:
Between the mangled remains of the two locomotives at Colwich lie the heaped-up bodies of three generations of coaching stock. Gary S. Smith

Single Line Operations

A number of times in recent years we have opened our newspapers to be greeted by photographs of the horrifying devastation caused by that most destructive of all railway accidents — the collision at high speed of two trains running head-on into each other on a single line. Fortunately, at least for railway passengers in Britain, these collisions have happened abroad but in countries that would normally regard their railway systems as being at least as technically advanced as ours — France, Germany, Holland and Canada.

Britain's railways were mainly constructed with double track, except for short branches, and lines in sparsely-populated areas. Yet despite many closures there are still hundreds of miles of single track in use today. The standard of safety on Britain's single lines has been very high for many years, thanks to a simple but ingenious piece of equipment known as the 'token'. Each section of single line between two signalboxes has its own token which every train through the section must carry, and as there is only one token available at any one time it follows that safety is assured, for not only are head-on collisions prevented but the possibility of a train crashing into one in front going in the same direction is also avoided. The token is sometimes very simple — just a piece of wood looking like 12 or 18in of broom handle, bearing a plate with the name of the section on it. In other cases, where it is part of the signalling equipment, it may be made of metal and shaped rather like a key (known appropriately as a key-token) or it may be a thick plastic disc rather like a large chocolate biscuit.

The system requires, of course, that drivers do not enter a section without a token (and that they obey the signals). They are strictly enjoined not to enter a section without a token. Very strictly indeed. The General Appendix goes so far as to utter almost blood-curdling threats: 'A driver will render himself liable to dismissal if he leaves . . . without the token'. Nowhere else in the whole panoply of Rules and Regulations is discipline enforced in such a forthright manner. Only in a general sense is dismissal mentioned elsewhere in the Rules. The offence of entering a single line section without a token has always been regarded as one of the most serious it is possible for a driver to commit — the Rule Book of a century ago contained the same wording, thus illustrating the remarkable durability of railway Rules whilst the rest of the world is changing out of all recognition around them.

A moment's thought, however, will reveal that the practice of having only one token for a section has its limitations. It requires trains to proceed from opposite ends of the section alternately (unless some means are adopted of conveying the token to the other end). It demands a rigid timetable and good punctuality. Special trains can only be operated with difficulty. These are problems which plagued the Central Wales line when it was worked on this system.

Necessity being the mother of invention, a way was found round the difficulty by having a number of tokens locked in a machine at each end of the section, the machines being electrically interlinked so that only one token for the section can be taken 'out' at any one time. This arrangement is known as the Electric Token Block system and has been the mainstay of single line working for over a century, resulting in a very high standard of safety apart from rare lapses. We have already met the Regulation of Railways Act of 1889 in connection with Block Systems. That Act also gave the Board of Trade powers to order that single lines should be worked on one of three systems, which included the Single Token and the Electric Token Block system.

For many years the two systems mentioned served their purpose adequately and efficiently but eventually it came to be recognised that the Electric Token system was in some cases rather elaborate and restrictive. What was really needed was a simpler but still safe system that did away with the token, and allowed trains to pass signalboxes without having to slow down to exchange the tokens. Another requirement was the ability to close signalboxes for a few hours without the problems this caused with electric token working. So far as trains following each other in the same direction over the single line were concerned, the same arrangements as applied on double lines ought to suffice — no token being necessary. The crux of the matter was to ensure that a train could not be admitted into a section if there was already one passing through it in either direction. Thus was the aptly named 'Tokenless Block System' born. It operates as follows. Track circuits are provided at each end of the section and after a train has occupied and cleared the track circuits on its entry into the section the Starting signal at neither end of the section can again be cleared (they are electrically locked) for another train in either direction until the first train has occupied and cleared track circuits at the far end of the section. Safety is assured provided drivers obey the signals, and the fundamental basis of signalling is that drivers do obey signals, although caution compels an admission that occasionally they do not. One of Canada's worst railway accidents occurred on Saturday 8 February 1986 on the Canadian National Railway in Alberta when a 114-car freight train wrongly left a section of double track and moved on to a single line to collide head-on at speed with an approaching transcontinental passenger train, killing 23 people and injuring 60. There was no token system in use and the accident would almost certainly not have happened if there had been. The Electric Token system may be old-fashioned but it is very safe.

A refinement of Tokenless Block operates in areas worked from power signalboxes where sections of single lines (usually short ones) are track-circuited throughout. After a signal has been cleared for a train to enter a section no signal can be cleared for a second train to enter the section from either end until all the track circuits have cleared after the passage of the first train. It is known as Track Circuit Block and also operates on those sections of double line where trains may pass in either direction on one track. It is very common over short stretches of line in junction areas (eg Lenton South Junction, see Chapter 8). A more recent development has been the signalling of long stretches of double line in such a manner that each track can be used by trains in either direction. The practice is known as 'bi-directional working' and allows one track to be handed over at quiet times to the Civil Engineer for maintenance. It is in use between Didcot, Swindon and beyond, and on parts of the Brighton line, and is being installed on the Midland main line south of Leicester. Without such a system, when one track has to be handed over for maintenance, trains in both directions have to be worked over the remaining line by a cumbersome, complicated and time-consuming procedure known in railway parlance as 'single-line working', often resulting in such serious delays to trains that operators divert trains over longer routes to avoid the affected section. Bi-directional signalling is expensive and in order to make the fullest use of it, facing crossovers capable of being used at fairly high speed need to be provided at regular intervals, thus increasing the cost. When a major resignalling scheme is being developed, any bi-directional proposals are always subjected to very close scrutiny on grounds of cost, and financial pressures being what they are, such proposals are often pruned or omitted altogether, which is a great pity because the cost is only marginal in relation to the scheme as a whole, and in consequence the remainder of the scheme (the main part) is not being used as productively as it might be, nor to its full potential. Furthermore it is much more expensive to go back afterwards and attempt to superimpose the bi-directional element on an already completed scheme. The Rugby-Coventry-Birmingham line is a good example of this; the bi-directional facility is badly needed there but no one has yet been able to make a sufficiently compelling financial case.

It might be mentioned in passing that the use of track circuits to prove that a section of single line is clear has a longer history than might be thought. Between the two wars the LNER had a number of installations in the North Eastern Area which used a 'transient' track circuit, and before a train was allowed to proceed on to a single line the section was swept by a track circuit current to prove that it was clear. Examples of such installations were: Castleford Old-Ledston 1926, Consett North-Blackhill 1930 and Northallerton-Ainderby 1939.

It is not often that bad weather turns out to have been a blessing in disguise. North of Inverness a single line snakes its way through the remote fastnesses of Northern Scotland over a length of 161 miles, before it finally reaches Wick and Thurso. It is a line which is no stranger to extremes of weather, and in January 1978 a severe blizzard brought down over 40 miles of telegraph wires. It is a line which was on Dr Beeching's list of closures as far back as 1963, and it has hung on since then by the skin of its teeth, thanks to the importance of and the increase in tourism in that part of Scotland. Nonetheless, the cost of replacing 40 miles of telegraph wires would have been a burden that the line could not have sustained and it seemed that its death-knell might have rung at last.

Operators, engineers and boffins from Glasgow and London met to look for a solution. Fortuitously the boffins had been carrying out research into the use of radio as a

Left:
Radio-equipped locomotive No 37261 skirts Loch Carron with the 10.55 Inverness-Kyle of Lochalsh on 19 July 1985. This was the first line in the world to be equipped with Radio Electronic Token Block. W. A. Sharman

communications medium in the regulation of train movements and it was put to them that if they could find a way to convey signalling messages from one signalbox to another by radio instead of by telegraph wire the day might yet be saved. The line, which was single throughout, with loops at stations so that one train could pass another, was signalled by the Electric Token Block system and that would be retained. So far as drivers and signalmen were concerned nothing would change; they would operate the signals and tokens exactly as before. What was needed was a means of conveying the signalling messages as safely and reliably as a telegraph wire. Radio alone could not do this — the transmitter would send out its messages to all and sundry, and the receiver would receive messages from all and sundry on its wavelength. Some form of code was needed, so that the receiver could instantly recognise and act upon messages which were intended for it, and reject all others.

The boffins set to work and quickly produced the solution — a small black box containing a micro-processor for encoding and decoding messages, which was attached to the Electric Token Block instruments. The system was brought into use in August 1980 and has worked effectively. As a spin-off, because an entire radio transmitting system had to be set up to deal with the signalling messages, it became possible to provide a radio link between signalmen and trains on the line. This is particularly useful in view of the long distances between some of the stations, the remote territory through which the line passes, and the effects of severe winter weather which sometimes cause trains to be marooned and lost. Thus at one stroke the line ceased to be a museum piece and leapt to the very forefront of technological progress.

West of Inverness there is another long straggling single line, hanging on to its life even more tenuously than the line to Wick. It leaves the Wick line at Dingwall then threads its way by mountain and loch 63 miles to Kyle of Lochalsh. Both lines were vital links and heavily used in the two World Wars and are evocatively described by Canon Roger Lloyd in his delightful book *Railwaymen's Gallery*. It is also one of the lines so charmingly brought to life in Alexander Frater's Odyssey *Stopping-Train Britain*. But sentiment alone is not enough to keep the line open; if it were the line would be extremely prosperous.

BR, with the Treasury breathing down its neck as usual, were faced with a stark choice: reduce the cost of working the line, or close it. At the same time, by happy coincidence, BR were considering how radio could be used to reduce the cost of working another line, which too was struggling to survive — the 48 miles long double track East Suffolk line between Ipswich and Lowestoft. If that line remained double, would a simple Train Despatching system, with commands transmitted by radio, be safe enough? The idea being developed was known as the 'basic railway'. All train movements on the line would be authorised by a central Controller using radio to give instructions directly to drivers. There would be no signalboxes or signals.

When ready to leave a station, a driver would radio to the Controller, giving his train identity number and the name of the station at which he was standing. He would then request permission to travel to the next station. If the previous train was at least *two* stations ahead permission would be given. All trains would stop at all stations and if the timetable was adhered to, trains would in any case be many miles apart. If for any reason a train lost time or broke down the Controller could be told by radio straight away.

Although this simple system might be acceptably safe on a double line it was not considered good enough for single lines. Train Despatching systems, although widely used

overseas, were outlawed in this country for very good reasons by the 1889 Regulation of Railways Act because they had caused too many head-on collisions. Overseas railways, as we noted at the beginning of this chapter, still have their collisions. At Flaujac in France, 32 passengers were killed in a head-on crash in August 1985 when two passenger trains collided on a single line worked under a Train Despatching system. However, even though a simple Train Despatching system by radio may not be thought safe enough on its own for a single line in Britain, could it form the basis of such a system if some means were found of retaining the concept of the token without requiring intermediate signalboxes for its operation?

Operators, engineers and boffins put their heads together again and pooled their views. The initial idea in the development process was for the token machines to be located on the platforms at stations, and linked together by radio. Drivers would operate the token machines themselves by radio-operated release from the signalman, and take out or replace a token. The Controller would tell the driver whether it was in order for him to take out a token and the equipment itself would ensure, as in normal practice, that only one token for a section could be out at any one time. The disadvantage of this idea was that it would require drivers to leave their locomotives in all weathers to operate the token machines and they might have to cross to the other platform to do it. Technical staff would have to travel to the stations to maintain the equipment.

The next idea was based on the use of a coded card rather like a bank card. The driver would stop his train alongside a card-machine and insert his card to book his train into the single line section. If the section was clear his card would be returned. If the section was not clear his card would be retained until it was, and an indicator would show 'Section occupied'. When the driver passed through the section and

Left:
Signalbox 'Key token' instrument. The spare tokens are housed at the bottom of the vertical slots. Author

Right:
RETB equipment fitted in the cab of an Inverness-allocated Class 37/4 locomotive. British Rail

reached the next station he would book himself out of the section. Tokens would not be used, except that the card could be regarded as a token, and the driver would not enter a section if his card were locked in the machine. The card-machines would be connected by radio and a micro-processor would ensure that no card could be returned from the machine to a driver unless the section was clear. The card would be a sort of electronic token. But somehow it did not feel like the ideal solution.

One day an operator and a boffin were having lunch together and musing over the various possibilities. Boffins by their very nature are full of ideas, and bang-up-to-date with the latest wizardry, varying from the highly impractical to the downright ingenious. Unfortunately their lack of down-to-earth practical experience sometimes makes it difficult for them to distinguish between the two. On the other hand operators, beset with practical difficulties, may be having to struggle to cope with them because they just do not know what whizz-bang solutions are being made available by technology and research; or do not recognise their potential because they do not properly understand them. But back to the lunch. 'What we need', said the operator, 'is a means of giving a token to the driver without the signalman actually having to hand it to him. We need a means of doing it remotely. Instructions given by voice alone are not sufficiently safe; there is too much possibility of misunderstanding. We must have something like a token to ensure safety.' 'Would you accept', replied the boffin, 'a radio system in which a centrally-located signalman could send a message to the driver which would then appear on a miniature screen in the driving cab?'

The conversation then went on as follows:

Operator: 'Could it print out the name of the section, say, Dingwall-Garve?'
Boffin: 'Yes.'

Operator: 'And could it be a unique message, so that once it had been given to one driver the same message could not be given to another?'
Boffin: 'Yes.'
Operator: 'And could it ensure that the message went to the intended driver, and not to any other?'
Boffin: 'Yes.'
Operator: 'And could it ensure, as with an electric token, that the signalman could not take back the message from the driver, without the driver's consent?'
Boffin: 'Yes.'
Operator: 'And could the system ensure that the driver couldn't accidentally "give up" the message while still in mid-section, by requiring co-operative action between both the driver and the signalman?'
Boffin: 'Yes.'
Operator: 'So the system could follow the Electric Token principles which we operators know and trust, with the sole difference that there wouldn't be a physical token?'
Boffin: 'Yes.'
Operator: 'Just a sort of electronic one?'
Boffin: 'Yes.'

And so the Electronic Token system was born. The lunch was worth it. The Kyle of Lochalsh line was an obvious one on which to try out the system. It was self-contained, operated by a captive fleet of locomotives and a limited number of drivers who knew that their jobs were at stake; had a sparse train service which could easily be controlled by just one signalman, and speeds were not high. A few moments' delay in carrying out radio procedures at stations would be of no importance. But two vital consequences would flow from the introduction of the system — (1) it would considerably reduce the cost of operating the line and so help its survival, and (2) the act of investment in ultra-modern equipment would be seen by the staff, by local people and by politicians, as an expression of BR's faith in the future of the line. It would be a great morale booster.

The system is based on the well-tried and very safe principles of the Electric Token system. The signalman 'hands' the electronic token to the driver, and for the transfer to be completed both signalman and driver must press a button on their equipment simultaneously. The token will then appear on the driver's console display and he will confirm to the signalman that he has correctly received it.

Instead of a Starting signal then giving the driver permission to enter the section, the signalman will give permission by radio. On entering the single-line section the driver will tell the signalman by radio as soon as the train is clear of the loop of double line at the station. This is important for two reasons — (1) as soon as the line at the loop is clear another train can be allowed to leave the loop in rear, and (2) if for any reason a driver had left a loop and entered the single-line section *without* the signalman's permission the signalman would realise this at once and tell the driver by radio to stop, also the driver of any other train heading towards him, thus ensuring safety.

In order to keep costs down, the points at loops are not worked by the signalman (who is likely to be many miles away) but are spring-loaded so that they always lie towards the same line. They can safely be trailed through by a train leaving the other line of the loop and proceeding in the opposite direction. It is necessary for them to be passed through in the facing direction at low speed as they are not locked, but it is in any case necessary for trains to enter the loops slowly because there are no safety overlaps; a train might be just running into the opposite loop from the other direction. When a train has entered a loop and has cleared the single line and the points, the driver will inform the signalman accordingly by radio. He will also confirm that his train is complete, ie none of it has been inadvertently left on the single line. Signalman and driver will press their buttons simultaneously and the electronic token will be returned to the signalman. The driver's console display will be cleared and the token will appear on the signalman's console display. If the section ahead is clear the procedure for token issue may then be repeated to allow the driver to proceed into the next single-line section. The signalbox computer ensures that tokens are issued in the correct sequence, keeps a record of all trains on the line and prevents the signalman from authorising conflicting train movements.

The Radio Electronic Token Block system, as it is called, is now in operation on the Kyle of Lochalsh line, the Highland line from Dingwall to Wick and Thurso, and the East Suffolk line. Plans are being developed for its installation on the West Highland line to Fort William and Mallaig, also on the line from Aberdeen to Inverness, and on the Cambrian line from Shrewsbury to Aberystwyth and Pwllheli. It is particularly useful for long single lines where the cost of installing the radio system can rapidly be recovered by savings in signalmen and the maintenance costs of lineside signals and signalboxes. There are, however, not really all that many lines of such a nature in Britain — probably not more than a dozen — but the system has enormous export potential, particularly for Third World railway systems. It can also form the basis of more advanced systems which can be applied to either double or single lines, by providing for tokens to be transferred without the train having to be stopped in a loop to do so. The points at the entrance to a loop can be operated, detected and locked by radio command, to avoid the train having to pass through them at low speed. Transponders located in the track can detect the position of the train and announce it by radio to the signalman. Magnetically-coded tail lamps can provide detection that the train is complete. Who knows, it might one day become the standard system on those lines with moderate speeds and a limited train service which do not qualify for full modern signalling with colour-light signals and continuous track-circuiting. The operator and the boffin might yet regret not having patented it!

Right:
On 1 August 1986 No 37415 approaches Fearn with a Wick/Thurso-Inverness service passing a 'Stop' board installed for the recently-introduced radio signalling system. David Brown

 # Trains without Guards

In 1985 the newspapers were full of reports about BR's proposals to withdraw guards from trains. Readers' letters bemoaned the imminent demise of the passenger guard, women feared for their safety from the attentions of less-reputable fellow passengers, and the leader writers thundered against what they saw as BR's lack of sensitivity and commercial wisdom. Had the newspapers got it wrong? Perhaps they had. It was never BR's intention to withdraw guards from *all* passenger trains but only from selected suburban services. Certainly not from InterCity services. But was the furore partly BR's own fault? Had it presented the proposals as clearly and thoroughly as possible? Had it made clear the limited effect of these proposals? Had it properly explained how safety would be provided for in the absence of a guard? Had it under-estimated the travelling public's desire for a 'railway presence' on passenger trains, even humble suburban ones, in order to reassure passengers in these increasingly violent times; and had it failed to realise how valuable such a 'presence' could be in reducing the loss of revenue from fare-dodging passengers?

BR's presentation of its proposals to its own staff may also have lacked sensitivity and imagination, and may have caused unnecessary unrest and opposition. Guards could be forgiven for gaining the impression that their jobs were to disappear in thousands overnight, rather than in stages over several years. Furthermore, BR may not have appreciated sufficiently the hidden commercial benefit of a railway presence on suburban trains; indeed its provision came about more as a result of trade union pressure for job protection than anything else. The National Union of Railwaymen was anxious to save as many jobs as possible and persuaded BR to regard as a trial the first scheme for working trains without guards, on the newly-electrified St Pancras-Bedford suburban service. It was agreed that the displaced guards would in the meantime act as Ticket Inspectors on those trains, and they have proved so successful at this that there is a case for such a practice being made permanent. The presence of a railway official on a train is also reassuring to the ordinary passenger. The trend towards the unstaffing of suburban stations and now the unstaffing of suburban trains is at variance with the need to maintain order in an environment that can at times be hostile, and some railway administrations have found it prudent to restore staff to previously unstaffed stations. Whilst this might be regarded as a semi-police function, it is more expedient in a variety of ways to use railway staff, who can carry out other duties as well. There is a strong marketing factor here — railways need to attract passengers, and that requires an attractive travelling environment.

BR had been attempting to introduce guardless trains since technology made it practicable to do so safely and economically by the early 1970s. However, the NUR was implacably opposed to any such moves, reinforced by resolutions at their Annual Conference. Quite naturally the guards were reluctant to see their jobs disappear, but a more astute union leadership might have accepted the inevitable and concentrated its efforts on obtaining the best rewards for all those who would be involved in the operation of guardless trains, whilst at the same time making the best possible provision for those guards displaced. As it turned out, the rank and file of the NUR

Left:
Guardless trains on the Midland: a Class 317 EMU heads through Hendon on the Up Fast line. Top centre is the tv screen angled towards the Down Slow line to enable the driver to check that all is in order to close the doors and depart, whilst just to its right is the tv camera pointing along the platform. Author

finally refused to be led into confrontation, and the operation of guardless trains began, albeit on a fairly limited scale.

So far as BR was concerned, there were those who looked upon the concept of guardless trains as the answer to the railways' economic problems. There were also those, somewhat shrewder, who recognised that a price would have to paid for union agreement to driver-only operation. Extra payments would be demanded by, and conceded to, those who might have to take on extra responsibilities. Costly equipment would have to be provided on safety grounds. The ultimate economy might be considerably less than had been hoped for. But BR had to achieve its ambitions for three reasons: one economic, one operational and one political. The need to make economies in the operation of trains speaks for itself. The operational case is simply that the ability to run trains without guards avoids being forced to cancel trains when no guard is available, a running sore, particularly in the London suburban area, caused by the inability to recruit sufficient guards and the economic necessity of keeping the establishment of spare guards to a minimum. The political case is the most interesting one. BR had to achieve success in its struggle with the NUR over the operation of guardless trains in order to prove to the government that the railway management meant business and that they were determined to comply as far as possible with the government's demand that the railway's dependence on public funds be reduced. It was hoped that the government would then be so delighted with BR's victory that it would release massive amounts of capital to be invested in electrification, resignalling, and the renewal of rolling stock, which is exactly what happened. Sir Robert Reid, chairman of BR, succeeded where Sir Peter Parker, the previous chairman, had failed. He provided a Conservative government with a number of resounding political victories, for which railways (and the railwaymen themselves) were duly rewarded. To be fair to Sir Peter, it has to be admitted that the industrial relations climate favoured Sir Robert, but it was a notable achievement nevertheless. The political acumen of the present chairman is one of his strongest suits. It is fascinating to consider whether the nationalised railways have not fared better under ideologically-opposed Conservative governments than under supposedly sympathetic Labour ones. It is also an interesting thought that if the NUR had not opposed driver-only operation there would have been no political victory and hence no reward. Perhaps after all the NUR leadership were more politically aware than they have been given credit for!

However, turning from the political and economic aspects of driver-only operation to the operational and safety implications, we might start by considering how the use of guards on trains came about in the first place, and why the practice has continued for so long. To find the answer to that question we have to go back to the very beginnings of railways, when they had just started to take over from the stage-coach. The first railway carriages were just like stage-coaches on a railway chassis. Stage-coaches carried guards to help passengers and to look after their luggage, and to assist with braking. It was a natural development therefore that railway carriages, modelled on stage-coaches, should have guards to do those things. One of the most important of the guard's duties in the days before continuous automatic brakes was to assist the driver to brake the train. This often required a number of guards and brakesmen, but when trains became fully braked they were no longer needed for that purpose. However, by then, guards had become an integral part of the working of trains and were retained. There was never much justification for having a guard on fully-fitted freight trains (ie trains which

are fully-braked throughout with the brakes on the whole train being operated by the driver) in steam locomotive days when there were always two men on the footplate.

The guard traditionally sat at the back of a freight train in his brakevan ('sat' is a euphemism — the guard braced himself in his seat and wedged himself as best he could as protection against the shocks, bumps and lurches of a normal journey). On a loose-coupled freight train, in which the wagons were coupled together by a simple three-link coupling which allowed a gap of a foot or so between the buffers of adjacent wagons, and which had no power brakes other than those on the locomotive, the guard had a number of important duties:

1 He used the handbrake in his van (called appropriately a brakevan, not a guard's van) to assist the driver to keep the train under control on falling gradients.
2 He used his handbrake to keep the couplings taut when travelling over undulating gradients, thus avoiding snatches which could lead to the breakage of a coupling. This was quite a skilful job on a 100 wagon freight train, which might be on two or three different gradients at the same time.
3 If the train accidentally broke into two portions when running, the driver would often be unaware immediately that anything untoward had occurred, but the guard would be there to bring the rear portion safely to a stand if he could. If the rear portion became derailed, the guard was in a position to protect the opposite line if it was obstructed by derailed wagons (and to protect his own train).

A guard on a loose-coupled train was a vital member of the train crew and absolutely essential. An experienced and capable guard could be of great assistance to the driver, although inexperienced and clumsy ones could be a nuisance to the driver, who might then say to the guard 'Leave the braking to me'. However, on fully-fitted freight trains there was no need for the guard to carry out any of these duties — the wagons were screw-coupled together so that the buffers were touching and the driver controlled the power brake on every wagon. In the case of a coupling breaking or an accidental uncoupling (rare events on such a train) the automatic brake would bring both portions to a stop without any action on the driver's part. Hence the name automatic brake. If for any reason the rear portion had become derailed the fireman could have looked after it in the absence of a guard. However, fully-fitted freight trains always carried a guard, who sat at the back ready to rush off with his flag and detonators in the event of an accident. The LNER actually went so far as to move the brakevan inside the train to ease the operation of dropping off or attaching a few wagons at stations en route, but with the stipulation that there must not be more than 20 wagons behind the brakevan.

With the advent of diesel haulage, needing only one man on the locomotive, the position is somewhat different, but before we go on to examine the effect of that on proposals to withdraw guards, let us see how the use of guards on passenger trains developed. The continuous automatic brake had become standard on all passenger trains before the turn of the century and it was rare for the guard to have anything to do with the brake during a journey. His duties developed in three main spheres, which are largely unchanged today — the safe and expeditious working of the train, commercial duties in relation to his passengers (called 'customer care' nowadays), and responsibilities for the safe carriage of mails and parcels.

The passenger guard's operating duties are mainly:

1 To see that his train is in good order before departure.
2 To satisfy himself, in co-operation with the driver, that the brake is working satisfactorily.
3 To see that all doors are closed before departure.
4 To 'protect' the train in case of accident, and look after the passengers.

The first three items arise before departure. The train should be in proper order before it leaves its depot, and station or depot staff are capable of carrying out all 'station' duties. It is when the train is out on the line that situations may arise to cause problems on guardless pasenger trains. If the train were to break down the driver would have to leave it unattended whilst he went for assistance. If it became derailed, and obstructed other lines, the driver could only protect one direction at once. If it caught fire the driver alone could not protect the train, go for assistance and look after the passengers. Whilst these might be thought to be remote dangers there would certainly be a lessening of safety standards if guards were to be removed without any additional compensating safeguards being applied, and this would be unacceptable in the launching of a new method of operation that would demand acceptance by the travelling public, the staff, the trade unions and of course the Railway Inspectorate of the Department of Transport. BR therefore drew up the following conditions to be applied in the operation of guardless suburban passenger trains:

1 Doors are to be power-operated by the driver.
2 Automatic Warning System (AWS) equipment must be provided.
3 If a platform is not manned, drivers must be able to obtain a clear view of the platform along the full length of the train.
4 Radio communication between driver and signalman must be provided.
5 The line must be track-circuited throughout its length.

These five conditions form the main requirements. Taken together they may provide an even higher standard of safety than applies with conventional train working. The driving of the train is unchanged, but the driver has the benefit of AWS and continuous track circuiting. So far as accidents are concerned, he is in constant radio touch with the signalman and he could, at least in theory, alert the signalman and so secure the safety of the line even *before* an accident, in the following manner. Normal radio calls from the driver to the signalman are dealt with in rotation but the driver has an emergency button and if he were to press it the signalman would be alerted at once. Details of the train would appear on the signalman's radio console and the signalman could ascertain from his diagram panel just where the train was. He could then put out a general radio call to all drivers in the area to tell them to stop (or proceed cautiously) and he could put the protecting signals to Danger. Thus, before the train concerned in the emergency could come to a stand, and long before the driver could telephone for assistance or use his track-circuit operating clip, as he would have to do on a conventional train, all trains in the area would have been warned and would themselves be coming to a stand. Safety would then be achieved much more quickly than under present conditions.

The question of the operation of doors on trains was dealt with at length in Chapter 5. On a guardless train, as there is no guard to see that all doors are closed before departure, nor to take action if anyone should attempt to join or alight just as the train is setting off, power-operated doors under the control of the driver are necessary. It is also necessary that the driver should be able to see along the full length of the train so that he can tell when it is reasonable to close the doors (for example he would not want to do it just as an infirm passenger was being helped in or out, nor when someone was just lifting a pram in or out), and so that he can be sure that no one is trapped in the doors. There is a general safeguard that, unless the doors are properly closed, an interlock will prevent traction power being applied to the train and it will be unable to move, but a scarf or strap may not be detected by the interlock and anyone so trapped could be dragged along the platform when the train started. Unless the driver can see clearly along the platform, means must be provided to enable him to do so. These take the form either of television cameras sighted along the train, with a TV screen on the platform opposite the driver's cab or, in suitable cases, a large mirror on the platform to enable him to see round the outside of a slight curve, or to see along a platform on the right-hand side of the train. If the circumstances are such that the driver cannot look back in safety as the train leaves a station, because of the presence of an overbridge or tunnel for instance, emergency stop plungers must be provided on the platform, for use by station staff or passengers if there are any present. This may be thought to be over-doing things a little, because the driver will have checked before he sets off that everything is in order and it assumes that someone is going to place himself in an irretrievable position of danger in the next two or three seconds. However, for a new venture such as guardless trains it is better, for purposes of public and staff acceptance, to be too safe rather than not safe enough. The requirements can always be relaxed in subsequent schemes if experience shows that they are unnecessary.

One of the more intriguing requirements stipulates that the driver's safety device (DSD), more popularly known as the 'deadman's handle', must not be capable of being neutralised whilst the train is in motion. On some stock the DSD can be rendered inoperative by the driver putting his 'forward/reverse' power controller into the 'engine-only' position, allowing him to coast along without having to depress the DSD pedal. It is strictly forbidden whilst the train is on the move but it is known to be done occasionally for various reasons. If it were to be done on a guardless train and the driver were to become insensible, a dangerous situation would arise. This requirement prevents it from being done; if the 'forward/reverse' controller is put into the 'engine-only' position at any speed above walking pace, the brake is automatically applied.

A public-address system is provided on guardless suburban passenger trains so that the driver can give any necessary instructions to passengers in an emergency, as well as making routine announcements. Consideration is also being given to a means of allowing passengers to speak to the driver. Whilst this could be misused by irresponsible passengers it would help to reassure law-abiding travellers, who could draw the driver's attention to unruly or intimidating passengers, enabling the driver to radio for police attendance at the next station. This would be far more effective than the passenger having to pull the communication cord, resulting in the train being brought to a stand away from a station and away from assistance.

The thought of a fire on a passenger train is always frightening, and although no passenger has been killed in a fire on a suburban passenger train for very many years, and although there is often little a guard could do in such a situation, it is necessary on guardless trains to provide an escape-route for passengers. Through access must therefore be provided between all coaches forming a multiple-unit, and passengers must be able to open emergency exit doors (whether end or side doors) from within the train. But with radio on the train, and public address, the situation

can be dealt with much more effectively than on a conventionally-manned train. The driver can radio for fire brigade assistance and stop his train at the most suitable point. In the meantime he can give the passengers whatever directions are most appropriate. The signalman will have stopped all trains, so that passengers jumping out of the affected train will not be in danger of being run down by other passing trains.

The question is often asked as to what would happen if the driver were to become insensible whilst driving, or be put out of action in a crash. In the first case the operation of the DSD would bring the train to a stand, and in addition the AWS at any Caution signal or severe speed restriction would automatically cause the train to be stopped. So far as the effects of a crash are concerned, the driver would almost certainly have time to press his radio 'emergency' button so that the signalman could take immediate protective measures. Furthermore the radio system is so designed that the signalman can speak to the passengers over the train's public address system. On a conventional train there is no guarantee that the guard will survive a crash and even if he is not killed he may be injured to such an extent that he cannot carry out his protective duties, a possibility that has always been accepted because it is unavoidable. On fully track-circuited lines, if debris from the crash obstructs another line it is likely to short-circuit the track-circuit on that line, which will automatically put the last approaching signal to Danger, and alert the signalman if he is not already aware of the emergency.

As a result of all these special arrangements, the operation of guardless passenger trains is very safe indeed; safer than many conventionally-manned trains. However, it is a costly venture and the pay-back is not as brilliant as might be thought. The balance sheet of costs and benefits is as follows:

Capital costs:
Provision of radio system and equipment.
Provision of CCTV or other equipment on station platforms.

Additional running costs:
Maintenance of additional equipment.
Extra payments to drivers and signalmen for extra responsibilities.

Savings:
A proportion of the guards' costs. (Some will still be required for ticket inspection and customer-care duties.)

Benefits:
Overall reduction in running costs.
A safer, more efficient service.
A more reliable service.
More productive use of manpower.

As guardless suburban passenger trains have not been operated for long, it is too early to assess the economic results of the arrangement, but it is to be hoped that BR will publish them in due course so that an informed judgement can be made. There are of course a number of imponderables. How much extra revenue will on-train ticket inspection produce? How many extra passengers will be attracted by a 'railway presence' in the passenger accommodation of the train? How much extra business will be generated by the increase in the efficiency of the service by the provision of radio, and the avoidance of the need to cancel trains when there is no guard available? The eventual verdict is likely to be a resounding vote of confidence in favour of the operation of guardless suburban passenger trains, but BR must take care to present the full facts so that the public can be reassured.

Left & right:
Mirrors to enable the driver to see along the train. An HST and an EMU are approaching the station on the Up Fast line. Seen at Potters Bar, September 1986. Author

The position of ASLEF (the Associated Society of Locomotive Engineers and Firemen — the drivers' trade union) in this matter is interesting. During the long negotiations (10 years or more) they have kept a very low profile. They have not suggested that the proposals were in any way unsafe (as NUR did) nor that the drivers would be unable to carry out the extra duties. They made a number of sensible detailed suggestions about the equipment to be provided. What they were chiefly interested in was the pay-off — how much extra money could they obtain for the extra work and responsibility; a very proper consideration for a trade union. But a cynic might remark that ASLEF was not losing any members, whereas the NUR was, and trade unionism is partly about the number of members. Falling numbers make it more difficult for a trade union to maintain an efficient administration, with good research facilities. The world of industrial relations becomes increasingly complex day by day, both in the technical and legal senses, and a trade union needs an expensive organisation to deal with it efficiently. ASLEF, being a small union, is particularly vulnerable in this respect.

The strict requirements for the operation of guardless suburban passenger trains, especially those concerning power-operated doors, radio and continuous track-circuiting, will have the effect of extending the period of the introduction of such workings over several years whilst the existing slam-door stock is replaced by power-operated door stock and sufficient funds are made available for resignalling and the installation of radio. So far, guardless suburban passenger trains only operate on the lines from King's Cross and St Pancras, and from Glasgow to the Ayrshire coast.

The safety requirements for the operation of freight trains without guards are naturally rather different in concept from those of passenger trains. Many of the problems associated with passenger train working do not arise, but there are other factors to be considered which are confined solely to freight train operations. Whilst the term 'freight train' will be used throughout, the arrangements also apply to parcels, mail and newspaper trains, empty coach trains and light locomotives. All trains must be fully-fitted, with the automatic brake operative throughout the train. Trains which have Post Office staff or newspaper sorting staff on board are regarded as passenger trains and are excluded from these arrangements.

The operation of freight trains has always been carried out at a safety level which, whilst not so high as that for passenger trains, was considered to be adequate but which did not, indeed could not, provide for every eventuality. In theory the guard observed the running of the train and took action to have it stopped if he observed anything untoward. In practice both his view, and his opportunities for observation, were very limited. He could not see much in the dark, his view along the train from the lookout windows of his brakevan was very restricted, and at speed the guard was often preoccupied with wedging himself in his seat to avoid being thrown around the van by its poor riding qualities. The number of occasions in actual practice when guards have initiated action to have their trains stopped, and have thus prevented a possible derailment, have been few. In the mid-1960s BR decided to abolish the use of brakevans on most fully-fitted freight trains, and place the guard in the rear cab of the locomotive where he could still observe the train. It caused a lot of industrial relations problems. The NUR felt that it reduced the status of the guard and suspected that it was the first step towards doing away with guards altogether. ASLEF felt that the sanctity of their domain, which they jealously guarded, was being infringed. However, the arrangement was finally adopted, but guards can often be seen travelling with the driver in the *front* cab. In freight train collisions in which the driver is killed or injured it is noticeable that the guard often suffers the same fate alongside him.

The other reason for having a guard on a freight train has traditionally been to protect his train and secure the safety of the line in case of accident or breakdown. The protection of his own train is much less vital nowadays with modern signalling and improvements in signalling controls, and the driver is responsible for protecting the line used by trains running in the opposite direction. On four-track sections the guard may have to protect the other line running in the same direction as his own train if it has become obstructed by wreckage, but most four-track sections nowadays are track-circuited and can be protected just as effectively by the driver using his track circuit operating clip. In any case, experience has shown that the guard's actions have rarely had any practical effect in avoiding a subsequent collision or reducing its effects.

In drawing up the safety requirements for the operation of freight trains without guards BR were particularly concerned about two factors — the propensity to derailment of short-wheelbase four-wheeled wagons, and the carriage of dangerous goods. During the 1960s and early 1970s the problem of derailments of what were at that time the standard wagons and vans became very serious. The vehicles concerned had a wheelbase of about 10ft and formed the great bulk of BR's wagon fleet, and many of them had been built since nationalisation. For reasons never really satisfactorily explained, derailments started to occur in freight trains travelling at about 50-55mph, a situation which had never previously been experienced. The number of such derailments increased year by year, each one ending in a pile of wreckage, and there was the ever-present fear that one day a passenger train would run at full speed into the heap of tangled metal and shattered wood. Fortunately there were very few really serious accidents involving passenger trains[1], but occasionally a second freight train ran into the wreckage, and once or twice a third freight train added itself to the heap. On one memorable occasion on the Erewash Valley main line of the former Midland Railway north of Toton, a coal train on the Up Fast line became derailed and the wreckage was run into by a train of iron ore on the Down Fast line. A third train on the Slow lines joined in. Fortunately there were no serious injuries but there was a heap of coal, wood, iron ore and scrap metal big enough to start up an ironworks. Both Derby and Toton breakdown cranes were engaged for 24 hours. The explanation of the cause of such derailments was often the same — a combination of minor faults in the wagon suspension (usually within agreed engineering tolerances), minor faults in the track (again usually within tolerances), and the speed of the train at or slightly above the maximum allowed. It was an unsatisfactory conclusion because there seemed to be no remedy, except the drastic one of reducing the speed at which the wagons were allowed to travel. This came down in stages from 60mph to 55mph, to 50, then to 45mph. Even this did not fully solve the problem and 16-ton coal wagons had finally to be restricted to 35mph. The effect on transit times was disastrous and a great deal of traffic was diverted to road by dissatisfied customers, especially after National Carriers Ltd was formed following the 1968 Transport Act. The solution to the derailments was never really found and it will always be a mystery as to why wooden-framed wagons could run happily at 60mph and above when hauled by steam engines on jointed track composed of 60ft rails laid on wooden sleepers, whilst the same wagons with steel frames could not be trusted to stay on the rails at much above 35mph when hauled by diesel locomotives, especially on long-welded rail laid on concrete sleepers, but it has

something to do with the greater flexibility and 'give' of wooden-framed wagons on jointed track on wooden sleepers, compared with the stiffness of steel frames on concrete sleepers. The problem was finally solved (or solved itself) with the replacement of the wagons by longer-wheelbase, higher capacity vehicles with improved springs and suspension, and with the reduction in freight traffic which allowed many wagons to be scrapped without replacement.

When the requirements for the operation of guardless freight trains were being drawn up, the derailment problem was still very much a live issue and it was decided that short-wheelbase wagons (defined as having a wheelbase of less than 15ft) should not be allowed to run in guardless trains except on continuously track-circuited lines with multiple-aspect signalling, so that if a derailment occurred it could be protected by the driver using his track-circuit operating clip, and there would be a signal-post telephone nearby from which he could report the derailment to the signalman. Longer wheelbase wagons, which are much less prone to derail, are allowed to run in guardless trains on non-continuously track-circuited lines as well as on those which are continuously track-circuited, but only where there is not a frequent passenger train service (not more than two per hour in each direction). There is no special precision or particular logic in this; safety is an art as well as a science and the running of guardless trains is a new art form. It is felt better to be more restrictive to start with, until some experience has been gained. The full requirements are listed in the appendix, and include details of those dangerous goods for which a guard must be provided. Once again it was felt prudent to be cautious in entering the untried area of the operation of freight trains without guards, when such trains are conveying goods of a dangerous nature. There are some types of dangerous goods which are hazardous in an unusual way, such as nuclear flasks containing irradiated fuel rods, or particularly toxic chemicals conveyed in tank wagons. On trains conveying such dangerous traffics a brakevan will continue to be provided at the rear of the train and a guard must travel in it, so that if the train has an accident the traincrew need not, indeed must not, walk alongside it in case of possible health risks from any leakage of the contents.

Radio communication between driver and signalman could be a useful aid in certain circumstances on guardless freight trains, but that applies also to trains with guards. It is not specially a matter of safety but rather one of expediency. A case for additional safety equipment can always be made out from a purely safety point of view, but the expenditure has to be justified in terms of the balance of probability. It is right and proper to spend money to guard against a hazard which can reasonably be foreseen, but it would be an extravagance to use limited funds to guard against an unknown or indefinable hazard, or one which may never happen.

Finally we should consider the economics of the operation of freight trains without guards. Apart from minor modifications to locomotives, the balance sheet shows a pure gain for freight trains running between yards, sidings and depots where there are BR or other suitable staff to carry out all the necessary terminal duties such as:

1 Placing the wagons on arrival.
2 Informing the computerised freight traffic control system, known as TOPS (Total Operations Processing System).
3 Uncoupling the locomotive.
4 Coupling the outgoing train, checking that it is fit and safe to travel, and noting any restrictions.
5 Informing TOPS.

6 Placing a tail lamp on the rear wagon.
7 Coupling the locomotive.
8 Carrying out the brake test.

The driver could certainly carry out some of these duties at unstaffed sidings, for which he would probably want extra pay, but there are technical problems in carrying out a brake test single-handed. More importantly, is it sensible to have a million pounds' worth of locomotive and wagons, to say nothing of their load, standing idle whilst the driver performs such duties? A judgement has therefore to be made as to whether it is more advantageous to carry a guard in certain cases, or even to employ terminal staff at previously unstaffed sidings. Each case has to be judged on its own merits.

Appendix 1

Conditions for One-Man Operation of Suburban Passenger Trains on British Railways

Rolling stock

Doors
Side doors to be power-operated and controlled by the driver. Interlock to be provided with the traction controller so that the train cannot be moved unless all passenger doors are closed.

Traction and braking control equipment
A form of driver's safety device, which the driver cannot neutralise whilst the train is in motion, must be provided.
   Application of the brake must automatically cut off the traction power.
   Automatic Warning System equipment must be provided, unless train stops are provided.

Through access between coaches, and emergency exit doors
Stock is to be fitted with end doors giving access between coaches within a unit, and between units where practicable.
   Passengers must be able to open emergency exit doors from within the coaches. These may be either end doors or a proportion of the side doors on each side of the train, or both. Opening of the doors is to be effected by conspicuously-marked, sealed-release handles or buttons. If only end doors are available as emergency doors, passengers must be able to get to either end of the train.

Train equipment
Track circuit operating clips shall be provided in each driving compartment.

Stations

Platform lighting
Platforms must be adequately and uniformly illuminated.

Manning of platforms and use of CCTV (closed circuit television)
If a platform is not manned, drivers must be able to obtain a clear view of the platform along the full length of the train. If necessary CCTV or other means may be provided to achieve this.

Emergency stop plungers
Where circumstances are such that the driver cannot look back in safety as the train leaves the station, emergency stop plungers are required on the platforms for use by station staff and passengers. Operation of an emergency stop plunger shall illuminate emergency Stop signals ahead of the platform and beyond any Starting signal.

Communications

Driver to signalbox or control
A system of continuous direct speech communication shall be provided between the driver and the signalbox, or a control centre in direct communication with the controlling signalbox, for the section of line in which the train is located.

Public address
A system of driver-to-passenger speech communication must be provided.

Signalling

All lines over which one-man operated suburban trains run in passenger service must be continuously track-circuited. This includes any adjacent running line that could be fouled by a derailed one-man operated train.
   AWS must be provided.

Appendix 2

Conditions for One-Man Operation of Fully Fitted Non-Passenger Carrying Trains on British Railways

Rolling stock

Automatic brake
The automatic brake, either air or vacuum, must be operative throughout the train in conformity with the appropriate regulations.

Traction and braking control equipment
A form of driver's safety device which the driver cannot neutralise whilst the train is in motion must be provided.
   Application of the brake must automatically cut off the traction power.

Train equipment
Track circuit operating clips shall be provided in each cab or driving compartment.

Signalling

Trains that include vehicles with a wheelbase of less than 4.5m
May run over passenger lines that are continuously track-circuited and equipped with three- or four-aspect colour-light signals, and over goods lines or loops adjacent thereto. May also run over non-continuously track-circuited passenger lines for short distances (up to 10 miles depending on circumstances) at the beginning or end of a journey, or intermediately, and also without restriction on single lines and on goods lines where these are not adjacent to passenger lines.

Trains composed of bogie stock or vehicles with a wheelbase of 4.5m or over
May run over the lines described above and in addition may also run over non-continuously track-circuited lines where passenger traffic is light (not more than two booked passenger trains per hour in each direction).

Light locomotives (single or in multiple)
May run over any line.

Traffic restrictions

The following dangerous goods must not be conveyed on one-man operated trains:

   Flammable gases in tank wagons, Class 2a.
   Toxic gases in tank wagons, Class 2c.
   Hydrocyanic acid.
   Explosives, Class 1.

[1] At Ashchurch on 8 March 1969 a 16-ton mineral wagon in a 57-wagon freight train from Birmingham, Washwood Heath, to Bristol, Stoke Gifford, became derailed only seconds before an express passenger train (the 10.40 Bristol-Newcastle) passed in the opposite direction. The coaches of the express were severely damaged by derailed wagons and two passengers lost their lives.

Obstructions on the Line

One of the perennial concerns of drivers is that of running into unprotected obstructions on the line. The driver cannot swerve and he will probably be too near to stop, especially if the obstruction is round a curve. In the darkness he will have no chance at all. There are many types of obstruction, but the ones we shall be concerned with in this chapter are:

Animals on the line.
Goods fallen from passing trains.
The effects of bad weather, eg fallen trees, snowdrifts, rock-falls, mud-slides.
Lorries and other vehicles running off the road.
Vandals.

Animals on the Line

It can be said that the railways have always had a duty to fence the line, going back to the 1842 Railway Regulation Act and beyond. This duty was to prevent cattle from straying on to the railway from adjoining land, and to prevent trespass *from* the railway. It was not originally intended to safeguard children from straying on to the railway and unwittingly putting themselves in danger, although it has come to be interpreted as such. There are about 20,000 miles of fencing alongside the railways of Britain, costing about £6 million a year to maintain. Some of the expenditure arises from damage caused by children, or by adults seeking a short cut.

The Rule Book tells drivers that if they see animals on or near the line, which they consider may endanger trains, they must tell the signalman as quickly as possible, and take other safety precautions. Since June 1986 the Rule Book has specifically said that a cow or bull or other large animal must be considered a danger to trains. The signalman, in turn, must stop trains and tell the drivers what has happened, and instruct them to take their trains forward cautiously. In this way subsequent trains are safeguarded.

Top:
The scene after the crash at Watford Junction on 23 January 1975. The driver of No 86209 survived his terrifying plunge down the embankment. British Rail

Above:
No 86209, the locomotive of the 22.15 Euston-Glasgow sleeper, seen where it came to rest at the foot of the embankment. The locomotive was to remain there for nearly three months, whilst the difficult operation to retrieve it was organised. British Rail

112

Each year there are thousands of instances of animals, mainly sheep, straying on to the line or on to the grassy area at the lineside, and many of these instances go unreported. However, about a hundred times a year trains run into animals on the line, and occasionally, once or twice a year, there is a derailment. Serious derailments are rare. Human fatalities are almost unknown. That was the case until Monday 30 July 1984.

The 17.30 express from Edinburgh to Glasgow that evening consisted of a Class 47/7 diesel-electric locomotive pushing six coaches. The leading vehicle had a driving compartment from which the locomotive and train were remotely controlled. Shortly after passing through Polmont, and whilst travelling at about 85mph, the train hit a cow and became completely derailed. The first coach turned right round and finished up on its side, and several other coaches were badly damaged. The behaviour of the coaches after the impact has interesting parallels with that of the coaches involved in the Lockington accident described in Chapter 12, as has the way in which fatalities occurred when passengers were thrown through the windows. Altogether 13 of them were killed and 17 passengers and railwaymen were seriously injured. In terms of fatalities it was BR's worst accident since the Hither Green derailment in 1967, when 49 passengers were killed.

Human trespass in the area was common and the fencing had to be repaired frequently. It is thought that the cow had gained access through a fence damaged by trespassers, and this problem of fence damage and trespass is very difficult to control, not only at Polmont but almost anywhere on BR. It is certainly not within the realms of practicality to prevent animals from getting on to the line, therefore BR took action in a number of directions after the accident, such as improvements to the Rules, the fitting of deflectors (cow-catchers) to Scottish Region push-pull trains and the equipping of driving cabs with radio to enable drivers to give early warning of animals on the line, or to be warned accordingly by the signalman.

Goods Fallen from Passing Trains

Once again the West Coast main line, and a sleeping car express, figure in these pages, in an accident that happened on 23 January 1975. The 22.15 sleeping car express from Euston to Glasgow was settling down to a steady speed of about 85mph on the approach to Watford Junction when the signals suddenly went to Red in front of it. The driver made an emergency brake application and had managed to reduce speed to 65mph when he suddenly saw looming up in front of him the bulk of another electric locomotive which had obviously been derailed and was leaning over towards him. He had hardly time to hang on tightly and pray that he would miss it, when the two locomotives struck each other a glancing blow, corner to corner, and his

Left:
The recovery of No 86209 involved the use of two 125-ton capacity cranes on 16 April 1975, with spreader beams to protect the locomotive's bodyside panels. A full account of the recovery of No 86209 appeared in the June 1975 issue of *Modern Railways.* Sparrows Crane Hire

Above:
The severely damaged remains of the leading locomotive of the Manchester-Euston train, Class 83 No 83003, being jacked up before removal. British Rail

Top:
Class 81 electric No 81016 being rerailed after the accident near Leighton Buzzard on 9 December 1982. David K. Smith

Above:
A view of the derailed coaches in the Leighton Buzzard accident. David K. Smith

locomotive cannoned off and shot down the embankment to the left. He was very lucky to survive his appalling ordeal, but the driver of the other locomotive was killed. Fortunately the sleeping cars became detached from the locomotive and did not follow it down the embankment but came to rest more or less in line along the track.

The cause of the derailment of the other train, the 19.10 express from Manchester to Euston, was clear. Some steel stillages had fallen from a passing freight train and had lain foul of the Up Fast line, on which the express from Manchester was just accelerating from its booked Watford Junction stop. It ran into the obstruction and was derailed towards the Down Fast line, but in doing so it cut the signal cables of the track circuits in that line, causing the signals to go to Danger in the face of the fast approaching sleeping car express. Had both trains met at full speed, ie at a combined speed of almost 200mph, the result would have been catastrophe on a grand scale. But accidents are always full of 'ifs'.

The train from which the steel stillages had fallen was company train No 6M50, the 20.12 from Fords of Dagenham to their Halewood plant. All the van doors had been secured and sealed before the train left Dagenham, but when it made a routine stop at Rugby for a crew change several van doors were found to be open. How could this have happened? They could not have worked open on their own during the journey because they were too well fastened. It was then found that the train had stopped twice for signals in the north London area, at Gospel Oak and Finchley Road, and police investigations led to the conclusion that the train had been attacked there by thieves, who had left the doors open. Vibration of the train during its journey then caused two stillages to fall out of the van just south of Watford Junction, to be run into by the express from Manchester. The cause of the accident was really a form of vandalism, although the robbers probably never thought of the possible consequences of their actions. Whether they would have been deterred had they done so is another matter.

Sleeping car expresses, and the West Coast main line, seem to occupy more than their share of the limelight in these pages (do they really suffer from a disproportionate number of accidents?) and by coincidence the same train was involved in another accident in the small hours of Thursday 9 December 1982. The express, now timed to leave Euston at 22.25, had left two hours late because there had been a defect in the electric train heating system. The train had just passed through Leighton Buzzard, travelling at about 75mph on the Down Slow line, when the electric locomotive, No 81016, ran into a steel rail which was thought to have fallen from an earlier engineering train. The derailed locomotive hit a bridge parapet, killing the driver and injuring the secondman. Twelve of the 14 coaches were derailed but stayed upright and in line. Only one passenger was injured.

The Effects of Bad Weather

The night of 9 December 1982 was extremely stormy in the south of England, with fierce winds and lashing rain. As the 21.46 electric multiple-unit train from Waterloo to Bournemouth was travelling at 90mph near Fleet (Hants) it ploughed headlong into a pine tree which had been blown over on to the line. It was BR's second train crash within 24 hours (the other one was near Leighton Buzzard, just described).

The train careered along for half a mile with the leading

vehicles derailed but fortune favoured the hundred passengers, none of them being hurt, although they had a very frightening experience. The driver was slightly injured but not detained in hospital. He said, 'We had a very lucky escape. It was pitch black, when suddenly there was a tremendous bang and the train started to bump all over the place. It seemed ages before we stopped.'

Lorries Running off the Road

The driver never knows where or when he will encounter an obstruction, and one of the hazards he has to contend with is that of cars and lorries running off the road on to the railway. Such an event, which cost the engine-driver and his mate their lives, happened in the small hours of 15 March 1976 near Annan, between Carlisle and Dumfries, when the driver of an articulated lorry attempted to negotiate a bridge carrying the A75 road over the railway. The lorry collided with the parapet and fell on to the railway line. At this stage the nearest approaching train was still 10 miles away, but by the time the alarm had been raised the train, the 20.55 express from Euston to Stranraer, had passed the last signal at which it could be stopped and its diesel-electric locomotive No 47274 crashed into the lorry at almost 80mph. None of the passengers was hurt but the lorry driver, who was later found to have three times the permissible amount of alcohol in his blood, was killed.

The Department of Transport have now recognised this particular hazard, and crash barriers have been erected at the sides of roads in locations where the railway could be imperilled.

Vandals

This cause of accidents stands out from all others in a number of ways. In the first place it is a misnomer to call the results of vandalism an accident; vandalism is a deliberate act where the perpetrator is either ignorant of the possible consequences of his actions, perhaps doesn't care, or in extreme cases really intends that those consequences should happen. In the second place it is so difficult to guard against.

Astonishingly, many of those carrying out acts of vandalism are too young to be prosecuted, or not much older. A few, thankfully only a tiny minority, are so wildly reckless in their actions that their soundness of mind must be questioned.

On 16 February 1979 a crowded HST from Paddington was travelling at about 65mph just beyond Reading when it ran into two lengths of rail which had been placed across the Down Main line in such a manner that one of them was angled upwards towards the approaching train. The vandals must still have been nearby when the HST hit the rail because it was the evening peak and the intervals between trains were short. We shall never know what the vandals hoped would be the outcome of their actions, nor whether they deliberately set out to derail the train with reckless unconcern for the deaths and injuries which might result, but even they must have been unprepared for the spectacular consequences of their actions. The upturned rail split the fuel tank of the leading power car, and immediately fire broke out, enveloping the first three coaches in flames before the train could be stopped. However, the fire did not penetrate the coaches and rapidly died out and the train was not derailed. Those who committed the outrage were never caught. It is thought that they must have had some railway knowledge because they managed to place the pieces of rail across the line without short-circuiting the track circuit, and they may have been people with a grudge against BR; perhaps former employees who had been dismissed.

A piece of rail was also used in another vandal attack

upon the railways on 22 May 1980. An Up sleeping car express on the East Coast main line had just left Edinburgh and had reached almost 70mph nearing Prestonpans, when it struck a piece of rail nearly 6ft long and weighing about 2cwt. The rail bounced along beneath the train with an enormous clatter, nearly frightening the sleeping car passengers out of their wits, until eventually it distorted the track and derailed all the coaches after the third one. They remained fairly upright and in line and there were no serious injuries. On this occasion the culprit was found — a 17-year old youth, who was committed to Borstal. History does not reveal whether this reformed him, but it certainly did not deter others — in 1985 six trains were derailed by vandals and there were 179 cases of trains running into obstructions, almost half of which were of railway material, mainly left behind after renewal or repair. So, at least part of the solution is in BR's own hands.

Below & bottom:
Derailed sleeping cars after the train had run into a piece of rail placed on the track by a vandal at Prestonpans on 22 May 1980. Iain M. Flynn

But lest it be thought that vandalism against railways is a recent social disease, it is apparent that our forefathers were also troubled by it. The Midland Railway Rule Book of 1883 even went so far as to quote part of the 1861 Offences Against the Person Act:

'Whosoever shall unlawfully and maliciously put or throw upon or across any Railway, any Wood, Stone or other Matter or Thing. . . with Intent to endanger the safety of any Person travelling upon such Railway, shall be guilty of Felony, and being convicted thereof shall be liable to be kept in Penal Servitude for Life, or for any Term not less than Three Years, or to be imprisoned for any term not exceeding Two Years, with or without Hard Labour, and if a Male under the age of sixteen years, with or without Whipping.'

The law is still in force today, although the penal servitude, hard labour and whipping have been replaced by simple imprisonment. It is often difficult to prove 'intent to endanger', especially in the case of younger people, but even without such intent the Act provides for two years' imprisonment. So the law is strict enough; catching the vandals in the first place is the difficulty.

Automatic Open Crossings

Not all the hazards that drivers have to face arise in the day-to-day signalling and operation of the railway. There is another category of hazard which may arise wherever railway and road cross each other on the level, and it introduces to our story another type of driver — the driver of a road vehicle.

1986 will not be remembered as a good summer, but the East Coast had the best of the weather and Saturday 26 July was fine and sunny there. In Bridlington station, the 09.33 stopping train to Hull, formed of a pair of two-car diesel multiple-units, was loading up with holiday-makers on their way home to Hull, some looking back on the enjoyment they had received, others looking forward to the familiar surroundings of home. None had any apprehension of possible danger in the relatively short journey ahead; after all, this was a quiet line with no high speeds so why should there be any cause for concern?

The train left Bridlington on time and set off on its 31-mile, 49min journey. At 09.55 it stopped at Hutton Cranswick station and after a few moments went on its way again. Everything was as normal as could be.

Three miles further down the line, at the closed station of Lockington, everything was normal too. One of the occupants of the railway cottages there saw her next-door neighbour climb into his blue Ford Escort van, as he did every Saturday morning, and set off towards the lane at the bottom of the station approach road. His route then took him over the level crossing at the old station.

The 09.33 train from Bridlington, now with about 120 passengers on board, approached the level crossing at almost full speed — between 60 and 70mph. At the controls its driver had no inkling of imminent disaster. Why should he? The line from Hull to Bridlington and Scarborough was peppered with level crossings and he had driven over it for

years. But that morning the malign hand of fate was working. It was not going to be another routine journey after all, neither for train driver nor for van driver, whose paths were destined to meet on the level crossing.

The train, weighing well over 100 tons, struck the van squarely in the middle and smashed it to pieces, scattering them far and wide, then careered on for 150yd before leaving the rails. The first coach reared up and turned completely round on itself, hurling passengers to their deaths through its broken windows, whilst the remainder of the train jack-knifed itself across the tracks. It was no longer a routine journey. Altogether eight passengers died, and 37 were seriously injured. A little boy of 11, a passenger in the Ford Escort van, also lost his life. It was one of Britain's worst-ever accidents at level crossings, equalled only by the one at Hixon, between Stoke-on-Trent and Colwich, on 6 January 1968, when an express from Manchester to Euston crashed into a heavy transporter lorry carrying an electrical transformer. Hixon level crossing had been modernised the previous year and automatic half-barriers with flashing red road traffic signals had been installed.

There were no automatic half-barriers at Lockington level crossing; only flashing red lights. This type of crossing at Lockington, known as an automatic open crossing (AOC)*, was devised by a working party of British Rail and Department of Transport experts in 1978 and the first one was installed in 1983 (at Naas, between Newport and Gloucester). Automatic open crossings were seen as a cheaper alternative to the automatic half-barrier crossing (AHB), the first one of which had been installed at Spath, on the now-closed line from Uttoxeter to Leek and Ashbourne, in 1961. By the end of 1985 there were 291 AHB level crossings, and 39 AOCs on BR.

Left:
The scene at Lockington after the train from Bridlington to Hull ran into a motor van on the automatic open level crossing. The van was almost totally destroyed by the force of the impact, whilst the two diesel multiple-units forming the train were completely derailed, with the leading vehicle turning through 180° before coming to rest.
The Press Agency (Yorkshire) Ltd

*Technically known as an AOCR — automatic open crossing remotely monitored. There is another type of crossing known as an AOCL — automatic open crossing locally monitored.

117

Drivers of
**LARGE or SLOW
VEHICLES**
must phone
and get permission
to cross

LARGE means
<u>over</u> 55′ long or 9-6″ wide
or 32·5 tons total weight
SLOW means 5mph or less

PARK HERE
AND USE
PHONE AT
CROSSING

ANOTHER TRAIN
COMING
if lights
continue to show

KEEP
CROSSING
CLEAR

KEEP
CROSSING
CLEAR

It might be appropriate at this stage to describe briefly the equipment and method of working of these two types of level crossings, which apart from the half-barriers are very similar. They are illustrated on pages 118-121 and consist of warning lights (amber and flashing red), and various traffic signs. There are no gates but AHB crossings have a lifting barrier which, when lowered, closes off half the road on the left-hand side. The warning sequence is initiated automatically by an approaching train when it occupies a track circuit designed to be long enough to give the necessary warning time of 27sec for trains travelling at the maximum speed allowed for that particular section of track. The amber light glows steadily for 3sec, followed by a minimum of 24sec of flashing red. At an AHB crossing the barriers descend after the lights have been flashing for 8sec.

Such times, measured in seconds, might be thought to reduce safety margins to an unacceptable level, but in fact there is no point in providing longer margins, which would merely encourage impatient car-drivers to 'jump' the lights. In theory there is no reason on safety grounds why the train should not go over the crossing as soon as the rear of any vehicle which is too near the crossing to stop when the amber light shows has passed clear of it. For this purpose 27sec is generally ample time, but the arrangement does mean that it is quite possible for people in a car to look down the line when going over a crossing and see a train approaching, even though the warning lights were not operating when the car passed them. This can give rise to incorrect allegations that the lights have failed.

The working of the crossing equipment is continuously monitored by a nearby signalbox, where there is an indicator to show that the main electric power supply is available at the crossing. So far as AHBs are concerned there is another indicator in the signalbox to show when the barriers are raised. AOCs have an in-built warning system that gives an audible alarm in the signalbox if all the red lights facing in one direction fail. At both types of crossing there is a telephone to the signalbox. An audible warning sounds at the crossing as soon as the amber light shows, but this is for the guidance of pedestrians, not vehicle drivers.

Above:
Britain's first automatic open crossing at Naas, between Newport and Gloucester, commissioned in 1983. At each side of the crossing there is a telephone connected to a signalbox. The cross and chevron above the flashing lights tell the road user that there are two railway tracks, although it is highly questionable whether many road users understand the meaning of this sign. British Rail (WR)

Right:
A typical automatic half barrier installation. British Railways

AHBs and AOCs may be provided on any railway line with not more than two running lines (a term which denotes lines other than sidings), but the maximum speed of trains over the crossing must not exceed 100mph for AHBs and 75mph for AOCs. The speed and volume of road traffic is of no consequence at an AHB but at an AOC it must not exceed 2,000 vehicles per day. Furthermore, the total number of road vehicles per day at an AOC multiplied by the total number of trains per day must not exceed 40,000, nor more than 600 in the peak hour. There is nothing magic or scientific about these figures — they are purely arbitrary and designed to reduce the chances of a train and a road vehicle being on the crossing at the same precise moment if something has gone wrong or someone has made a mistake. The limitation to 75mph is designed to reduce the effects of a collision if the one-in-a-thousand chances turns up. At Lockington it did turn up and even at 60-70mph caused devastation.

Automatic level crossings are not interlocked with railway signals and such signals may show Clear whether or not the lights are flashing, and irrespective of the presence of a road vehicle on the crossing, but there must be a signal capable of being placed at Danger not further away than 10min running time for the fastest train. This is not only to allow trains to be stopped in case of emergency but also to allow abnormally heavy or slow lorries, or herds of animals, to cross the lines safely by telephone arrangement with the signalman.

Automatic crossings are capable of being switched to non-automatic operation when necessary, for example when one of the tracks is being repaired, or when nearby road works may cause vehicles to tail back on to the crossing. In such cases a railwayman will be stationed at the crossing, and he will operate the barriers and lights manually. Trains approaching the crossing will be stopped by the signalman and the drivers will be warned to approach the crossing cautiously and not to proceed over it until they have received permission from the man at the crossing that they may do so. Operations of this nature, the details of which are not known to road users, may sometimes give rise to stories and rumours that the lights were seen not to be working properly, or that they had failed.

The advantages of automatic level crossings may be summarised thus:

1 They avoid failures of the human element on the part of railway staff employed to operate crossings with gates. Fatal accidents occasionally occur at such crossings.
2 Gated crossings often have railway signals protecting them. Trains sometimes crash through the gates when the driver inadvertently slides past the signal, and if there happens to be a road vehicle in the way the results can be disastrous for its occupants.
3 Automatic crossings avoid the heavy manning costs associated with gated crossings.
4 The flow of road traffic is speeded up. Automatic crossings are closed for less than a minute when a train passes; gated crossings for three or four minutes because it is necessary to swing the gates across the road and clear the railway signals in time to give a clear indication at the Distant signal to an approaching train which may be up to 2 miles from the crossing. If the signal is not at Clear when it comes into the driver's view he will slow down ready to stop at the signal at the crossing, which may cause it to be closed to road traffic for longer than normal.
5 When trains pass over a level crossing at short intervals, either from opposite directions or where one closely follows another, the interval between the trains may be too short to allow the gates to be swung open (or manned barriers to be raised), thus the gates or barriers may have to remain closed across the road whilst two or even three trains pass. The delay to road traffic can be considerable, especially if a long queue builds up, as it does in the rush hour at busy crossings. Automatic crossings go a long way towards solving this problem — they will open between trains even if only 10sec is available before the next train 'strikes in' and triggers off the warning lights.

There are, of course, disadvantages. Automatic crossings are safer than *some* gated crossings, but they are not

necessarily safer than manned level crossings provided with full-length lifting barriers and flashing road traffic signals, nor with such crossings unmanned but monitored remotely by closed-circuit television. One of the less desirable effects of automatic crossings is that they may be said to transfer the responsibility for safety at the crossing from trained and reliable railway staff to road users who may occasionally act recklessly, irresponsibly or carelessly. It could be argued that if the road user wants to kill himself by his own stupidity, so be it, but that philosophy is only tenable so long as those actions do not endanger the lives of railway passengers. And of course it is not always a question of stupidity; it may be a simple failure of the human element.

In this connection we must make a distinction between AHBs and AOCs. It is hardly possible for a road user to cause a collision at an AHB crossing through carelessness or lack of attention — the half-barrier sees to that. It can only be caused by stupid recklessness. Not so at an AOC, however. There is no half-barrier to wake up the day-dreaming car-driver, and the stupid driver can 'jump' the lights without the tell-tale zig-zag round the barriers. But all this was foreseen when AOCs were devised, hence the limitations which were imposed.

But let us now return to Lockington. Was there a system failure at the crossing? It seems very unlikely indeed. Two witnesses saw the red lights flashing normally as the train approached the crossing, although they were on the opposite side of the crossing to the Ford Escort van driver. Nevertheless, it is technically inconceivable that the lights should flash normally in one direction and fail completely in the other, and yet be found to be in proper working order when tested afterwards. Furthermore such a failure would have sounded an alarm in the monitoring signalbox. No such alarm was received; and it must be said that wrong-side failures of level crossing automatic equipment are very rare indeed.

Perhaps we shall never know exactly what happened at

Below:
A poster issued in 1962 in connection with the installation of an automatic half barrier level crossing at Stallingborough on the line between Barnetby and Grimsby. Note that early crossings of this type had only the two flashing red lights.
British Railways

Below right:
A modified version of the automatic half barrier crossing, installed at Ripe, Sussex, in 1970. New features included an amber light giving advance warning before the flashing red lights. The illuminated message 'Another Train Coming' denotes the passage of another train before the barriers rise.
British Rail

Lockington. The van driver, the one man with the key to the explanation, was badly injured in the crash and it often happens in such circumstances that the memory of those moments preceding the accident is blurred or completely erased. However, there are a number of important factors peculiar to this case, which go far to render it untypical.

In the first place the van driver lived in the railway cottages almost next to Lockington level crossing. Although the crossing had only recently been modernised he can hardly have been unaware of it. It cannot have been the case that he suddenly came upon it and was confused by its method of operation. Secondly the van driver did not approach the level crossing by driving straight along the road towards it; had he done so he would have had the benefit of all the warning traffic signs, plus the full 24sec of flashing-red road traffic signals. The two witnesses previously mentioned gave evidence of how visually-arresting the lights were. But the van driver did not have the benefit of the warning traffic signs, nor a good long view of the flashing lights; on the contrary he turned on to the lane leading over the level crossing only a few yards from it. In such circumstances, especially if pre-occupied at the start of a journey, might it not be possible to overlook the lights, especially if they were in view for only a few seconds against a bright sky background?

There is another consideration too. Experienced car drivers do not concentrate consciously on every aspect of their driving. On the contrary, much of it is done as an automatic reaction. We do not consciously say to ourselves 'I am approaching a left-hand bend, therefore I must turn the steering wheel in an anti-clockwise direction'. We do not say to ourselves 'I have now accelerated to 30mph on the level so it would be appropriate for me to change from third gear to fourth'. No, for much of the time car driving is done on 'automatic pilot', because the procedures have been so completely absorbed. Consider therefore someone who has regularly driven over a gated crossing. His mind is then programmed: 'Gates across the road. I must stop, as there is a train coming'. If the gates are not across the road his mind is equally programmed 'No train coming, it is safe to cross'.

Let us then apply this philosophy to the events of the morning of the accident and let us surmise as follows: The van driver set off on his journey, turned on to the lane and approached the crossing. His driving was on 'automatic pilot'; perhaps his mind was pre-occupied. His 'automatic pilot' was programmed to look for gates across the road. There were no gates across the road so the reaction of the automatic pilot was to drive over the crossing. The warning lights, visible only for a few seconds, did not penetrate the consciousness. It must be stressed that this is only a surmise, but it is a possible explanation of events.

But if we accept the surmise for the sake of argument, what does it prove, and what considerations flow from it?

In the first place we have already concluded that the circumstances of the accident were untypical and we ought not to condemn automatic open crossings on the basis of this one accident alone. On the other hand, though, if the 'automatic pilot' theory is accepted it would surely have detected the presence of a lowered barrier at an AHB crossing and the driver would have stopped clear, so we might therefore conclude that AOCs are unsuitable but AHBs are acceptable, *but only in the special circumstances of the Lockington accident*. That consideration would not apply to the normal user of an automatic open crossing because the visual impact of red flashing lights for up to 24sec would surely penetrate the consciousness and overcome the automatic pilot, even without the presence of a lowered barrier. It must be accepted, however, that AOCs are marginally less safe than AHBs; that has always been the accepted view, hence the restrictions on their use.

There are a number of other advantages that AHBs possess over AOCs. There is always a temptation to a reckless or impetuous road user to jump the lights, and it is easier to achieve at an AOC, where a driver may sneak across hoping he will not be noticed, whereas at an AHB it is necessary to do a very obvious zig-zag round the lowered barriers, which also entails going over the double white line and possibly reducing speed, an undertaking likely therefore to deter all but the most foolhardy.

Another advantage of AHBs concerns the situation which arises when a second train approaches the crossing just as the first train has cleared it. A day-dreaming car driver switched on to automatic pilot might well set off over the crossing as soon as the first train has passed, even though the lights are still flashing, but would hardly drive through a lowered barrier. It has to be admitted therefore, that it would be easier to set off unwittingly over the crossing at an AOC than at an AHB, even though a flashing sign is provided at AOCs which reads 'Another Train Coming'. This possibility too was recognised when AOCs were devised, hence the restriction on the combined volume of trains and road vehicles, which helps to reduce the number of occasions when two trains pass over a crossing in quick succession. It should be noted that the lights will cease to flash (and the barrier will rise at an AHB) if the road can be opened for at least 10sec before the approach of the second train triggers off the warning lights.

It might be argued that AOCs are as safe as AHBs when properly used, but this ignores the day-to-day realities of the situation and in practice AHBs are safer than AOCs. The retort might then be 'So what? Are we to have the same standard of safety equipment at *every* level crossing regardless of the degree of peril and regardless of cost?' If the answer to that question is 'yes', then we should have full-length manned barriers at every level crossing because that is what such an answer would entail. But where is the logic in such a demand? And apart from that, why should we demand a much higher standard of safety at a place where rail crosses road than we do at a place where road crosses road? There are many busy, dangerous crossroads which do not even have traffic lights, and even the busiest, most dangerous crossroads do not have barriers with a man to operate them, nor even half-barriers, nor have local

Left:
Non-automatic crossings often cause lengthy delays to road users. These manually-operated full-length barriers are at Thatcham, near Newbury. D. E. Canning

residents ever demanded that they should be so equipped. So we ought not to apply double standards. The type of equipment to be provided at a railway level crossing should be appropriate to the degree of peril, and it would be illogical to act otherwise. But consequent upon that decision is the need to accept an occasional accident without causing an uproar and setting up special government reviews, which happened after the Hixon accident and has happened again after the Lockington crash.[1] It is understandable that the government may wish to calm people's fears about safety at level crossings but it might also be thought of as an insult to the integrity and professional competence of railway managers and a reflection on the standing and independence of the Railway Inspectorate of the Department of Transport.

Finally, the question arises as to the future of automatic level crossings. AHBs have been in use since 1961 and they have been widely installed. There is sufficient experience to indicate that they are acceptably safe in most situations and the site conditions for suitability are strict and clearly defined. Their acceptability was confirmed both by the Inquiry held by Mr E. B. Gibbens QC into the Hixon accident in 1968 and by the joint BR/Railway Inspectorate team which re-examined the question in 1978, and studied continental practice, where the automation of level crossings, both with and without barriers, has proceeded much further than in Britain. However, even continental practice is not perfect. The French Railways had their own 'Hixon' in July 1985 when a push-pull express from Le Havre to Paris, being propelled at nearly 100mph, ran into a lorry on an automatic level crossing at Saint-Pierre-du-Vauvray. Seven passengers were killed and 55 injured. The crossing was equipped with four half-barriers, which British practice has always considered undesirable and potentially dangerous.

Wrong-side failures of equipment at AHBs in Britain are very rare and most accidents are caused by motorists zig-zagging round the lowered barriers. This is a deliberate act and whilst the motorist is at liberty to risk his own life he should be deterred with all the force the law can command from hazarding the lives of innocent railway passengers. Perhaps he should be charged under Section 34 of the Offences Against the Person Act 1861, which provides that any unlawful act, 'which endangers the safety of persons conveyed on the railway shall be a misdemeanour, punishable by imprisonment for two years', rather than be charged under the Road Traffic Acts with a traffic offence and receiving a small fine.

So far as automatic open crossings are concerned, it is too early yet to judge whether they are acceptably safe because they have only recently started to be installed, and there were only 47 of them in use at the time of the Lockington accident. The events at Lockington were not wholly typical but inevitably the accident, being so serious, has brought the question into prominence. BR might have been able to take a relaxed attitude in the days when a heavy steam locomotive at the head of a train could be expected to toss aside any car that got in its way but it is not a valid attitude today, as was so tragically demonstrated at Lockington when a small van succeeded in completely wrecking a

Lockington level crossing looking east, the scene of one of Britain's worst-ever level crossing accidents on 26 July 1986.

100 ton train. And it is not just DMUs and push-pull trains which are at risk. On 4 May 1982, the 13.35 express from Glasgow to Aberdeen, hauled by a heavy main-line diesel-electric locomotive, collided with a farm trailer on a field-to-field farm crossing of private occupation status at Nairn's Crossing near Forteviot, just south of Perth. The whole train, except the last coach, was derailed, and most of it plunged down an embankment into a field, but no one was killed and only four passengers were seriously injured.

The crux of the argument between AHBs and AOCs really boils down to a question of cost. AHBs are acceptably safe. AOCs are less safe than AHBs, but they may still be acceptably safe in certain circumstances. They are somewhat cheaper, but does the saving justify the reduction in safety? Or to put it another way, is the increase in safety of an AHB worth the extra cost? There is no definitive answer.

There are just two other matters to be dealt with. After an accident such as this, the question is always raised as to whether some form of guard or cow-catcher at the front of the train would have avoided the derailment. It is a question that has been raised many times but has rarely been seriously considered. However, after the Polmont accident on 30 July 1984, when an Edinburgh-Glasgow push-pull express being propelled was derailed after running into a cow, resulting in 13 passengers being killed, a form of deflector was designed and fitted to such trains in Scotland. The front-end design of locomotives and multiple-units, and of the first vehicle of push-pull trains, needs to be re-examined to see whether they can be made more resistant to derailment after colliding with road vehicles at level crossings or with heavy animals or objects on the line.

The second matter is really one of clarification. There is another type of automatic open crossing, known as an

Labels on the image:
LOCOMOTIVE
TRANSFORMER FROM LORRY
REAR OF TRANSPORTER
WRECKED SIGNAL BOX
ICE CAR
TRACTOR
TRANSPORTER
LEVEL CROSSING

AOCL (automatic open crossing locally monitored) where safety is monitored by the driver of an approaching train. There is no difference in equipment or operation so far as the road user is concerned, but the train driver is required to approach the crossing at such a speed as will enable him to stop safely short of the crossing if it is obstructed when it first comes into his view. There is no telephone from the crossing to a signalbox and the train driver himself checks that the flashing red warning lights are working by observing a duplicate flashing light (white) at the side of the line. The speed of trains must not exceed 55mph but in practice speeds are usually lower. The experience of Lockington brings into question whether the speed limit of 55mph is too high, bearing in mind that the train involved at Lockington was only travelling about 10mph faster than that and if Lockington had been an AOCL the collision would still probably have happened. The speed of 55mph, selected by the 1978 Review team, is purely arbitrary, based partly on continental experience and partly on the excellent safety record at AOCLs before 1978 when the limit was 35mph. Perhaps 45mph would be a suitable compromise — it would have little practical effect on day-to-day operations and would improve safety margins.

As a postscript to this question of safety at automatic open crossings, it is interesting to reflect upon another accident at a level crossing just a mile north of Lockington, almost exactly 10 years earlier. This accident happened on 20 June 1976 at Kilnwick level crossing, when the 09.30 passenger train from Hull to Scarborough, consisting of seven diesel multiple-unit coaches, ran into a saloon car. The car driver was killed but it is notable that although the train was travelling at its maximum speed of 70mph, only its front bogie was derailed and no one on the train was hurt, yet in almost identical circumstances at Lockington 10 years later nine people died and many were injured. It would therefore be unreasonable to attribute the death-roll to the automation of Lockington level crossing, and thereby to condemn the whole principle of the automation of level crossings. There could just as easily have been a similar death-roll at Kilnwick, which at that time was not automated but was equipped with gates, worked by a crossing keeper (at the subsequent Public Inquiry he was

Above:
Hixon Crossing 1968: the scene of chaos after the 11.30 Manchester-Euston express struck a transporter carrying a 120-ton transformer on 6 January. Keystone Press Agency

found to be not at fault). The number and severity of casualties in a railway accident are purely a matter of luck, and safety measures should always be directed at the causes of accidents and their *potential* consequences, not the actual ones.

One final point — Lockington might well be considered a perfect example of a level crossing eminently suitable for conversion to an automatic open crossing; there are only a handful of road vehicles and two trains per hour, the approach road is straight and level and leads to nowhere in particular, and the traffic is local in character, yet a mile up the road there is a situation of much greater danger where the lane crosses the busy, high-speed main road from Hull to Bridlington, which is full of cars, coaches, and 38-ton six-axle articulated lorries, all travelling (some illegally so) at 50-70mph; and there are not even any traffic lights. Such a dangerous situation would not be tolerated on the railway for an instant.

At the time of writing, neither Major King, the Inspecting Officer who held a Public Inquiry into the cause of the accident, nor Professor Stott has issued his Report. But the fact remains that safety at automatic open crossings is largely dependent on the actions of road users. Railway passengers are entitled to expect safety standards to be applied by trained and reliable railway staff and not to be at the mercy of any Tom, Dick or Harry driving a road vehicle. On those grounds automatic open crossings ought not to be used by trains travelling at high speeds. Above about 45mph half-barriers ought to be provided.

[1] A committee has been set up by the Department of Transport under the chairmanship of Professor Stott with the remit 'To review the safety record of automatic open crossings, to consider the lessons gained from the experience so far, and to make recommendations to the Secretary of State for Transport.

⑬ Conclusions

Anyone reading the preceding chapters may be forgiven for concluding that rail travel in Great Britain is not as safe as its reputation would suggest and certainly not as safe as it could be. The evidence presented in this book could lead to a conclusion that the railways have often been slow to apply remedial safety measures, that deliberations have lacked a sense of urgency, that design work, testing and implementation have been unduly protracted, and that action when finally taken has been half-hearted and reluctant, giving the impression that BR didn't really believe that it needed to do anything. But would such a judgement be unduly harsh and unfair? It cannot be denied that, on the evidence, it has often in the past been a question of too little and too late. One must hope that this is no longer the case, but there is still much to be done in the interests of greater safety, and there can be no standing still.

However, protracted or not, there is no doubt that the actions which BR have taken over the years have borne fruit — in the late 1970s and early 1980s there were four individual years (1976, 1977, 1980 and 1982) in which no passengers were killed in train accidents. In 1983 only two were killed, whilst 1985 was another clear year. In the 10 years 1976-1985, 45 passengers lost their lives in train accidents on BR, which is about as many as are killed on Britain's roads in two or three *days*, and fewer than died in one single airline disaster at Manchester Airport in 1986. The Transport Act 1962, which sets out BR's duties, merely says that the British Railways Board should have *due regard* to efficiency, economy and *safety of operation*. No doubt the draughtsman of that Act found it as difficult as others have done to lay down precise safety standards. Absolute safety is unattainable in practical terms.

There are, however, other considerations. Apart from any

Below:
The old . . . Class 47 No 47712 *Lady Diana Spencer* passes beneath the semaphore gantry on the way out of Stirling, heading the 11.05 Aberdeen-Glasgow service on 25 August 1984. W. A. Sharman

moral duty not to kill passengers there are commercial and business implications. A serious collision these days might not cause any passenger deaths but can cause millions of pounds worth of damage. Those same coaches whose design has contributed so greatly to the saving of lives in an accident are in consequence very expensive. So is the track, the signalling and the overhead electrified line equipment. The interruption to the train service may last for days, which causes not only an immediate loss of revenue but also mars the railway's reputation for reliability. And even though passengers might not be killed many are injured, some very severely; and drivers are often killed. So what more ought to be done?

By comparison with continental railways BR has lagged behind in a number of areas: in the provision of radio communication between drivers and signalmen, in equipping coaches with power-operated doors, but most of all in equipment to help the driver. The reasons are partly financial — continental railways receive far more money from their governments than BR does — but there are others. The splendid safety record during the late 1970s and early 1980s did much to strengthen a feeling within BR that a sufficiently high safety level had been reached and that little of a major nature remained to be done. There was also a certain rigidity of attitude that saw no need to do anything more to help the driver, 'He's paid to obey signals' was an oft-heard saying, but as the use of AWS became more and more widespread, signs began to emerge that the concept of the system, being merely advisory, had an inherent flaw. Nonetheless, flawed though it is, AWS has been, and still is, of enormous value, but in the 30 years that have elapsed since the present system was finally approved, technology has moved on and there are now more effective systems available. There is an amply-demonstrated and over-riding need for BR to do more to help the driver and it should tackle the problem with vigour, with determination and, above all, with urgency. It will take several years for such action to bear fruit and in the meantime there could be more accidents, more deaths and injuries and more destruction. One can only hope that BR will not allow sectional interests and short-term pressures to deflect it from the pursuit of such an objective.

To return to the two questions with which this chapter opened: Is rail travel as safe as its reputation suggests? and is it as safe as it could be? To the first question the answer must be 'yes'. BR's reputation as a safe means of transport is deservedly high (despite occasional lapses). The record speaks for itself. To the second question the answer has to be 'no'. To give any other answer would be to fly in the face of the evidence in this book. But there is a third question — *ought* rail travel to be safer? There is no apparent commercial need; BR's current safety levels attract passengers rather than deter them (although that might be a reflection on the competition rather than a credit to the railway). Would substantial investment in increased safety attract more passengers? It seems unlikely. So where is the pay-off? Why should BR spend some of its precious funds on greater safety, for no competitive gain, rather than on improved stations, faster trains, more luxurious coaches, etc, which would improve its competitive position? I believe that the reasons why it should might be summarised as follows:

1 Another accident of the 'Colwich' type could well result in a long casualty list. BR would then be forced to take action.

2 The public's expectation of safety levels will not remain static. It never has done.

3 The Department of Transport will continue to expect a gradual improvement in safety standards.

4 The Health & Safety at Work Act 1974 requires a high standard of safety. Commercial matters are not a factor in the reckoning.

5 Higher speeds will demand a more effective safety system.

6 A more advanced safety system would avoid the cost of double-manning of trains running at more than 100mph.

7 The cost of junction signalling would be reduced.

8 Millions of pounds would be saved by the reduction in the number of serious accidents.

9 The expenditure on improved safety, though substantial, would be spread over many years.

The long saga of accident prevention on Britain's railways has shown generally continuous, although somewhat uneven, improvement and progress. Throughout this history the Railway Inspectorate of the Department of Transport (and its predecessors) have acted as the guardians of public safety. Their conclusions and recommendations, following inquiries into accidents, have most often been accurate and appropriate, indeed, if any criticism can be levelled at them it is that they have not always in the past pressed their recommendations as strongly as perhaps they ought to have done. Theirs is a hard task, and they have a fine line to follow between on the one hand making over-extravagant demands and on the other having too much regard for the railway's financial difficulties. On balance, though, they have carried out their responsibilities with skill and distinction and their reputation is high. Their published reports on acccidents are models of narrative layout, clarity and logic, and my only complaint is that they are absurdly expensive — the Wembley Report, published in February 1986, cost £4.90 for just 12 pages and a couple of diagrams, which goes far towards defeating the whole purpose of issuing public reports, if the public don't buy them because they are too expensive. Few railwaymen will purchase them at that price, yet they are the very people who ought to be buying and studying them.

As our story has unfolded in the preceding pages it is uncanny how often sleeping car expresses have figured therein, sometimes even the same ones, yet they form only a small proportion of the total number of express trains. It can only be coincidence? The West Coast main line south of Crewe has also been frequently mentioned but here there is perhaps a more logical explanation — it does have the reputation of being BR's busiest main line. Yet its rival, the East Coast main line south of Doncaster, has hardly had a mention.

And finally, so far as the individual passenger is concerned, he or she need have no fears about safety, despite all that I have written. Even on the basis of a daily journey to and from work a passenger would have to live for many thousands of years to have an even chance of being killed in a train accident. So take heart, and continue to travel by the most comfortable, most enjoyable and safest means of transport ever devised. Generations of railwaymen have dedicated themselves to seeing that it is so.

Below:
... and the new: a multi-aspect colour-light signal in the Glasgow area. GEC

Index

DANGER ON THE LINE
STANLEY HALL

PART TWO

Contents

Introduction and Acknowledgements

My first book on railway safety standards, and accidents to trains on British Rail, published in 1987 under the title *Danger Signals*, was concerned mainly with the operational aspects of railway work, under the control of drivers, guards and signalmen. This second book ventures into the realms of civil, mechanical and signal engineering and explores the technical aspects of accidents of which the driver is often an unwitting and unwilling victim or observer. However, as in *Danger Signals*, it also attempts to look beyond the obvious cause of an accident, and explores the way in which the conditions necessary for accidents are created, such as the impact of new technology, errors made by technical staff, the effect of management action or inaction, and the influence of the changing railway environment. It is, however, not a technical treatise, but is aimed equally at the professional and the layman, at the railwayman and that large body of people interested in railway activities.

Chapter 10 discusses the accidents at Purley, on the Southern Region's main line from Brighton to London, and at Glasgow Bellgrove, which happened within two days of each other in March 1989. The causes of accidents such as these where drivers pass signals at Danger were fully explored in *Danger Signals*, but they are of such significance in safety terms that it was felt to be essential to include an examination of them in this book.

I have taken as my starting point the nationalisation of railways on 1 January 1948, with only an occasional reference to events or accidents before that date, therefore the book is essentially concerned with the modern railway. Because of my background as a railway operator it is also an operating view of the railway scene, concerned with trains and the general running of the railway, as influenced by technical matters, such as the track, bridges, rolling stock, and the conveyance of dangerous goods.

Technical innovation is often a two-edged sword. It removes previous causes of accidents but may easily create other, new, and sometimes unforeseen hazards. Technology pushes at the boundaries of knowledge and experience, indeed that is how progress comes about, but the act of venturing into the unknown can have a downside so far as safety is concerned.

The theme of the book is safety, and it explains how today's very high standards have been achieved. I am writing these very words as I travel in High Speed Train comfort and safety through thick fog at 125mph, confident that the skill and care of engineers of all disciplines will get me to my destination on time and in one piece. By contrast, tonight's newspapers may well contain reports of multiple pile-ups on motorways, of people being trapped in their burning cars, and of the general mayhem which seems to afflict our motorways and trunk roads during fog and frost.

Accidents by their very nature indicate that something has gone wrong, or that someone has made an error, but the ultimate responsibility may well lie with the management of British Rail, because it is they who decide how the railways should be operated, and the extent to which the effects of human error should be guarded against. Accidents are almost bound to result in criticism but I hope that my comments are always fair and take account of the constraints, whether financial, political or legal, which often bear harshly upon BR. The views expressed in this book, and the criticisms, except where otherwise attributed, are mine alone, and I have striven to achieve an objective and dispassionate viewpoint.

In my descriptions of certain accidents I have attempted to give the reader a feeling of what it must have been like to have been involved, whether as passenger, driver or guard, and this necessarily entails a degree of dramatisation. I make no apology for this — accidents *are* dramatic and they *are* frightening.

This book would not have been possible without the enormous help I have received from the officers of the Railway Inspectorate of the Department of Transport, and from their Accident Reports, also from the Annual Reports of the Chief Inspecting Officer. I am also very grateful for the help and encouragement given by my family and friends, and to those of you who were kind enough to buy my first book *Danger Signals*, because that has encouraged me to write this book. I must also express my gratitude to those of my friends and former colleagues who have kindly read the drafts and given me their helpful comments.

Finally, I would like to acknowledge the help I have received from the following in the provision of material and with help in research:

The British Railways Board
British Timken, Duston, Northampton
British Transport Police
Chartered Institute of Transport
Cowans Boyd, Carlisle
Dorman Traffic Products Ltd, Southport
Graviner Ltd, Slough
National Railway Museum, York
National Union of Railwaymen
Procor (UK) Ltd, Horbury Junction.

1
Fires on Express Passenger Trains

Imagine that you are a passenger on an express train. Perhaps you are reading, or chatting, or just looking out of the window enjoying the view of the countryside. You catch a faint whiff of something burning. You do not recognise it but you think it might have come from outside, and you dismiss it from your mind. A few minutes later the smell intrudes into your consciousness again, only this time it is a little stronger and more acrid. You look round to see if you can detect where the smell is coming from, and you notice that one or two of your fellow passengers are also looking round in a concerned sort of way. In the rest of the coach life is going on as usual — family parties playing games, people eating and drinking and chatting happily. Some just sleeping.

Suddenly you get a definite smell of something burning, and a feeling of alarm starts to rise within you. You begin to wonder whether you should do something, but what? Go for the guard? No, you decide that would be futile; it would take too long, and in any case you don't want to fetch the guard on what might turn out to be a wild-goose chase if nothing can be found when you return. Pull the communication cord? You look to see where it is and spot a red handle near the ceiling on the opposite side. But suppose it is a false alarm? Would you have to pay £50? Perhaps it would be better to move away further down the coach, just in case. After all, you don't want to make a fuss, and look a fool when it turns out to be nothing. But even

whilst these thoughts are chasing each other through your mind you notice a definite puff of dark smoke. Others do too, and the normal chatter of the coach is replaced by a more agitated hubbub. Voices are raised. People start to move away. Someone calls, 'fetch the guard'. Someone else shouts, 'is there a fire extinguisher?' Then, a small tongue of reddish-yellow flame licks up the wall. Passengers nearby start to move away in a hurry, but their way is impeded by the throng of other passengers blocking the aisle. Within seconds thick black suffocating smoke and fumes begin to curl down the coach along the ceiling, flames shoot up the wall to the roof and a mad scramble breaks out to get away from the fire. But the train is full. There are over 70 passengers in that coach. Some are elderly and not very agile and there's only one way out — through the door at the far end. But that door is blocked with a huge press of bodies jammed together in their panic and anxiety to escape. However, the train is slowing down because the communication cord has been pulled, but the flames are now rapidly advancing down the coach towards the

Below:
London & North Eastern Railway prewar third-class open saloon coach, with bucket-type seats. Six schoolboys lost their lives in a fire in a coach of this type in 1941, when a lighted match lodged between a seat and the side of the coach.
Ian Allan Library

Above:
Class A3 Pacific No 60035 *Windsor Lad* at Edinburgh Waverley on a train for Perth. This was the locomotive on the train involved in the fire at Penmanshiel Tunnel on 23 June 1949.
Eric Treacy/Millbrook House Collection

terrified trapped passengers, who can already feel the intensity of the heat. There is only one way of escape left — through the windows. People are already hammering on them but the windows are tough and double-glazed. Fortunately, someone remembers that there is a hammer provided for just such an emergency, fixed to the wall in a glass case. This is no time for standing on ceremony. A fist smashes the glass and the precious hammer is plucked from its housing. There is now a desperate race against time. Can sufficient windows be broken in the remaining few seconds before people are burnt to death or become unconscious from carbon monoxide poisoning? And how many people will be able to escape before being overcome?

It is a fearful scenario. And yet it takes only a few seconds for a small, smouldering fire to become a sheet of flame, if conditions favour it; therefore it is obviously vital for designers and builders of railway coaches to have full regard for the possibility of fire. Their success may be measured by the fact that, with the single exception of the Taunton fire in 1979, no passenger has been killed in a train on fire since 1951. Before that, fires were more prevalent, especially in the earlier days when coaches were built entirely, or mainly, of wood, and lit by gas, which was housed in tanks underneath the coaches themselves.

By the beginning of World War 2 steel was in general use for coach underframes, and the use of steel sheet for sides and roofs was becoming prevalent, but the body framing and the interior fittings were still generally of wood. However, throughout all the perils of World War 2 there was only one case where passengers were killed in a train fire, and that was at Westborough on 28 April 1941. Boys were returning to their public school at Ampleforth near York after the Easter holiday, and about 100 of them were travelling in two reserved open third-class coaches with bucket-type seats attached to the rear of the 12.45pm King's Cross to Newcastle express. Some of the boys were indulging in the stupid boyish prank of flicking lighted matches about and one match lodged between the seat and the side of the coach. The seats had roll-round foam rubber cushioning, which was very inflammable, and there was a small initial fire which within seconds was out of control. The communication cord was pulled and the train stopped near Claypole, about 10 miles north of Grantham. Both coaches, and the rear brakevan, were all burnt down to their underframes and six boys lost their lives.

In view of the conditions which existed in Britain in April 1941, when night after night whole city centres were set on fire by German air attacks, it is not surprising that the Westborough fire attracted little attention. In more normal times it might have led to action being taken to reduce the likelihood of such fires developing so quickly, but in the event little was done and it is surprising that eight years were to pass before there was a further serious fire.

Thursday 23 June 1949 was a fine, dry, warm day. The 7.30pm express from Edinburgh to King's Cross left on time, with 'A3' Pacific No 60035 *Windsor Lad* hauling 12 coaches, the last four of which were:

Corridor third No 1498
Corridor brake composite No 1148
Buffet car No 9124
Corridor brake third.

The train was about half-full and it passed Cockburnspath, 35 miles from Edinburgh, at 8.31pm with speed down to about 25mph on the 1 in 96 gradient. The signalman there watched it pass his signalbox and saw nothing wrong. About 5min later a passenger in the fifth coach went to the buffet car at the rear of the train and noticed no trace of fire in coach 1148 next to it. However, only a few moments later when he re-entered the brake compartment of coach 1148 on his way back from the buffet car, he saw passengers running into it from the corridor, with clouds of thick, black smoke following them. The guard was already putting the brake on and the train stopped quickly, enabling the passengers to jump out.

Coach 1148 was built by contractors for the London & North Eastern Railway (LNER) in 1947. It had a steel underframe and sheet steel external panelling, with wooden framing and interior fittings. It was of the latest LNER postwar design, with a small guard's-compartment, two first-class compartments, three third-class compartments, and two transverse corridors with outside doors. The transverse corridors were unusually located towards the centre of the coach instead of at the ends, a feature of the design which was intended to reduce the distance a passenger had to walk from an outside door to a compartment. On the evening of the fire the coach conveyed one first-class passenger and 14 third-class. One of the third-class passengers suddenly saw flames about a foot

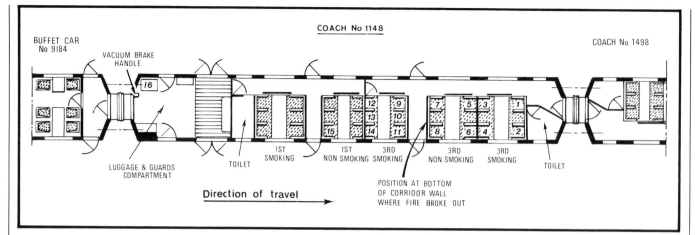

COACH No 1148

BUFFET CAR
No 9184

VACUUM BRAKE
HANDLE

16

COACH No 1498

LUGGAGE & GUARDS
COMPARTMENT

TOILET

1ST
SMOKING

1ST
NON SMOKING

3RD
SMOKING

3RD
NON SMOKING

3RD
SMOKING

TOILET

POSITION AT BOTTOM
OF CORRIDOR WALL
WHERE FIRE BROKE OUT

Direction of travel

deep, accompanied by black smoke and a roaring sound, moving along the top of the corridor towards him. He at once pulled the communication cord, shouted to his companions, and ran into the corridor, through the flames, to safety. The flames immediately entered the open doorway of the compartment, blocking the escape route for the three other occupants. They were thus trapped and had no alternative, if they wanted to avoid being roasted alive, but to break the window and jump out. One of them was severely injured in doing so. All the other passengers were able to escape from their compartments in time, although some were burnt in doing so and suffered from the effects of smoke and fumes.

The astonishing feature of this fire was the rapidity with which it spread. Within little more than a few seconds it had raced along the corridor ceiling from end to end, down to the floor and into the compartments. The coach and the one next to it, No 1498, were swiftly burnt down to the underframes. If the train had been full, and travelling at express speed, there would almost certainly have been a

Top:

Coach No 1148 and the Penmanshiel fire

Above:

Postwar LNER third-class corridor brake coach of the type involved in the Penmanshiel Tunnel fire on 23 June 1949. It was built in 1947 and has an oval toilet window, which was distinctive of the period. *Ian Allan Library*

heavy death toll, but in the event no one was killed. The cause of the fire was probably a carelessly discarded cigarette end.

The train stopped with the first eight coaches already inside Penmanshiel Tunnel and the train crew quickly split the train next to the burning coach. The front portion was taken forward to Grantshouse, where it arrived at 8.50pm, only 10min after the train had first stopped and with many passengers possibly unaware that there was anything amiss. It is an interesting comment on the emergency arrangements in those days that the first ambulance did not arrive until 9.45pm, over an hour after the train had stopped, closely followed by the fire brigade, despite the fact that the scene of the fire was immediately alongside a main road, but, as it happened, the injured had already been taken to hospital by cars and buses.

Tests were subsequently carried out to discover why the fire had spread with such rapidity, and some remarkable evidence emerged. A small twist of paper was placed on the floor of a similar coach, against the wall of the transverse corridor, and lit. The effect was astounding. In less than 10sec the whole transverse corridor was filled with flames and the test had to be abandoned to avoid the coach being completely destroyed. In the next test a lighted match was thrown into a corner of the corridor. Nothing happened for 10sec, then the surface of the wall suddenly burst into strong flames 2ft long. Some 15sec later the flames had reached the ceiling, and within another 10sec the entire corridor was in flames, and the fire had to be extinguished immediately.

When built, the interior woodwork of this type of coach had been sprayed with three coats of clear cellulose lacquer, and a panel taken from one of the coaches was sent after the fire to the Fire Research Organisation for tests. They found that the inflammability of the surface was, by a very large margin, the worst in their records. The LNER, in its specification to the contractors, had given details of the various paints to be used, which were all of the ordinary oil-bound kind. How cellulose came to be used was never discovered, but passengers in that coach during its two-year life had been travelling unwittingly in a time-bomb. When it exploded into flame they were lucky not to have been burnt to death, or asphyxiated by smoke and fumes.

The lessons of this accident were taken to heart and the cellulose coating was quickly removed from all the LNER coaches which had been sprayed with it. However, even whilst this remedial work was being done there was another train fire, in which lacquer containing nitrocellulose was a factor, although not the main one.

Thursday 8 June 1950 was also a fine, warm, dry day. The 11.00am express from Birmingham to Glasgow was making its way laboriously up Beattock Bank, 40 miles north of Carlisle, and as it passed Greskine signalbox at 4.53pm the signalman there watched it go past at about 30mph. Everything appeared to be normal. Ten minutes later he noticed from the track-circuit indicators in his signalbox that the train had not yet passed the Harthope Intermediate Block Home signal 2½ miles ahead, then 5min after that he received a telephone call from the signal to tell him that the

Above right:
One of Eric Treacy's favourite locations — Harthope, on the climb to Beattock Summit, and the site of the tragic fire on 8 June 1950:

1. **'Royal Scot' class 4-6-0 No 46157 *The Royal Artilleryman*, shedded at Edge Hill, on a short train of six ex-LMS coaches.** *Eric Treacy/Millbrook House Collection*

2. **'Princess Coronation' class Pacific No 46224 *Princess Alexandra* on the Down 'Royal Scot', with a complete rake of 15 ex-LMS coaches in early British Railways livery.** *Eric Treacy/Millbrook House Collection*

Right:
Trains at Greskine — before and after electrification:
1. **'Clan' class light Pacific No 72005 *Clan Macgregor* on a Carlisle-Perth parcels train, on 1 August 1964.** *Paul Riley*

2. **1S19 Bristol-Glasgow sleeper, with Class 40 diesel-electric No 40016 hauling dead electric No 81015, on 4 June 1978.** *Derek Cross*

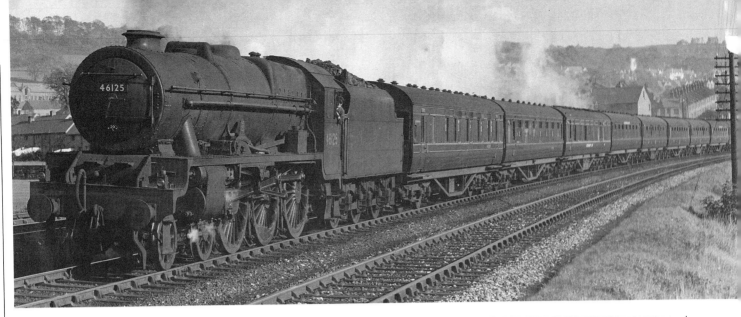

1

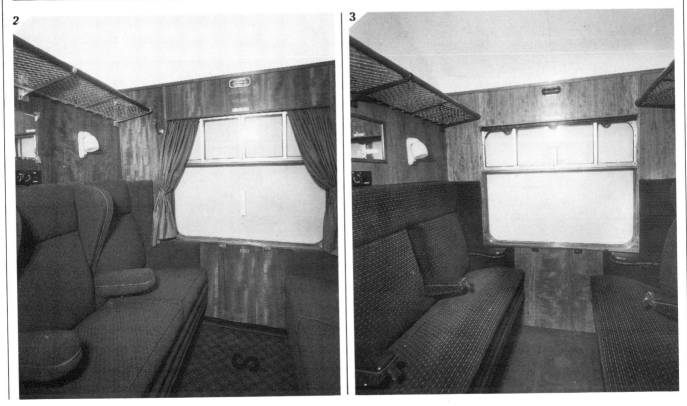

2

3

Left:

A typical London Midland & Scottish Railway express, in very early BR days, with a 12-wheeled dining car. The train is the Down 'Thames-Clyde Express', headed by rebuilt 'Royal Scot' class 4-6-0 No 46125 *3rd Carabinier* bearing a 20A shedplate (Leeds Holbeck), and is seen approaching Marley Junction between Bingley and Keighley. *Eric Treacy/Millbrook House Collection*

train was on fire and had been stopped. There were 10 coaches on the train, the first four being:

Corridor brake third
Corridor composite No 4851, in which the fire broke out
Corridor first No 1073
Dining car.

Coach No 4851 had three first-class compartments and four third-class. There were only five passengers in the coach — a mother and two young children in one compartment, and two ladies in the next one.

The train had left Carlisle at 4.02pm on the final part of its journey. In coach 4851 everything seemed normal. The restaurant car attendant brought a tea tray to the young family, and half an hour later he called to collect it. One of the ladies went to the toilet. All were unaware of the fearful events about to engulf them, although some had noticed a vague smell of something burning since the train left Carlisle.

When the train passed Greskine signalbox the signalman had had a clear view of the left-hand side of the train and was certain that there was no sign of smoke or flame coming from his side of it. At the same time the fireman had looked back from the engine along the right-hand side and had seen no signs of fire. And at this precise moment the lady in coach 4851 had gone to the toilet. All were unaware that the 'fire-bomb' which had been ticking away quietly for hours was about to explode.

At 4.56pm, 3min later, normality had changed dramatically into terror and death. The lady who had gone to the toilet came out into the corridor, and to her amazement

Left:

An LMS-pattern composite corridor coach, built in 1949; the type involved in the Beattock Summit fire:

1. Exterior view
2. First-class compartment
3. Third-class compartment

The exterior body panels and the roof were of steel, but the body frames, partitions and linings were of wood. *BR*

Below:
Coach No 4851 and the Beattock fire

found that it was full of smoke. She could also feel the heat of the fire, but she had chosen a fortunate moment to go to the toilet because it was next to an outside door through which she was able to escape. Her companion was not so fortunate. A few moments after being left alone she was suddenly horrified to see dark smoke pouring down the corridor. She grabbed her handbag and started to make her way towards the end door, then she saw the young mother with two small children trapped and helpless in the next compartment. Compassion overcame self-preservation and she went in to help to carry the children to safety. She was joined immediately by a man from the next coach who reached across and pulled the communication cord. It was his last act. A huge fireball of flame and hot gases erupted into the compartment and killed all five of them instantly. The man and lady had paid for their compassion and gallantry with their lives.

On the engine, the driver had just passed over Harthope Viaduct, travelling at about 30mph, when he noticed from his vacuum brake gauge that the vacuum was falling. He concluded at once that the communication cord had been pulled and looked back along the left-hand side of the train. He saw dense smoke pouring out of the second coach (4851) and immediately made a full brake application, which stopped the train in about 15sec. By now flames were shooting from the windows of coach 4851. With great presence of mind, and assisted by his fireman, he uncoupled behind the third coach (which by this time was also on fire), drew forward the front portion of the train including the two burning coaches, uncoupled again in front of the burning coaches and drew forward again, thus isolating them and preventing the fire from spreading along the rest of the train. The rear portion of the train was now standing without an engine on the 1 in 74 gradient falling back towards Carlisle, with only the vacuum brake and the guard's handbrake to hold it. The vacuum brake would slowly leak off, so the following train, the 'Royal Scot', was brought up behind for safety reasons.

Among the many acts of gallantry that afternoon might be mentioned that of Ganger Moffat. He was on duty on the line checking expansion joints in the rails, when he heard a train approaching and, looking up, he saw smoke and flames coming from the second coach (4851). The driver was already making an emergency stop and the train came to a stand with the blazing coach only a few yards away. He assisted two ladies from the rear door of the first coach (next to 4851), then, learning that there was another lady at the end of the coach on fire, he climbed up into that coach and found her standing in a dazed condition in the corridor against the lavatory wall. Having helped her out he re-entered the coach, went into the lavatory and seeing no one there, he entered the three first-class compartments.

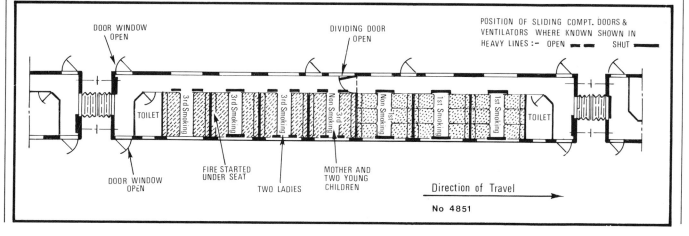

No 4851

The smoke was now becoming so thick that it was difficult for him to see anything at all, so he groped about on the seats but did not find anybody. His breathing had by now become badly affected but he pressed on and reached the next compartment. The smoke suddenly cleared and there was a burst of flame which swirled round the whole compartment. In that instant Ganger Moffat caught a momentary glimpse of the still figure of a woman seated, almost in repose. She was already dead. It is an oddity that those who lose their lives in a fire are often found in quiet and natural attitudes whereas one might expect at least some sign of panic or frantic attempt to escape. After all, if you were trapped in a compartment with a wall of fire rapidly advancing towards you, you would hardly sit quietly waiting for it to consume you like a latter-day Joan of Arc. What had happened is what happens in so many cases of fire — the victims are struck down in an instant by hot gases or carbon monoxide poisoning and that is what had happened in this case.

Ganger Moffat tried to enter the compartment but was forced back by the heat. He was rapidly losing consciousness but managed to crawl along the corridor and escape. He too almost lost his life attempting to rescue others, an act of gallantry for which he was awarded the British Empire Medal. Indeed, the train crews in both this accident and the one at Penmanshiel Tunnel acted with great presence of mind and promptitude in dealing with a difficult situation which they had never previously encountered. They deserved, and received, great praise.

The sad deaths of the young family, together with those of the two passengers who had tried to help them to escape, naturally aroused a great deal of public interest and concern. Anxiety was expressed in Parliament, not only on the subject of fire precautions on trains but also on the whole question of fire considerations in the design of passenger coaches. The public inquiry into this fire was held by Col R. J. Walker of the Railway Inspectorate, Ministry of Transport. In his report he concluded that some time before the train reached Carlisle a lighted match or cigarette end had been carelessly thrown down on to the floor by someone travelling in the compartment next to that one occupied by the two ladies. It found its way under the heater beneath the opposite seat, into a collection of dust and bits of paper behind the heater in the space between the heater and the partition wall separating the two compartments. The partition was made of plain softwood. A small smouldering fire started in the rubbish, spread to the partition and the seat, and continued to smoulder for an hour or more. All that time the fire was using up the available oxygen in the compartment, the doors of which were closed, and forming carbon monoxide and other gases. The temperature was also rising quickly.

Before gases produced in this type of fire will ignite they require both oxygen and the right temperature, but because the gases were produced in a closed compartment they would not ignite, whatever their temperature, because there was insufficient oxygen. However, the smouldering fire eventually burnt a small hole through the partition, allowing gases and smoke to escape into the next compartment, which was empty, and into the corridor. This probably happened a minute or so after one of the ladies left her compartment to visit the toilet, an act which fortuitously saved her life.

The man who died had been travelling in the next coach and, noticing the smoke, went forward to investigate. He came upon the lady in coach 4851 who was now alone, then the two of them moved forward to escape, without realising the potential danger of the situation and the high temperature of the gases inside the closed and empty compartment. They immediately saw the young family and

entered their compartment to help to evacuate the two young children. At this precise moment the burning hole in the partition wall reached such a size that the correct conditions of temperature and air mixture were produced, and the gases ignited. The temperature in the closed compartment shot up, breaking a window in the corridor side. The main volume of gases rushed into the corridor, mixed with the air, and burst into flame with a huge ball of fire. It was in effect a slow explosion and the heat which it generated was enough to kill instantly anyone within range. It was this fireball which killed the five passengers, and it also set the whole of the coach on fire.

In 1950 much thought was being given to the detailed design of the new British Railways standard coach, known subsequently as Mk 1, and there were plans to build 1,189 of them in 1951. All the circumstances of the fire in coach 4851 were therefore examined in great detail, to see to what extent they could be guarded against in the new coaches. These factors were as follows:

1. The location of the heater underneath the fixed seats made it difficult to clean behind the heater, and allowed fluff and odd bits of paper, etc to accumulate. To overcome this problem the seats in the new coaches were made removable and wire mesh grilles were fixed underneath the front of the seats to prevent rubbish from finding its way through to the back. Although this was a good idea in theory it made it harder for the cleaning staff to clean behind the heaters and could even have led to increased danger if the cleaning were not carried out conscientiously.

2. The partitions between the compartments were of plain deal boarding. It was decided to protect the boarding in new coaches by covering it with asbestos millboard.

3. The interior finish used in coach 4851 was a special lacquer which had been used for the previous 13 years. It had a matt finish and required only a very thin coating, and one of the reasons for its use had been to reduce the fire risk. However, it contained a certain amount of nitrocellulose and as a result had a fairly high flammability. It was decided not only to discontinue its use but also to remove it from existing coaches.

4. If inflammable materials such as wood and furnishings were to continue to be used in coach construction it was felt to be important to provide additional doors away from the ends of the corridors. This feature had already been incorporated in the design of the new BR Mk 1 side-corridor coaches by the provision of a central transverse corridor, with an additional door in the corridor side (two in the case of composite coaches), but the Railway Executive had considered it unnecessary to provide them in open-type coaches.

5. Fire extinguishers. Up to 1948 fire extinguishers on the London Midland & Scottish Railway and the London & North Eastern Railway were only carried in restaurant cars and guard's vans. In both the Penmanshiel and Beattock fires, extinguishers would have been useless because the fires were far too big when discovered, to have been capable of being put out by hand-held extinguishers. However, the Railway Executive felt that it ought to be seen to be taking some positive action, and provided them in all coaches, but in fact,

fires on trains were so rare that if these two fires had not happened it would have been difficult to justify the provision of extinguishers in every coach.

Two serious fires in two years was much more than the statistical average, but railway accidents are no respecters of statistical averages. But three in three years was highly unlikely. However, fate thought otherwise.

The famous 'West Riding' train from King's Cross to Leeds, which had covered the distance prewar in 2hr 43min hauled by one of Sir Nigel Gresley's equally famous streamlined Pacifics, had become by 1951 the 3.45pm from King's Cross to Leeds, taking 3hr 45min, although with a much heavier train. On Saturday 14 July 1951 the train consisted of 14 coaches hauled by a Class A3 Pacific engine No 60058 *Blair Atholl*, marshalled as follows:

Twin open brake third, Nos 1738 and 1737
Twin open first
Twin restaurant open third
Corridor composite
Corridor third
Corridor brake third
Corridor composite brake
Corridor composite
Two corridor thirds
Corridor brake third.

Seating capacity, excluding the restaurant car, was 96 first-class and 316 third-class, and the train was actually carrying 10 first-class and about 340 third-class passengers. The first six coaches were articulated twin-sets

specially built by the LNER in 1937 for its high speed trains
the 'Coronation' and the 'West Riding'. The coaches were
designed to a very luxurious standard, with seats at tables,
arranged with two seats at one side of the centre gangway,
and single seats at the other. The only exit doors were in the
vestibules at the extreme ends of each twin-set. The
underframes were of steel, and the bodywork consisted of
steel exterior panels with teak framing and softwood
interiors. The whole of the interior was covered with a
leathercloth fabric known by the trade name of Rexine.
Significantly, the fabric was coated with nitrocellulose.

With two such serious fire hazards — the location of the
doors and the presence of nitrocellulose — the question
arises as to whether the railway administration, which in
1948 had become the Railway Executive, should have
allowed such coaches to continue in service, now that the
risks had been pointed out so dramatically and forcefully at
Penmanshiel and Beattock. However, the railways were
short of coaches. They had lost a lot during the war from
German bombing, and new building had been restricted
since 1939. After the war the shortage of steel had
restricted the number of coaches which could be built.
Many of the express coaches in use in 1951 had fire hazards
of one sort or another, indeed some still had wooden bodies,
and to have taken them all out of service would have made
it impossible to run an adequate train service. What is
more, the railway's record of fire safety was excellent —

there had been only three serious fires on trains since 1939.
One wonders whether any of the passengers in the three
twin-sets felt any qualms about their safety, and whether
any, more knowledgeable or more cautious, chose to travel
in the ordinary coaches, hoping that they had had any
nitrocellulose removed. The decision by the Railway
Executive to allow these twin-sets to remain in service, or,
to put it more accurately, the failure to consider whether
the twin-sets should be allowed to remain in service or not,
was severely criticised by Col Walker in his Report.

However, to return to the events of 14 July 1951. About
40min after leaving King's Cross a passenger who was
sitting in the rearmost seat on the left-hand side of the
second coach of the twin-set next to the engine (coach
No 1737) noticed a wisp of smoke rising up the side of the
coach near the armrest. She called the attention of a
passing pantry boy, who returned to the fifth coach, the
restaurant car, and informed the conductor. This man went
to have a look, then went back to tell the guard, who was
riding in the ninth coach. The guard went forward and,
lifting the seat, saw that smoke was coming from the corner
of the floor, between the edge of the carpet and the side of
the coach. He at once jumped to the conclusion that the
smoke was coming from an axlebox running hot. Incredibly,
instead of stopping the train at once so that the axle did not
have time to disintegrate, and derail the train, he decided to
write a note which he intended to throw out of the train at
Huntingdon, about 10min away, asking for the train to be
stopped at Peterborough for examination. He even went to
the dining car for a potato to act as a weight for his note.
Being unable to find one he threw the note out anyway. It
was found next day, and it was perhaps fortunate that the
smoke was not from a hot axlebox, which might well have
collapsed and caused a serious derailment, with many
casualties.

After the guard had left to write his note, the smoke
increased and the passengers became more uneasy. One of

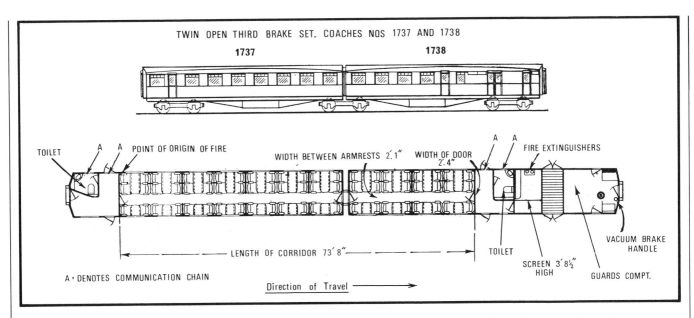

TWIN OPEN THIRD BRAKE SET. COACHES NOS 1737 AND 1738

1737   1738

TOILET — A A POINT OF ORIGIN OF FIRE — WIDTH BETWEEN ARMRESTS 2'1" — WIDTH OF DOOR 2'4" — A A FIRE EXTINGUISHERS

LENGTH OF CORRIDOR 73'8"

A = DENOTES COMMUNICATION CHAIN

Direction of Travel ⟶

TOILET — SCREEN 3'8½" HIGH — GUARDS COMPT. — VACUUM BRAKE HANDLE

Above:
Twin-set Nos 1737 and 1738, the coaches of the Huntingdon fire

them decided to pull the communication cord, and as the train came to a stand just beyond Huntingdon flames appeared and suddenly spread with great rapidity up the sides and into the roof. In a matter of seconds the fire was spreading quickly forwards along the sides and roof of the coach. At once all the passengers tried to escape but the only available exit was through the intercommunicating door into the next coach and then through a single door into the vestibule at the leading end of that coach. Both coaches were full and in addition some soldiers and sailors were standing in the vestibule, so that there were probably about 75 people in the twin-set. The flames were accompanied by dense and choking fumes and smoke which quickly filled the coaches; and in the alarm and excitement the centre aisles of both coaches became blocked with passengers at once. Others were unable to leave their seats to get into the aisle at all because of the crush. People were therefore trapped between the solid crush of passengers at one end and the rapidly advancing flames at the other. There was only one way of escape left open to them — by breaking the

windows and climbing through. It was literally every man (and woman) for himself. But train windows are not easy to break even in the haste and incentive of a fire breathing down your neck. The glass has to be tough, and it was only the efforts of the soldiers and sailors in helping to break windows that enabled some passengers to escape with their lives, but 22 passengers and the guard received burns and other injuries in escaping, including nine seriously hurt.

The cause of the fire was thought to have been a piece of live coal from the engine firegrate falling on to the track then bouncing up and lodging in a small hole cut through the floor of the coach to allow an air duct to be taken through. The space between the duct and the sides of the hole had been filled by asbestos at one time but it had fallen out unnoticed, as the carpet and underlay covered the hole completely. The floor was deal boarding.

After the Penmanshiel fire two years earlier the Railway Executive had set about examining all of its 25,000 coaches

Below:
Smoke and flames pour from the windows of the second and third coaches of the 3.45pm from King's Cross to Leeds near Huntingdon on 14 July 1951. *Times Newspapers Ltd*

M 4784

Above:
BR standard Mk 1 second-class open coach, with centre doors. Seen at Bristol Temple Meads on 17 November 1984.
M. J. Collins

Below:
BR Mk 2 second-class open coach, 1967 pattern, with centre doors. Exterior and interior views. *BR*

for the existence of nitrocellulose. By the time of the Huntingdon fire all but 1,000 had been examined. Over 8,000 coaches were discovered to contain inflammable surfaces and almost 7,000 had been dealt with. Nitrocellulose-coated cloth presented a new problem, which had to be dealt with quickly to make it less vulnerable to fire, and this was done. It is difficult now to understand how such a dangerous material came to be used in the first place; it would have been easy to have tested it for flammability, when its latent defect would have immediately become apparent. There was perhaps some complacency in railway circles about fire hazards, based in part on an excellent safety record, although in mitigation it has to be said that the twin-sets for the LNER's streamlined services were designed to be staffed with attendants, similar to the practice on Pullman trains. It is clear that the fire hazards of using them as ordinary coaches without attendants had not been appreciated.

The need for additional external doors which had been demonstrated at Beattock was not accepted by the Railway Executive for its new open-type coaches, and even after the Huntingdon fire they were unconvinced, and suggested that the steps they had already taken would sufficiently reduce the risk of fire. They refused to budge from this standpoint at first, but finally gave way and agreed to incorporate additional doors in the new BR Mk 1 open stock. The additional cost was in fact negligible.

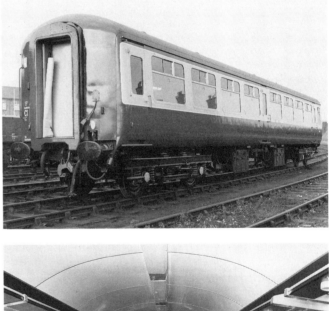

This issue of additional doors presents one of the few cases this century where the Railway Inspectorate has felt sufficiently strongly that some action ought to be taken, but which is being resisted by the railway authorities, that it has sought the help of the Minister. Strange as it may seem, the Railway Inspectorate had no powers to compel railways to adopt different methods or use different materials on existing railways, but could only recommend or apply pressure. The Minister supported the Railway Inspectorate and ultimately made a statement in Parliament that additional precautions were to be taken to minimise the risk of fires, and one of these was the provision of centre doors on the new open coaches. The Minister had the ultimate power, had the Railway Executive continued to prove obdurate, of sacking the chairman and appointing one who would carry out his wishes. The Railway Executive accepted the inevitable and gave in. Whilst it may be difficult to understand why it was so obstinate, the Railway Executive was strongly of the opinion that the measures it had already taken regarding the use of fire-resistant materials and finishes in the design of the new standard

coaches would completely overcome any possibility of a repetition of the fires that had occurred at Penmanshiel, Beattock and Huntingdon. What is more, they were proved correct. There was no repetition, and there was never any need for the additional doors in open coaches to be used for the rapid evacuation of passengers in a fire, but the weight of public opinion, not always the best guide, and illogical on this occasion, was too heavy to be resisted. In later years, in the design of Mk 2 coaches, the additional centre doors were eventually dispensed with.

However, the saga was not yet complete. Railwaymen have long held a superstition that accidents always come in threes, but there was to be a fourth, near Fordhouses, about four miles north of Wolverhampton on the main line to Stafford of the former London Midland & Scottish Railway (LMS). Nor was there long to wait, as the fourth fire occurred as early as 14 March 1952, whilst the argument about additional doors was still raging. The circumstances were in many ways similar to those of the Beattock fire. It started in a pile of rubbish behind the heater underneath the seat, and began to smoulder. The passengers told the guard, who was in the same coach (a corridor brake third) and he directed a fire extinguisher as best he could on to the seat and the back, but it was difficult for him to deal with the area beneath the seat as it was fixed in position. When the extinguisher was empty and the fire was apparently out, the compartment was evacuated, the doors were closed, and the guard stopped the train by using his emergency brake valve.

The train came to a stand about 400yd from a station, and the guard and fireman examined the underpart of the coach for signs of fire, but could find nothing wrong. They decided to continue into the station so that passengers could be evacuated if necessary, and as the train stopped in the platform the compartment burst into flames, in a repetition of the Beattock fire of 1950. Fortunately all the passengers had already moved into other coaches or on to the platform and no one was injured. By chance, there was a wartime Supply Depot alongside, whose fire brigade was located next to the station. They quickly came into action and directed hoses on to the burning coach in a very short time, but despite this the coach continued to burn fiercely and was almost completely destroyed. The coach, moreover, had been built as recently as September 1950 to the previous LMS design. Incredibly, although nitrocellulose had been shown to be a highly dangerous substance when used in the interior finish of railway coaches, it was found to have been used in this coach, even though it was built 15 months after the Penmanshiel fire and three months after Beattock. What is more, the coach was one of those which had been tested for nitrocellulose and had been passed as safe. The Railway Executive found itself totally discredited.

Fordhouses proved to be the last serious train fire for many years, even though coaches built by the pre-

Below:
BR Mk 2c second-class open coach, without centre doors, but with a low ceiling incorporating ducts for air-conditioning.
BR

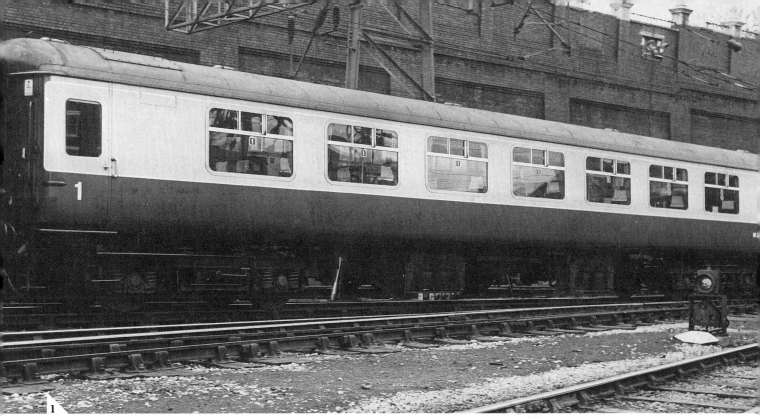

nationalisation companies continued in service for a long time. The new standard coaches, designated Mk 1, had a very good fire safety record, and this fine record was continued in subsequent series of coaches in Mks 2 and 3, to such an extent that over 30 years passed before another serious fire occurred (discounting for the moment the Taunton fire of 1978, which was an oddity, and which will be dealt with later).

British Railways Scottish Region operates an excellent express service of trains between Edinburgh and Glasgow — fast, frequent and comfortable, using very modern Mk 3 air-conditioned coaches built to a very high standard of fire resistance. On 22 August 1983 the 18.30 train from Edinburgh to Glasgow consisted of one of the usual push-pull sets and was being propelled by a Class 47 diesel-electric locomotive. It was marshalled as follows:

Brake open second-class, with driver's compartment
Open first-class, Mk 3
Three open second-class, Mk 3.

The train was well filled, and the weather was sunny and warm.

As the train neared the end of its journey a lady travelling in the fourth coach of the five-coach train went to the toilet at the rear of her coach. When she came out of the toilet she was amazed and horrified to see orange and yellow flames about 2ft high right across the gangway connection between the two coaches, so she went straight back into the toilet. Realising that if she stayed there she might well be trapped and burnt to death, she plucked up all her courage, opened the toilet door again, and rushed through the thick black smoke back into the coach. Luckily for her the automatic sliding door worked quickly but even so she felt the intense heat on her back and her hair was singed.

Meanwhile, other passengers in both coaches had seen the thick black smoke in the vestibules and the communication cord had been pulled. As the train quickly slowed down and stopped near Cadder signalbox, smoke and fumes began to pour into both coaches and passengers rapidly began to move away in fear and anxiety.

What happened then was almost a repeat of the Huntingdon fire. The fourth coach was quite full and people quickly moved towards the sliding door at the far end of the coach. Unfortunately it was defective and not working automatically, but could be opened by hand. However, in the haste and near-panic of the situation those passengers nearest the door failed to appreciate what to do and decided that they were trapped. The coach was rapidly filling with thick black smoke, making it difficult either to see or breathe. The only way out was through the windows, but fortunately there were sufficient passengers with the presence of mind to use the emergency hammers. Everyone was therefore able to escape with no more than cuts and bruises, but with the lasting memory of those awful moments of terror, although in escaping they had unwittingly put themselves in mortal danger of a different kind. Most of the passengers who jumped out of the windows landed on the opposite running line, where they stood around for some minutes whilst they recovered themselves. If another train had been coming on that line they would have been mown down.

Because of the materials used in the construction of the coach the fire advanced only slowly and was put out quite quickly and easily when the fire brigade arrived. One end of each of the two coaches was severely damaged, but significantly the seats themselves had not caught fire. The essential difference between Huntingdon and Cadder showed that the lessons had been well learnt. The fire at Cadder progressed much more slowly and burned much less fiercely than at Huntingdon, thanks to the use of fire-resistant materials.

The cause of the fire is thought to have been the same in four of the five fires examined in this chapter — the careless act of throwing down a burning cigarette end. At Cadder it eventually ignited the polyurethane foam used in the gangway end unit at the rear of the fourth coach, and it was fanned into flame by the draught of air in the speeding train. Both the fourth and fifth coaches had been built in 1975 with foam gangway units, but because the units had not stood up to the wear and tear of daily service they had been replaced as necessary by a later rubber bellows design introduced on all new stock a year later. Critically, the original foam bellows unit was still in use at the rear of the fourth coach. Foam ought not to have been used in the first place from a fire hazard point of view, and after a foam gangway had caught fire near Acton on a Paddington to Bristol IC125 unit on 5 July 1981, although causing little damage, they should all have been removed. Unfortunately they were not removed quickly enough, and the task was not completed until early 1984.

The fire in a sleeping car train at Taunton on 6 July 1978 was in one way the worst of all. It claimed 12 lives. But the cause was almost stupidly simple. The main store for the supply of clean bed linen to Western Region sleeping cars was at Old Oak Common, the coaching stock depot near Paddington. Clean linen was sent down each night in the sleeping car train to Plymouth and Penzance for use the following night on the return journey. Before May 1977 it had been loaded in the guard's van of the Plymouth portion of the train, but the formation of the train was then changed, and as there was no longer a guard's van in the Plymouth portion it had to be sent in the sleeping cars themselves. There was no suitable accommodation in the sleeping cars for bags of linen so they were merely stacked in one of the vestibules — a practical but unsatisfactory solution. Practical because the sleeping car attendants only used one of the vestibules in each coach to receive intending passengers, being the one nearest their cubicle. Unsatisfactory because it tended to block one of the limited number of exits in case of fire or other emergency demanding rapid evacuation. It was the first mistake of several.

The second factor was the construction of the sleeping cars themselves. The one concerned in the fire was vehicle No W2437 and had been built in 1960 by Metro-Cammell Ltd to a British Railways design. It had been fitted with a heating system worked by steam supplied by the locomotive, but with the changeover from steam to diesel locomotives, and the difficulty of finding a design of oil-fired boiler which could withstand the rigours of being installed on a vibrating diesel locomotive (plus the expense of carrying a second man on the locomotive merely to oversee the boiler), a decision was taken to change over from steam to electric heating. Sleeping car W2437 was modified in 1976, and as part of that modification an electric heater was fitted on the vestibule wall outside the attendant's cubicle. Significantly, it was not provided with a protective wire mesh guard, because it was thought that luggage would never be stacked there. This was the second mistake.

The third factor in the lead-up to the disaster was the method of heating and ventilating the individual sleeping berth cubicles. Air could be drawn either from outside the vehicle, or from inside through an opening in the end wall of the vestibule next to the attendant's cubicle — the one with the electric wall heater. Some of this air was then blown through ducting along the roof of the sleeping car and into each individual cubicle.

BR Mk 1 sleeping cars, exterior and interior views. The single berth compartments were first-class, and the double berth second-class. *BR*

The stage had now been set for disaster and it is only surprising that it had not happened sooner. There had in fact been a potential disaster a few years earlier when a smouldering laundry bag containing linen had been discovered against a vestibule heater in a sleeping car on a Glasgow to Euston train, but it was quickly dealt with. The obvious lesson was not taken to heart.

On the evening of Wednesday 5 July 1978 the two sleeping cars forming the Plymouth portion of the 21.30 from Penzance to Paddington (including car No W2437) were platformed at about 22.30 so that the passengers could join the train and go to bed without having to wait for the arrival of the main train at about midnight. The five or six bags of clean and dirty bed linen were already in their deadly positions in the vestibule next to the heater, which at this time was cold. The main train arrived at 23.50. It coupled up to the two Plymouth sleepers, and set off for Paddington on time at 00.30. The heating was now on and the bags of linen began to warm up. The electric wall heater began to overheat because it was covered by the bags of linen, and the linen itself began to smoulder. Smoke and gases, including deadly carbon monoxide, began to be given

off, and were then sucked into the heating and ventilating system, along the roof ducting and into the sleeping-berth cubicles, where most of the unfortunate occupants never knew what killed them. A small number awoke and managed to escape with their lives. The train was stopped at Silk Mill signalbox, about half a mile short of Taunton station, at 02.41, by the communication cord being pulled. Car W2437 was now on fire but the disaster was over. Death had already taken place. It had all been so deadly simple.

One question that might be asked straightaway is — what were the sleeping car attendants doing? How could so much smoke and heat be given off without the attendant knowing about it? Each attendant looks after two coaches and the attendant in the Plymouth portion had been travelling in the sleeping car next to W2437. After Exeter he had had a wash and brush up in an empty berth, had gone to the lavatory, and on emerging he saw smoke coming from W2437. He knocked on a few doors in the sleeping car next to W2437 and shouted something about fire, then passed out. It was the attendant in the next pair of sleeping cars who pulled the communication cord. But there is no way of guaranteeing that attendants will be in the right place, or will stay sufficiently alert, to detect a fire as soon as it starts to give off smoke.

So far as the Taunton fire was concerned the means of preventing a repetition were very simple and staightforward. A wire mesh grill over the vestibule heater would have been sufficient; but Taunton was looked upon as merely the tip of the iceberg. Sleeping car fires had been

happening two or three times a year, mainly caused by electrical defects, but had been extinguished before they got out of control. Also the Taunton fire had revealed a number of unsatisfactory features. But its worst feature was that it provided a convenient stick with which to beat BR and a number of prominent people, including MPs, were not slow to use it. One or two managers within BR, who ought to have known better, also jumped on to the bandwagon. Red herrings abounded and a state of near-panic gripped British Railways. Certainly, after the disaster things needed to be tightened up but, perhaps inevitably, there was an over-reaction, culminating in a shopping list of 'things that needed to be done'. BR felt impelled to take every conceivable action that could be devised, despite the fact that before Taunton no one had been killed in a sleeping car fire since at least World War 1, and probably long before that. The sleeping car attendants suddenly found themselves a beleaguered species. They were required to explain to all sleeping car passengers as they joined the train, the action that the passengers should take in case of fire. Notices were posted in the compartments in three languages. Attendants were supplied with portable warning horns worked from a compressed-gas canister, with which they were supposed to run up and down the corridor, in case of fire. These might have been sensible measures if fires in sleeping cars had been a nightly occurrence, but they have to be viewed against a background of millions of sleeping car passengers conveyed safely without being disturbed by fires. One other

illustration will suffice. The standing instructions in the Rules and Regulations said that all external doors were to be left unlocked, but it had long been the practice for attendants to lock the doors on the platform side at the far ends of the pair of coaches they were responsible for. This channelled the flow of passengers through the doors at the inner ends of the pair of coaches, enabling the attendant to deal with each passenger as he arrived, and to show him to his berth, in an orderly fashion. It also helped to keep out drunks and other undesirable people and provided security for the passengers' belongings. It was what is known in the trade as 'practical railway working'. It had no bearing on the number of casualties in the Taunton disaster but there were some complaints from the emergency services that they could not gain access to the train through some of the doors. As a result, the instruction was reissued and re-emphasised, but BR went even further. Previously the gangway door between the sleeping car portion of a train and the ordinary coaches had been kept locked to prevent ordinary passengers from passing through the sleeping cars and possibly causing a disturbance. Even this sensible instruction was revoked by BR. It was quickly reinstated however, when a senior Board member was disturbed one night shortly afterwards by a party of drunks. He learnt the hard way that railway conditions in the dark hours are often quite different from those which apply during office hours, and that there is usually a good reason for the Rules and Regulations being laced with a modicum of railway commonsense and practicality.

147

E 10654

Inter-City Sleeper

C3

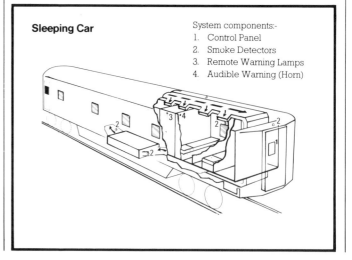

Above and left:
BR Mk 3 sleeping cars, introduced in 1981, exterior and interior views. The interior view shows the double berth mode. *BR*

Below:
Typical Graviner Fire Protection System

Sleeping Car

System components:-
1. Control Panel
2. Smoke Detectors
3. Remote Warning Lamps
4. Audible Warning (Horn)

Taunton had a far more serious effect in a completely different direction. It occurred just at the time when BR was planning to replace its existing fleet of sleeping cars by the new Mk 3 version. Two hundred and thirty-six new vehicles were authorised in 1979 at a cost of £39 million but the design was extensively revised to incorporate the recommendations of the Railway Inspecting Officer. This increased the cost by several £ million and the order had to be reduced by no fewer than 26 vehicles to keep within the authorised cost. Graviner Ltd supplied a sophisticated and elaborate smoke detection system, to be fitted in every berth and in other sensitive locations. Warning horns were fitted in each berth, and elsewhere. Each berth is virtually a self-contained steel chest, and all decorative materials, furnishings and bedding were chosen for their fire-resistant qualities. In the event of smoke or fire, alarm horns sound, a warning lamp in the corridor is illuminated outside the berth concerned, and flashing arrows direct the attendant to the affected location. Internal doors are automatically closed. This is an impressive list of safety features, and shows what can be done to make sleeping cars safe against fire — but at a price. If Taunton had not happened would the Mk 3 sleeping cars have been any less safe in practical terms without all these features, and if the answer is 'yes' why had they not been incorporated in the original design?

Mention has been made several times of the actions of traincrews in case of fire. It is deeply ingrained in every railwayman's subconscious mind that if a vehicle catches fire the train should be split both in front of, and behind, the burning vehicle so that it is isolated, and the fire is prevented from spreading to the rest of the train. It is very pleasing to note how promptly and effectively this was carried out in the incidents that have been described, and it reflects great credit on the railwaymen concerned, particularly when it is remembered that most traincrews have no experience of trains on fire. One moment they are proceeding quite normally on an everyday journey. The next moment, without warning, they are faced with a grave and rapidly-worsening emergency and have to spring into action and deal with it as though it were a regular occurrence. Such occasions almost always bring out the best in railwaymen, often at some danger to themselves. One of the bravest acts took place at Soham, on the Ely to Newmarket line of the LNER, during the night of 1 June 1944. Driver Gimbert was in charge of 'Austerity' 2-8-0 No 7337, with a trainload of bombs. Looking back as he approached Soham he saw that the first wagon was on fire. Quickly he stopped his train, the fireman uncoupled behind the blazing wagon, then Gimbert set off again with the intention of leaving the wagon in open country in case its 10-ton load of bombs should explode. He didn't get very far. There was a tremendous explosion and the wagon simply disappeared. Fireman Nightall was killed instantly, and Driver Gimbert was seriously injured but survived. Both men did what they knew instinctively was expected of them, and both were honoured with the George Cross, the highest award for civilian bravery.

There is now a British Standard Code of Practice for fire precautions in the design and construction of railway passenger rolling stock (BS6853:1987) so there should be no more serious fires on InterCity trains, but Taunton and Cadder both showed just how easily events can conspire to create very hazardous situations. The code of practice was prepared under the direction of the Fire Standards Committee, with BR involvement, and is addressed to the designers of railway passenger rolling stock and those responsible for its maintenance, modification or refurbishment. It gives advice on the choice and testing of materials, the provision of fire barriers, and means of achieving safe evacuation from a train on fire. It owes its origins to the initiative of Lt-Col Townsend-Rose who, during his inquiry into the Cadder fire, was disturbed to find that no standards appeared to exist on this question. He therefore convened a working party to draw up such standards, and these formed the basis of the British Standard.

Fires are distinct from other types of railway accident. In a collision or derailment the passenger learns pretty quickly — in a matter of seconds — whether he is going to live or die (unless, as at Harrow in 1952, another train ploughs into the wreckage at high speed). In a fire, by contrast, the situation just gets worse and worse, and unless the passenger can escape, he's dead. And he dies in a particularly horrifying way too. So it is right that railway coaches should be as safe from fire as possible, especially as the fire brigade is unlikely to be able to reach the scene of a train fire quickly enough to be of value in rescuing passengers. This is no reflection on the efficiency of the fire service, but merely a recognition of the realities of the situation — it may be some time before the alarm can be raised, the nearest fire brigade may be several miles away, and there may be considerable difficulties of access to the train. By contrast, passengers will have escaped from the train, or met their death, within a very few minutes. Even at Taunton, where conditions were extremely favourable — the train stopped near a signalbox and therefore the alarm was raised straightaway; the fire station was nearby; and there was good road access — 15min elapsed between the communication cord being pulled and the arrival of the fire brigade. The railway situation is unique, and fire precautions have to be designed accordingly.

Below:
Locomotives frequently catch fire. Class 31 diesel-electric No 31256 was producing a lot of smoke and fumes near Hayes (Middlesex) on 10 September 1978. The other locomotive was No 31252. *D. H. Rayner*

2
Hot Axleboxes

Axleboxes are of two main types — plain bearing and roller bearing. Plain bearing axleboxes date back to the earliest days of railways, and consist simply of a whitemetal bearing underneath the springs of the vehicle or bogie, and resting upon the end portion of the axle, which is known as the journal. Bearing and journal are enclosed in a metal case (the axlebox), the whole being kept upright by axlebox guides attached to the wagon body, so that the wagon body can move up and down as the springs deflect under load or

Below:
10in x 5in Plain Bearing Oil Axlebox (cast steel, open-fronted)

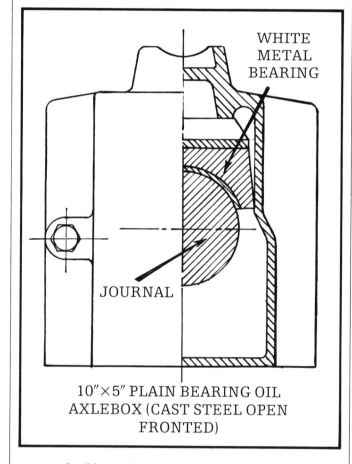

WHITE METAL BEARING

JOURNAL

10"×5" PLAIN BEARING OIL AXLEBOX (CAST STEEL OPEN FRONTED)

as a result of irregularities in track levels. This method of vehicle body suspension has been in use for many, many years, and hundreds of thousands of wagons were built to this design under the British Railways Modernisation Plan of the mid-1950s. Some of them are still in use, mainly by the Civil Engineer's Department.

It will readily be appreciated that the rotation of a dry, smooth axle journal underneath the plain whitemetal bearing will create friction and heat, leading eventually, if unchecked, to the journal becoming red-hot and breaking off, leaving one corner of the wagon completely unsupported and one wheel with no weight on it. At this stage, rapid derailment is inevitable. To avoid this happening, some form of lubrication is essential.

For many years grease was the normal means of lubrication, and a small army of men was employed, scattered throughout the length and breadth of the railway system, to refill the axleboxes. They were known, appropriately, as greasers, and could be found in every marshalling yard and goods yard of sufficient size.

In a later development, grease was replaced by oil as the lubricant, but it was not practicable merely to fill the axlebox with oil, as happened with grease, because the oil could not be prevented from leaking out at the point where the axle entered the box. The problem was overcome by placing a felt pad against the underpart of the journal, with the pad being supported on a spring mechanism, and a wick taking oil from the sump at the bottom of the axlebox, which thus allowed the rotating journal to carry around continuously a film of oil on its surface, and thereby providing adequate lubrication between bearing and journal. Needless to say, the axlebox needed constant

Below:
Traditional private owner's coal wagon, produced in hundreds of thousands, and equipped with grease axleboxes.
Ian Allan Library

Bottom:
A later-generation coal wagon, the standard British Railways 16-ton all-steel mineral wagon, with side and end doors, built at Derby in 1949. Equipped with oil axleboxes.
Ian Allan Library

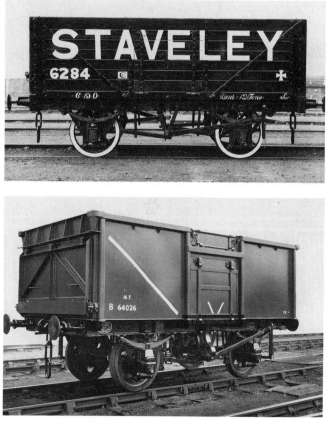

examination and replenishment, and the army of greasers became an army of oilers and greasers. The pads required regular replacement to avoid surface glazing preventing the free flow of oil. The prevention of axleboxes overheating thus depended on every axlebox being examined regularly; easy enough to achieve with passenger coaches but not quite so easy with goods wagons unless an inordinate number of men were employed. And so the hot axlebox became a part of everyday railway life.

Regulation No 17 of the Regulations for Train Signalling required each signalman 'to be careful to notice each train as it passes to ascertain whether there is any apparent necessity for having it stopped at the next signalbox for examination, and if he observes or becomes aware of anything unusual in a train during its passage, such as ... a hot axlebox, he must send to the signalman in advance the ''Stop and examine train'' signal' (seven consecutive beats on the bell communication between the two signalboxes). The signalman in advance, on receiving the bell signal, would then immediately put his signals to Danger, both to stop the approaching train and also to stop any train going in the opposite direction in case the train with the hot axlebox had in the meantime become derailed and wreckage was obstructing the opposite line.

Signalmen quickly learned how to recognise a hot axlebox, especially at those signalboxes where trains had already run long distances from a marshalling yard. The squealing of a dry axlebox running hot can be heard from quite a distance and is readily recognisable. It is a distinctive sound, unlike any other railway noise. When the oil pad becomes dry it warms up, and will eventually give off both smoke and smell; and the smoke is easily visible from the signalbox provided that it is on the same side of the line, and that there is sufficient light, either natural or artificial. The guard sitting at the back of the train might hear the axlebox squealing, or see the smoke as the train rounds a curve. He might also smell the smouldering pad. On a train fitted throughout with the continuous brake he can stop the train by the use of his emergency brake before any great harm is done, but on a loose-coupled train he would wait until his train passed a signalbox, and then, in the words of the Rule Book 'make every effort to attract the attention of the signalman', who would then promptly apply Regulation 17. The fireman would also look back down the train at frequent intervals.

Hot axleboxes were a frequent occurrence on goods trains, and, as might be expected an organisation developed to cope with them. The wagon with the defective axlebox was detached from the train and put into a siding at the signalbox at which it had been stopped for examination. Men known as carriage and wagon examiners visited such sidings regularly, or could be sent for specially if necessary. If the bearing and journal were undamaged, the wagon could have a new oil pad fitted and be sent on its way after being oiled, but if any damage had been caused the wagon would have to be sent on a slow train to the nearest wagon repair depot. In the worst cases special arrangements would have to be made to repair the wagon *in*

Below:
The type of goods train on which hot axleboxes were a frequent occurrence. Former Great Western Railway '28XX' class 2-8-0 No 2893 heads a goods train through Sonning Cutting, near Reading, on 16 May 1964. *Brian Stephenson*

situ, and it was often necessary first to tranship the load into another wagon. Special tranship gangs existed in some places but if they were not available the local permanent way gang was often glad to help out on overtime, or at the weekend, in order to supplement its rather meagre basic wage.

Wagon repair depots were established in all the bigger yards and depots. Quite often they were privately owned, as were many of the wagons prior to nationalisation in 1948, and some of the larger repair firms were nationwide, Wagon Repairs Ltd being one of the best known.

The organisation for detecting and dealing with hot axleboxes proved quite adequate for the task right up to the 1960s, but then several changes took place which considerably increased the hazard. Hot axleboxes have to run for several miles before they reach a critical stage, and as long as there were plenty of lineside signalboxes to maintain supervision there was little problem, but several factors were occurring simultaneously which had the effect of continuously reducing the amount of lineside observation. These were:

1. Minor signalling schemes, allowing intermediate signalboxes to be closed.
2. The automation of level crossings, allowing the staff to be withdrawn.
3. The abolition of signalboxes, when sidings or branch lines were closed permanently.
4. The abolition of signalboxes, no longer required owing to a reduction in the number of trains run, or the closure of such signalboxes during quiet periods.
5. Power signalboxes were being developed, covering ever-increasing areas, with little or no actual observation of trains.

The other main change taking place in the 1960s was the increase in the average speed of freight trains, brought about by the replacement of steam locomotives by diesel or electric traction, and the decrease in the number of trains run unbraked, ie without power brakes being operated on any of the wagons. Actually, the braking power of a diesel locomotive is less than that of a steam locomotive, and for some years during the transition period it was necessary for various stratagems to be employed to deal with the situation on unbraked trains, some costly, some inconvenient, and some both. The main ones were:

1. Shunting out all the available power-braked wagons in a train, so that they could be marshalled in the front portion, thus providing what became known as a 'fitted head', and considerably increasing the brake power available to the driver. There was a sliding scale allowing the train load to be increased proportionately to the increase in brake power. In practice the complicated calculations of train weight and brake power together with the nuisance and inconvenience of having to shunt out odd wagons from a train up to 60 or 70 wagons long meant that trains were rarely made up to their theoretical maximum load, and no amount of blandishments, threats and exhortations from higher management could ever achieve it.

2. An additional locomotive could be coupled to the train locomotive to provide extra brake power — an expensive solution and normally employed only over short distances.

3. A new vehicle, known as a brake tender, was designed. It was basically a short bogie wagon with heavy weights to increase adhesion, and power brakes on all four axles. The brake tenders were attached next to the locomotive, either singly or in pairs, and could be either propelled or hauled. As a stopgap they had their uses but were universally unpopular. They caused extra shunting and never seemed to be there when wanted. Locomen did not like propelling them, and eventually during one of their more intransigent periods refused to do so any more.

Below:
English Electric Type 3 No D6767, complete with brake tender, heads a freight train on the Up East Coast main line at Relly Mill, near Durham, in June 1967. *John E. Hoggarth*

The upshot of all this was that freight trains ran faster and faster, with less and less lineside supervision. A dangerous situation was developing, which had to be countered. Hot axleboxes had to be identified, and trains stopped, before disaster struck. Fortuitously, a similar situation had arisen in the United States a decade earlier and the railways there had sought a technical solution, resulting in a piece of equipment being designed known as a hot axlebox detector (HABD), which was installed in the track and scanned the two ends of each axle passing over it; then compared the temperatures and sounded an alarm in a monitoring signalbox if they were seriously different because one end was overheating. The signalman could then stop the train and deal with the defective wagon. Technically, all hot objects radiate heat energy, known as infrared, which is invisible but can be detected by an infrared camera (the scanner). The scanner always looks at the same point on the axleboxes of each passing train.

BR started to install lineside HABDs in the 1960s and by now there are about 200. They have never been entirely satisfactory. The level at which they are set has to be sufficiently low to detect an incipient hot axlebox, yet not so low as to give rise to false alarms triggered off by such things as locomotive exhausts. In practice it has not been found possible to strike the happy medium, in fact signalmen have been told to ignore alarms relating to ac electric locomotives, diesel-mechanical multiple-units and, as can well be imagined, steam locomotives in steam. HABDs were originally set for plain bearing axleboxes, but roller bearings (described later in the book) run warmer and to avoid false alarms the HABDs needed to be set very accurately, which stretched the capability of the equipment to its limits. Reliability was also a problem, as was the supply of spare parts. The whole subject demanded a great deal of management attention, which could not always be given when other more urgent or more important questions arose. There was a difficult learning curve for both management and technicians alike, and a number of unsatisfactory situations arose. Machines which had

become unserviceable, or which had been switched off because they had generated too many false alarms, were removed from site to a workshop without being replaced and were often away for months waiting parts. During all this time there were loopholes in the safety defences. For example, on 20 September 1979, train No 8M79, the 03.40 Tyne Yard to Toton, conveying 38 wagons of coal with a fitted head of 16 wagons became derailed and caused considerable track damage and disruption about 1½ miles north of Thirsk when an overheated journal eventually became so hot that it broke off from the remainder of the axle. The wagon concerned was a 21-ton coal hopper. There should have been two HABDs between Tyne Yard and Thirsk — one at Croxdale, near Ferryhill, about 36 miles from Thirsk, and one at Danby Wiske, near Northallerton, about nine miles away. Both detectors were out of order waiting spares, the one at Croxdale since 1 July and the one at Danby Wiske since 21 July. Nor was the Thirsk derailment exceptional. Barely a week later, train No 8V63, the 02.10 Tinsley to Severn Tunnel Junction was derailed at Water Orton, approaching Birmingham, by a journal burning off. The hot axlebox had been picked up by the HABD at Lea Marston, a short distance away, and the signalman at Saltley powerbox, upon being alerted by the alarm, had put his signals to Danger, and the train was already slowing down. However, when the accident was being investigated it transpired that the previous HABD was no less than 36 miles away at Duffield, yet it was well known that 25 miles was the absolute maximum safe distance between adjacent HABDs. As at Thirsk, a casual observer might have been forgiven for concluding that BR had been gambling on safety, gambling that a wagon would not run hot and spread itself all over the tracks. It was not a deliberate gamble, of course; in the one case it was bad management, in the other a considered judgement of risk, but whatever it was it came off, although that was really just good fortune and one really ought not to pray good fortune in aid of safety. However, these were bad days for railways. Morale was at rock bottom, there was constant strife between BR and the trade unions, the financial squeeze was so severe that mere survival was counted success, and there was a lack of positive direction. Small wonder that HABDs did not receive enough managerial attention — they were well down the list of priorities.

One might ask what the nation's watchdogs were doing at this juncture. Perhaps the Railway Inspectorate of the Department of Transport was not fully in the picture, not aware of the extent to which safety was being hazarded day by day. The role of the Railway Inspectorate is a difficult one; on the one hand there is no point in its making unreasonable and impossible financial demands on BR, yet on the other hand it must not allow sympathy with BR's financial predicament to sway its judgement. It is a fine line but there are occasions when it must stand firm if it feels that the overall demands of safety are being neglected because money is tight. This was one of those occasions, because the sums of money involved were not large. It was the era of BR Chairman Sir Peter Parker's famous phrase — and he was a master of the elegant and persuasive phrase — 'the crumbling edge of quality'. BR assured the Railway Inspectorate that the phrase did not apply to safety, and that it would impose speed restrictions, or take equipment out of service, before dangerous conditions were reached, but it is clear that this weighed upon the mind of the Chief Inspecting Officer Lt-Col I. K. A. McNaughton, for in his Annual Report for 1979 he commented upon the increase in significant train accidents from 220 in 1978 to 243 in 1979 by saying that:

'In looking for an explanation of this increase . . . I would suggest that part, at least, arises from the direct or indirect effects of the continuing financial problems facing railway management.'

He was right. The problem continued to give cause for concern, and in his 1981 Annual Report his successor, Maj C. F. Rose, returned to the attack:

'. . . so far at least, the Railway's policy of putting safety before operational or commercial considerations has prevented any serious erosion of their traditionally high safety standards.'

His use of the word 'serious' can hardly have been unintentional, and the inference is that he *did* consider that there had been *some* erosion of safety standards.

Maj Olver returned to the subject in his Report dated 30 April 1986, on the derailment at Birtley which occurred on 1 August 1984. After seriously criticising the civil engineering department, he concluded:

'. . . with the ever-increasing manpower economies being introduced throughout British Railways, I consider it is essential that frequent checks are carried out at all levels to ensure that the new organisation is working efficiently and that it has not led to shortcomings . . . The slimming of the permanent way organisation, while not resulting in a detectable drop in safety standards, has no longer got the comfortable margins that it had of old.'

Worries about hot axleboxes are now largely, although not entirely, in the past, thanks to a simple but remarkable invention — the roller bearing. In a plain axlebox the bearing rests directly on the end of the axle (the journal) and friction between the two when the axle rotates is prevented by a film of oil. In a roller bearing axlebox a 'race' of rollers acts in the same way as, and replaces, the film of oil.

The advantages of roller bearings are that they require no maintenance between shopping and run hot very much less frequently than plain axleboxes. When they do run hot it is not due to lack of lubricant (except where there has been a failure to grease), but is usually caused by incorrect reassembly after shopping, or occasionally by mechanical failure, mainly where the 'cage', which holds the rollers in the 'race', breaks. In such circumstances the temperature of the axlebox rises very quickly indeed, to such an extent that the journal end can become overheated and break off within three to five miles. It will be seen, therefore, that HABDs provide only a slight defence against a roller bearing axlebox overheating — they would have to be positioned every two to three miles to provide effective cover, rather than the 25-30 miles which is the current practice.

However, when the use of plain bearings has been eliminated it will then be possible to set HABDs to act only for roller bearing axleboxes. HABDs located at 12 to 18-mile intervals will then give some degree of safety.

As the lineside hot axlebox detector is not a totally satisfactory solution to the problem, other answers have been sought. The West German railway network (DB) has considered the possibility of applying sensors to each

Below:
The essential parts of a Timken roller bearing, showing the race of roller bearings, and the cup. *Author's Collection*

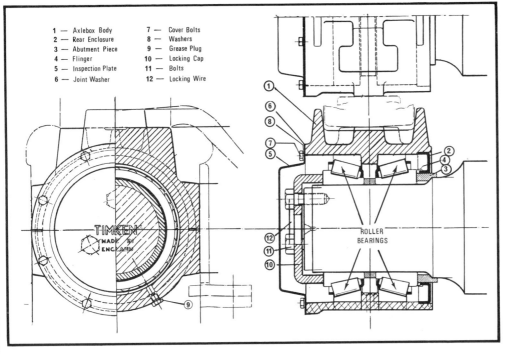

1 —	Axlebox Body	7 —	Cover Bolts
2 —	Rear Enclosure	8 —	Washers
3 —	Abutment Piece	9 —	Grease Plug
4 —	Flinger	10 —	Locking Cap
5 —	Inspection Plate	11 —	Bolts
6 —	Joint Washer	12 —	Locking Wire

Left:
Side, End and Top Elevations of a Timken Roller Bearing

Below and bottom:
Insulated fish vans fitted with roller bearing axleboxes for use on the express fish trains between Aberdeen and King's Cross via the East Coast main line. The train is seen ready to leave Aberdeen on 20 January 1958. Note the two vans marshalled behind the brakevan for quick detachment en route. *BR*

journal bearing housing, but has found it costly. British Timken has experimented with a fusible plug incorporated in the axlebox, which emits dense smoke when running hot, but this is not entirely satisfactory as it depends on the smoke being seen, and the train being stopped, within a few miles — very difficult to achieve on most of BR's main lines.

Roller bearings were first introduced on Britain's railways in 1928, on the Euston-Watford dc service of the London Midland and Scottish Railway, but development was very slow and mainly confined to steam locomotive axles. It was to be 30 years before roller bearings started to come into widespread use on BR. On 20 January 1958 the first fish train to be composed of vehicles fitted with roller bearings left Aberdeen for King's Cross. Some 275 fish vans were provided for the Aberdeen fish trains, the vans being identified by a blue circle painted on the body side. The trains were known as Blue Spot fish trains, and because the vehicles had an unusually long wheelbase, they were allowed to travel at more than 60mph. In the 1960s roller bearings became the standard fitting for all new construction, both on freight and passenger vehicles, and with the rapid withdrawal of older types of vehicles in the 1970s and 1980s the great majority of vehicle axleboxes are now the roller bearing type.

Some of the plain bearing axlebox vehicles taken out of traffic use were adopted by Civil Engineers for departmental use, but in some cases the axleboxes were not changed to roller bearing because of the cost and the relatively short remaining life of the vehicles. However, some types of vehicle in departmental use may not receive the standard of maintenance which is given to traffic wagons, and as a result they occasionally run hot. On 20 July 1985 a wagon loaded with prefabricated track en route from Crofton depot, near Wakefield, to Newcastle triggered a hot axlebox detector near Thirsk and signals were placed to Danger ahead of it. At the same time, the axlebox burst into flames and before the train could be stopped the journal end had burnt off and derailment had occurred. Engineering Dept wagons are a source of worry even to the engineers themselves. One engineer, writing in BR's own house journal as recently as March 1988 expressed his fears that sooner or later there would be a major mishap with one of these vehicles. He was to be proved not far wrong.

Above:
Standard British Railways 21-ton coal hopper wagons, equipped with roller bearing axleboxes. These were a special batch of vacuum-braked wagons serving West Drayton Coal Concentration Depot. *BR*

Right:
A civil engineering department 'Grampus' wagon, fitted with oil axleboxes, off the rails at Redhill, Southern Region, on 13 October 1984. The cause in this case was not a hot axlebox. Its neighbour has already been fitted with roller bearing axleboxes.
Alex Dasi-Sutton

Below right:
Class 58 freight locomotive No 58004 heads a train of empty 32-ton coal hopper wagons through Nottingham station on a return merry-go-round working from Staythorpe power station (near Newark) on 1 November 1985. The entire fleet of 32-ton hoppers is equipped with roller bearings. *Gary Grafton*

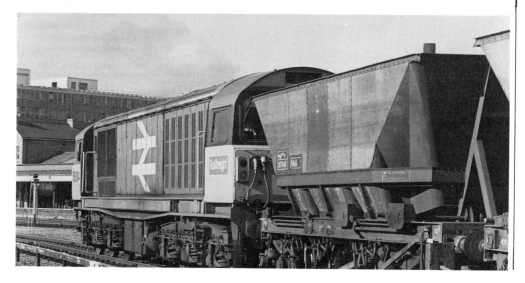

Only a few months later, on 12 July, a departmental wagon loaded with concrete sleepers and being conveyed on the 16.58 freight train from Workington to Willesden became derailed at Hademore, on the West Coast main line near Lichfield, causing severe damage to several miles of expensive track. Fortunately, no other train was involved. The cause of the derailment was a hot axlebox. This particular wagon was fitted with FAG roller bearing axleboxes.

Failures of roller bearing axleboxes, though relatively few, can have dramatic results, but surely none more so than those which overtook train 6M08, the 01.40 Haverton Hill (Teesside) to Glazebrook (Lancs) on 20 December 1984. The train was conveying 13 bogie tank wagons loaded with a total of 835 tons of petrol, and was examined before the start of its journey. It ran quite normally to Healey Mills yard, near Wakefield, where a fresh traincrew took over for the next stage of the journey. Again the journey was quite normal as the train ran along the Calder Valley through Brighouse and Sowerby Bridge, heading towards the Pennines which in this area reach over 1,500ft on the bleak and boggy moorlands. The train climbed the gradually steepening gradient towards the 2,885yd long Summit Tunnel, with the final five miles at 1 in 182. The signalman at Hebden Bridge, seven miles from the tunnel, watched the train go by. He saw nothing untoward. The train looked just like all the other oil and petrol trains which passed his box. Little did he know that catastrophe was only minutes away.

In the driving cab everything was perfectly normal and routine too. The driver had applied full power to haul the heavy train up the gradient, then as the tunnel mouth loomed up and he reached the summit he eased off power and sounded his horn as he entered the tunnel. Tunnels, even those as long as Summit Tunnel, hold no fears for drivers these days. It is merely a bit darker in there than it is outside; quite unlike the days of steam locomotives when tunnels were stinking holes full of smoke, and loathed by traincrews. The train was running smoothly through the tunnel at about 40mph when the driver suddenly felt the locomotive shudder and noticed that the automatic air brake pressure gauge had suddenly dropped to zero. At the same moment he felt the brakes go on and immediately deduced that the train had broken in two.

As he climbed down from the locomotive in the inky darkness, lit only by the backglow of his headlight, he had little or no inkling that this was to be one of the most terrifying days of his life. He knew what he had to do — consult with the guard to see what was wrong, and then see whether the opposite line was obstructed in any way. If it was, it was then the driver's duty to go forward as quickly as he could, waving a red light to warn the driver of any train approaching the obstruction. What he failed to do, which in the event was of no consequence, was to place a track-circuit operating clip on the opposite line straight away. A track circuit is an electrical train-detection device which feeds a low current through the running rails. When vehicle wheels run on that section of track they short-circuit the electric current. The short circuit is detected by the apparatus, which places the last approaching signal to Danger, and illuminates an indicator in the

Above left:
A block trainload of 100-ton
oil tankers, seen near
Beattock with a Class 86
electric locomotive in charge.
As a matter of interest, would
the oil companies allow their
road tankers to run about the
country in such a
disreputable state? *BR*

Above:
Sowerby Bridge West, in the
Calder Valley, showing a
Blackpool-Bradford train.
L. A. Nixon

Right:
Class 37 No 6942, at the head
of a train of coal empties,
descends the Calder Valley
after leaving Summit Tunnel
on 2 June 1971, and is seen
passing through Todmorden.
J. H. Cooper-Smith

signalbox. It is a device which is at the very heart of the modern signalling and safety system, and can be operated equally well by a track-circuit operating clip, which is a simple device carried on all locomotives and multiple-units. It consists of two spring clips joined by a piece of wire. In an emergency the clips are placed one on each rail, and in an instant there is a short circuit and the signals are switched to Danger. It is certainly the quickest and most effective way of preventing a train in the opposite direction from running into an obstruction, provided that it has not already passed the last signal. If it has, no power on earth can save it because it will have crashed headlong into the wreckage in as little as a minute.

But to continue with our story. The driver climbed down on to the track and walked towards the other end of his locomotive, where the guard had already alighted. The scene was like something out of Jules Verne. There they were, in the middle of the tunnel, three-quarters of a mile from either end, with the back glare of the locomotive headlight eerily lighting up the surroundings, and clouds of dust and petrol fumes rolling towards them. They knew that they were carrying 835 tons of four-star petrol. They knew how even a saucerful of petrol could cause quite a blaze; then suddenly there was a 'whoosh' of flame down the train somewhere. What terror gripped them can scarcely be imagined. For all they knew, the whole 835 tons might explode into flames at any moment, and there was only one way the flames could go — along the tunnel. They ran for their lives, half expecting with every step to be overtaken by searing flames. The relief when they finally reached the tunnel mouth was enormous. Nor did they know what lay behind them in the tunnel. They had seen a whoosh of flame, they suspected that the train had become divided, but they did not know that most of the tankers had become derailed and that some of them were on their sides lying on the opposite line. If another train had been approaching, the resulting crash in the confined space of the tunnel among tens of thousands of gallons of highly-inflammable four-star petrol would have been too awful to contemplate. Luckily, the tanks lying on their sides on the opposite line had short-circuited the track circuit, so the vital signal at the tunnel mouth was already at Danger.

The traincrew used the telephone at that signal to raise the alarm, and immediately the whole emergency organisation sprang into action. On the railway, breakdown trains were alerted and arrangements were made to cancel trains or divert them from the blocked route. Key personnel were called out. Police, fire and ambulance services were at once notified, and they responded very quickly. The accident happened at about 05.50 and the alarm was raised just after 06.00. By 06.08 Greater Manchester Fire Service Control had received the call for assistance and had notified the West Yorkshire Fire Service Control at 06.13. Fire engines arrived at the Manchester end of the tunnel by 06.16 and at the Yorkshire end at 06.22 (the tunnel lies across the county boundary). Such promptness was most commendable, but thanks to the foresight of BR and the fire service a practice had already been held to test the response time, in view of the fact that the tunnel lies in two different fire service areas.

The firemen entered the tunnel from both ends to assess the situation, which could hardly have been more difficult or novel for them. They extinguished several small fires and appeared to have the situation under such good control that they felt it would be safe for the locomotive and first three tankers to be removed from the tunnel. The driver and guard were still there and they very bravely agreed to go back into the tunnel, even though the terror of recent events was still fresh in their minds. At last they reached the locomotive, but then found that the coupling between the

Above:
The scene deep inside Summit Tunnel on 20 December 1984, just before the great fire erupted. The firemen are seen dealing with what were thought to be small and isolated pockets of fire. Their courage in such circumstances is greatly to be admired.
Brian Saville/ West Yorkshire Fire Service

third and fourth wagons was too tight to be lifted off the drawbar hook, the fourth wagon being derailed. At this stage they must have felt like calling the whole thing off but with great determination they stuck to their task. The driver reversed the locomotive and pushed the front three wagons against the fourth so that the buffers could be compressed and the couplings slackened. It was successful and the traincrew gingerly took the locomotive and front three undamaged tankers out of the tunnel into the open air. The relief they felt when they finally emerged into the daylight can be imagined, and the bravery they displayed was a great credit to the railway service.

By 09.45, 4hr after the accident, it appeared that everything was under control and that the railway breakdown gangs could soon move in to clear the line and reopen the route to normal traffic. In the event it was to be eight months before that happened. A fierce fire broke out with great fury and suddenness, and had the flames not been able to escape up two of the tunnel's 12 ventilating shafts it is likely that a number of firemen would have perished. The fire was so intense that flames shot out of the top of the two ventilating shafts to a height of 150yd, with great quantities of air being sucked into the tunnel to fan the fire. It burnt uncontrollably for 24hr, causing considerable damage to the tunnel lining.

The first people to enter the tunnel after the fire had a daunting experience. They had no idea what they would find. The tunnel might have collapsed, or it might be in a dangerously unstable condition ready to do so, but in fact the old tunnel had stood up to its ordeal remarkably well, especially as it had been built in the early days of railways as long ago as 1840/41, for the Leeds & Manchester Railway. George Stephenson had been Engineer-in-Chief and had done his job well. It was, incidentally, the first railway tunnel through the Pennines.

Major accidents often have minor causes and Summit Tunnel was no exception. Whilst the Inspecting Officer who conducted the subsequent inquiry, Mr D. Sawer, was examining the debris in the tunnel he discovered the journal end which had burnt off the leading axle of the

fourth tank wagon. The wagon had then become derailed, although the train actually parted between the sixth and seventh vehicles. The defective wagon was No PR82689. It had been built in 1968 by the Standard Railway Wagon Co for hire to Total Oil, and was purchased by Procor (UK) Ltd in 1971. It had originally been constructed to carry Class B heavy oil products but was converted in July 1984 to carry Class A light oil products before being hired to ICI. In November 1984 during the course of normal maintenance the wheelsets were found to require attention and the vehicle was despatched to Rail Car Services at Gloucester.

Reconditioned wheelsets were fitted and on 10 December the vehicle was returned to traffic and sent to Haverton Hill. From then on it was only a matter of time before it fell to pieces. It had actually made one round trip to Glazebrook and was on its second when the accident occurred. Why it should choose to happen in the middle of Summit Tunnel is one of those quirks of fate.

The axlebox bearing which failed had been manufactured by British Timken and had been refurbished and reassembled by the British Steel Corporation. It is probable that the failure resulted from incorrect reassembly or incorrect fitting on the journal. Such a simple cause, costing millions of pounds! No doubt BR was relieved that it had insured itself against the cost of major accidents, but it has to pay hefty annual premiums to do so. At one time BR stood all its own losses arising from accidents, but the cost of the Britannia Bridge fire over the Menai Straits in 1970 seriously unbalanced BR's budget and it was felt to be better to even out the cost of major accidents (ie those costing several million pounds) by means of an annual payment of an insurance premium. Failures of roller bearing axleboxes on bogie tank wagons are quite rare, and the failure rate has been calculated at one per four to five million vehicle miles run.

Those who are opposed to anything with the word 'nuclear' in it were up in arms about the possibility of a train conveying a flask containing irradiated fuel rods being involved in such a fire as the one at Summit Tunnel. Whether the flask could withstand those temperatures over such a long period of time without the contents leaking is problematical. It has never been tested, nor is anyone likely to go to the trouble and expense of mounting such a test. The chances of a petrol train becoming derailed and catching fire in the middle of a tunnel are millions to one. So far as is known it has never happened before, not even a derailment, let alone a derailment and fire. And the chance of a train conveying a nuclear flask being so near that it had actually passed the last signal when the derailment occurred must be of such an order of magnitude that it is quite incalculable. Yet, the suggestion was seriously made that BR should timetable its trains so that nuclear flask trains are not planned to pass petrol trains in a tunnel. This is taking contingencies to extremes and is about as sensible

Above and Below:
Two views of the Britannia Bridge over the Menai Straits, after the fire in 1970. The sagging bridge and the smoke-blackened stone towers can clearly be seen.
John H. Bird/E. N. Kneale

as telling a pedestrian that he should not cross a road if a motor vehicle is likely to pass within the next three weeks. Fortunately BR took a pragmatic view — it agreed that it would avoid timetabling such trains to pass each other in a tunnel, but wisely made no stipulation about the actual day-to-day running.

Finally, it is interesting to speculate on what might have happened if neither police nor fire brigade had attended,

and if the whole incident had been dealt with by railway staff alone. After all, the fire brigade was unable to prevent the fire from burning itself out, although its action in keeping the fire under control during the early hours did enable the locomotive and three tank wagons to be rescued, which might not otherwise have been the case. But that is perhaps being unfair. Individual firemen acted with great bravery, and some might well have lost their lives. No one had experienced such a situation before and there were fears that the whole 835 tons of petrol might create a gigantic fireball, consuming everything in its path over a wide area, almost in the nature of an explosion. It was obviously sensible to take precautions, such as the evacuation of nearby residents. Police and fire services are very sensitive on this issue, following a number of serious eruptions and fireballs during derailments in North America. On 24 Feburary 1978 at Waverley in Tennessee a derailed tank wagon of propane exploded as it was being pumped out, and 12 people were killed. On 10 November 1979 at Mississauga, a Toronto suburb, a quarter of a million people had to be evacuated because of the danger that a tank wagon containing chlorine might rupture and release clouds of the poison gas which claimed so many lives on the Western Front in World War 1. Adjacent tank wagons in the derailed train were burning and exploding. The cause of the derailment was a hot axlebox of the plain bearing type. The Canadian Transport Commission recommended that, amongst other things, roller bearings should be fitted to tank wagons conveying inflammable liquids and that hot box detectors should be installed at 20-mile intervals in built-up areas.

To return to the subject of lineside hot axlebox detectors. Whilst they will detect an overheating roller bearing axlebox, such overheating can occur over a relatively short distance and may lead to catastrophic failure within a few miles. Obviously, HABDs located 25 to 30 miles apart do not provide continuous cover and consideration is being given to locating them on the approaches to long tunnels, viaducts and long bridges so that a train with a defective bearing can be stopped and be prevented from becoming derailed whilst actually in the tunnel or on a viaduct or long bridge. HABDs work best when they are located on straight and level track, and where the train has not recently been braking. It is also convenient to have a siding nearby into which a vehicle with an overheated axlebox can be detached. Whilst the first priority must be to identify an incipient hot axlebox, it is inconvenient if unsuitable siting gives rise to a lot of false alarms, and it is very inconvenient if an axlebox is discovered to be in such a bad state that it is not safe to take it forward yet there is no siding nearby into which it can be detached. These factors tend to determine the optimum location of HABDs but there is a need for some compromise here if safety is to be assured.

When the alarm sounds in a signalbox the instrument tells the signalman the number of the axle in the train, and whether it is the left-hand or right-hand side of the train. The signalman will then stop the train, and any other that may be approaching, in case of derailment, and inform the traincrew of the details. Driver or guard will then check to see how hot the particular axlebox is, but if nothing appears to be amiss the train may proceed forward at not more than 20mph to a place where technical staff are available. Alternatively the vehicle may be detached. If the axlebox is hot the vehicle must be detached, and no movement must exceed 10mph, but if there is any doubt about the wisdom of moving the vehicle at all it must not be moved until it has been examined by technical staff, who would authorise such movement if appropriate.

The frequency of false alarms on passenger trains, and the need to carry out these instructions, caused a lot of delay, and it was necessary to introduce some relaxation. Genuine hot axleboxes on passenger trains are quite rare, therefore if nothing can be found after an alarm the train may run forward at normal speed but an examination must be carried out within 50 miles either by technical staff or by the passage of the train over another detector. If neither is available, and everything seems to be in order, the train may run forward another 50 miles.

It will have been noted that in the discussion of the Summit Tunnel fire, all three parties (Railway Control, the police and the fire service) knew immediately that the train was conveying petrol. How this came about will be revealed in the next chapter.

3
The Transport of Dangerous Goods

The railways of Britain have been carrying dangerous goods ever since they were built, although it is interesting to reflect that they only did so on their own terms, in contrast to the general run of goods traffic for which the railways were common carriers and were obliged to carry anything that was handed to them, until freed from that obligation by the Transport Act 1962.

Reading through the old books of regulations, one is immediately struck by the way in which certain commodities have now passed into history, such as celluloid, calcium carbide, charcoal, saltpetre and oily waste; reminders of our industrial past. No mention then of some of today's hazardous commodities, such as liquefied petroleum gas and hydrocyanic acid, and the one that causes the most excitement of all — spent nuclear fuel. Our forefathers never dreamt of the marvels of the nuclear age, nor had any inkling of its dangers.

In this chapter we shall consider the problems surrounding the conveyance of certain types of dangerous goods, and the safety organisation which exists for dealing with the effects of an accident to a train conveying such traffics. One of the potentially most hazardous traffics is spent nuclear fuel, and it is certainly the traffic which appears to cause most concern in the public mind, mainly because the effects of an accident in Britain causing radiation leakage from a flask containing irradiated nuclear fuel are unknown. There is simply no experience of such an event because it has never happened, whilst the effects on the human body of radiation from other sources often take so long to manifest themselves, especially if the dosage is small. There is also the problem of the safe disposal of nuclear waste. These factors tend to make the nuclear power industry a focus of attack by pressure groups of all kinds.

There are a number of nuclear power stations around Britain's coastline, mainly of the Magnox reactor type, although there are some advanced gas-cooled reactor stations. Each fuel element for a Magnox reactor consists of a bar of uranium metal encased in a tube of magnesium alloy, called Magnox. Gas-cooled reactor fuel elements are made up of pellets of uranium oxide in stainless steel tubes, 36 of which are held together in a graphite sleeve.

Both types of fuel element are manufactured by British Nuclear Fuels at Preston, and are transported to the power stations by road. At this stage the elements are perfectly harmless and can safely be held in the hand, but after use in the reactor they are highly radioactive. A Magnox fuel element for the Sizewell power station is about a metre long and weighs 25lb. Each of Sizewell's two reactors contains about 26,000 elements, which remain in the reactor for up to 11 years. After use the elements are stored for three months, and then taken by rail in specially constructed containers known as flasks to British Nuclear Fuels' reprocessing works at Sellafield, on the line between Barrow-in-Furness and Whitehaven, in Cumbria. Each flask contains 200 Magnox fuel elements or 20 gas-cooled reactor

Below:
The result of inattention in the driving cab. Class 47 locomotive No 1614 had been hauling a train along the Up Goods line at King's Norton, near Birmingham, on 27 May 1970, but the driver failed to stop at the signal, and the locomotive ran into the buffers in the dead-end. The driver admitted having fallen asleep and there was no AWS on the Goods line to alert him. The accident, which happened in a built-up area, could have had disastrous consequences as there were five tank wagons of butane liquefied petroleum gas in the train, but fortunately the tank barrels were not ruptured.
Paul Cotterell

9900

SHELL BP

9900

Highly Inflammable

for repairs advise
Shell-Mex and B.P. Ltd
Shell-Mex House, London

W.B. 15'-0"

LOAD BUTANE 18 TONS
PROPANE 16 TONS

21-3-0

Above:
A propane/butane tank wagon, first registered in 1963 and built by Chas Roberts & Co of Wakefield. Gross laden weight 40 tons. Equipped with roller bearing axleboxes and the vacuum brake. *Ian Allan Library*

Left:
Class 25 diesel-electric No 25307 passes Cark signalbox on 28 July 1982 with a block trainload of nuclear flasks for Sellafield. *Noel A. Machell*

Above, left and below left:
A spectacular demonstration of the ability of a nuclear flask to withstand the impact of a 250-ton train at 100mph. Staged at Old Dalby, near Melton Mowbray, on BR's Research Department test track. The locomotive was No 46009.
Colin J. Marsden/
Colin J. Marsden/
Nicholas Sargeant

elements and is filled with water. A flask is essentially a massive steel box with 14in thick walls, which are designed not only to absorb radiation but also to be proof against breakage, heat or leakage. The flasks (which conform to internationally agreed standards) have to be capable of withstanding a fall of 30ft on to an unyielding surface; and to convince sceptics of the tremendous strength of the flasks the Central Electricity Generating Board arranged a spectacular demonstration in 1984 in conjunction with BR. The CEGB bought from BR a redundant Class 46 diesel-electric locomotive and three Mk 1 coaches, and equipped the locomotive with remote control (no one wanted to stay in the cab during the test!). They then positioned a flask, at its most vulnerable angle, on the line to simulate the worst derailment conditions, and drove the 250-ton train into it at 100mph, having carefully assembled the nation's press and TV beforehand. The locomotive was wrecked but the flask, to everyone's relief, was undamaged. Everyone, that is, except the anti-nuclear lobby who protested that it was not a representative test. What would happen, they said, if the flask was in a petrol fire for an hour (in what circumstances it is difficult to imagine, other than the Summit Tunnel fire, which in any case was a million to one chance), or fell off a high viaduct (when did a train last fall off a high viaduct on to an unyielding surface in Britain?). There has to be some regard to the balance of probabilities even when dealing with spent nuclear fuel. There have now been more than 10,000 safe journeys since flasks first began to be carried, with only one or two very minor derailments of no consequence whatsoever. Yet, the subject of the transport of flasks is a very delicate one and the consequences of radiation leakage are so unpredictable that it is quite proper and essential that all sensible and practical safeguards should be taken. But even if the flask were to be

Left:
On 19 April 1982 Class 25 diesel-electric No 25032 is seen leaving Blaenau Ffestiniog with a nuclear flask from Trawsfynydd power station. Note the guard's brakevan at the rear of the train — all trains conveying nuclear flasks must have one. *M. M. Hughes*

cracked in some way, and some of the water lost, the only effect would be to contaminate the ground in the vicinity, with no major threat to health. So long as the elements themselves remained undamaged, radioactivity would be contained; and in the worst case — damage to the fuel elements — many hours would elapse before there was any release of radioactivity which was not entirely confined to the vicinity of the flask. It is the objective of the emergency organisation to ensure that expert personnel and emergency services reach the scene during that period and take emergency action.

All trains conveying flasks have a brakevan at the rear, in which a guard must ride. In the event of an accident the guard and driver must not proceed along the train towards each other for the purpose of ascertaining the extent of the accident, but must immediately set off in opposite directions to protect the obstruction, to warn approaching drivers to stop, and to raise the alarm either by telephone or by going to a signalbox. The signalman will then inform the Area Operations Centre or Regional Control, which will call the fire brigade and notify the CEGB Alert Centre. The police, both British Transport and County, will also be called out, together with the railway breakdown service.

The CEGB Alert Centre is manned round the clock and would call out a Flask Emergency Team, supplemented if necessary by specialist advisers, and would also give advice on action to be taken in the meantime. Helicopters would be used where appropriate to enable the Flask Emergency Team to reach the scene of the accident with the least possible delay. If there was any suspicion of radiation leakage the police would arrange any necessary evacuation, but this is extremely unlikely as the Flask Emergency Team would have more than sufficient time to take remedial steps. To sum up, therefore, a train conveying a nuclear flask is very unlikely to have an accident in which the flask itself is directly involved; the flask itself is unlikely in the extreme to be dangerously damaged, and finally if it is, the Flask Emergency Team would have time to take remedial action. The danger area would be no more than a 50yd radius from the flask. Frequent exercises are held with the CEGB and the emergency services in order to test the emergency procedures.

Most railwaymen are more concerned with the dangers arising from the carriage of other commodities, such as hydrocyanic acid (hydrogen cyanide), known as HCN for short. This normally travels in block trainloads of tank wagons from Grangemouth, near Falkirk, to the ICI works at Haverton Hill, near Stockton-on-Tees. HCN is a liquid which is extremely poisonous by inhalation, by ingestion and by contact with the skin. It is also highly flammable and the vapour can form an explosive mixture with air. The tank wagons have additional protection at the sides and ends to minimise the damage in the event of a collision, and the tank barrels are painted white with a horizontal orange band round the barrel.

As with nuclear flasks, these trains convey a brakevan at the rear in which a guard must ride, and in the event of an accident the driver and guard must not proceed towards each other to see if the other line is obstructed but must immediately set off in opposite directions to raise the alarm and seek assistance. This instruction is designed to avoid the traincrew from having to pass near any tanks which may be leaking. Signalmen are aware of any train conveying HCN, because such trains are signalled by a special 'Is line clear?' bell signal 2-1-7. In power signalbox areas the train is known by its four-character identification code. Even when the tanks are empty they are considered to be dangerous because of the vapour they contain.

One of these trains was derailed near Ferryhill on 9 December 1975. The police and the fire services were called out, together with a specialist team from ICI at Haverton Hill. As it was not known initially how serious the leakage was the police decided to evacuate several nearby streets as a precaution. It turned out to have been unnecessary, but it was a sensible measure. The derailment was caused by substandard track, according to the Inspecting Officer, Lt-Col Townsend-Rose, in his Report.

Whilst nuclear flasks and HCN are relatively new traffics, the railways have been carrying explosives almost since they were first built. The regulations and instructions designed to ensure that explosives are carried safely have therefore been developed over a long period of time. Enormous quantities of explosives were carried safely during World War 2, with only two exceptions — the explosion at Soham in 1944, described in Chapter 1, and the

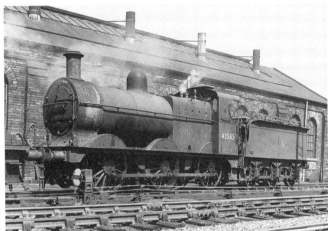

Above:
Ex-Midland Class 3F 0-6-0 No 43579, the engine involved in the Bootle explosion in 1945, is seen trundling a trainload of Barrow Ironworks empty coke hoppers through the cutting near Calverley & Rodley on 16 May 1951. *Leslie Overend*

Left:
Sister engine No 43585 is seen resting between duties outside Hellifield shed, on 29 June 1961. These simple, sturdy machines had a very long life. *G. W. Morrison*

Below left:
The gigantic crater at Bootle, after a wagon of depth-charges blew up on 22 March 1945. The first five wagons of the train are standing beyond the crater. This photograph was taken by a local railway inspector and may be the only one in existence of this disaster. *Inspector Redman, per Norman Stubbs Collection*

explosion of a wagon of depth charges at Bootle. Every 1,000-bomber raid needed eight complete trainloads of bombs, to say nothing of 28 trains of petrol.

The story of the Bootle explosion illustrates yet again the courage of traincrews when faced with a sudden emergency. Driver Goodall and Fireman Stubbs booked on duty to work the 5.55pm freight train from Workington to Carnforth on 22 March 1945. They had 58 wagons, including, next to the engine, seven wagons of 'government traffic' from the ammunition depot at nearby Buckhill, labelled 'Dangerous'. Their engine was an old Midland Class 3F No 3579. They were good engines for their size, but when worked hard they inevitably threw out sparks from the chimney. When passing through Bootle the fireman noticed the reflection of flames from the station buildings and when he looked back he saw to his horror that one of the ammunition wagons, the sixth from the engine, was burning furiously. The driver gradually brought the loose-coupled train to a stand and the fireman jumped off just before it did so. He quickly threw the coupling off behind the blazing wagon, despite the imminent danger, then ran back to the engine. Immediately the driver drew ahead with the blazing wagon then stopped again. The risk of a tremendous explosion was increasing with every second that passed. The fireman jumped down again and very courageously approached the blazing wagon, despite the great heat and the obvious danger that it might explode at any moment, blowing itself and him to smithereens. He managed to uncouple the blazing wagon and despite a natural inclination to put as much distance as possible between himself and the wagon he still had the presence of mind to apply its handbrake, lest it should follow them down the gradient — a nightmarish thought. Back to the engine he went again, heart pounding both from his exertions and from apprehension, then the driver took the remaining five wagons forward to what he thought was a safe distance. The fireman then considered his next duty, as though he had not done enough already. He knew that the 9.20pm passenger train from Barrow was due and he knew that he had to stop it before it reached the danger area. His devotion to the job saved his life. He grabbed the detonator case (detonators are small explosive devices which are intended to be fixed to the rail head in case of emergency and are exploded by the wheels of a locomotive passing over them, which alerts the driver and warns him to stop) and stuffed his pockets with them. Taking a lamp from the engine he ran forward along the line to warn the approaching train.

The next thing he knew was when he recovered consciousness, to find himself lying by the side of the track, temporarily deafened. A huge cloud of debris blotted out the moon. The blazing wagon had exploded, and the depth charges had blown a crater 60ft across and 45ft deep. The fireman returned to what remained of the engine to find that his driver had been blown to pieces, but he still remembered that he must stop the passenger train. Finding that the engine was still moveable he drove it forward to the next signalbox, at Silecroft, keeping a sharp lookout for any sign of the passenger train. To his relief he found it standing safely in the station at Silecroft. The signalman had kept it there, having received the 'Stop and examine train' bell signal from the signalman at Bootle, who had seen the wagon on fire.

It is pleasing to be able to record that Fireman Stubbs received the George Medal from King George VI for his outstanding bravery and resourcefulness. He not only lived up to the traditions of the railway service — he enhanced them.

Many years later, there was a rather frightening incident at Howe & Co's Sidings signalbox, near Armathwaite, just south of Carlisle on the line to Settle and Leeds, in 1969. Hot axleboxes were not uncommon on that line, in view of the sustained high speed achieved by freight trains on the long, falling gradients, and the distance which the trains had run since their last examination.

Signalmen were accustomed both to keeping a good lookout, and to detaching defective vehicles without fuss. One night a van containing high explosive shells was detached from a train with an axlebox on fire, but because the fire was thought to have burnt itself out the fire brigade and military authorities were not informed, as they ought to have been. Several hours later the signalman was greatly alarmed to see smoke and flames coming from inside the van, and he sent for the fire brigade. By the time it arrived the van was well alight, and shortly afterwards it exploded. This was the first explosion on the railways since 1945, but it was not the only explosives scare in 1969.

The conveyance by rail in peacetime of military ammunition and explosives is not as uncommon as might be imagined, particularly to NATO forces in Western Europe. On 22 October 1969 a special train left a depot in Hampshire en route to Felixstowe Docks. It consisted of 27 standard covered vans of 10ft wheelbase and conveyed 117 tons, mainly ammunition. The train left Temple Mills during the late evening, hauled by a Class 37 diesel-electric locomotive, and set off on the last leg of its journey. As the train was passing through Chelmsford the signalman saw sparks coming from it, and he realised straightaway that something was wrong. Almost immediately he heard the noise of a derailment, so he put all his signals to Danger and sent the 'Obstruction Danger' bell signal to the signalboxes at each side — Witham and Ingatestone.

Luckily there was no train approaching from the opposite direction.

On the locomotive the driver had been running his train at about 45mph, the maximum speed allowed for 10ft wheelbase wagons, and had shut off power on the falling gradient approaching Chelmsford. He was just starting to reapply power as the train passed through the station, when he felt a slight snatch or jerk followed by the feel of the brakes being applied. Suspecting that something was wrong he looked back and saw sparks coming from the train, so he made a full brake application immediately. As soon as the train stopped both he and his secondman jumped down from the locomotive on to the track. After telling his secondman to go forward to protect the train and warn any approaching driver to stop, he himself went back to look at his train. He was quite horrified by what he saw — almost the entire train was derailed and four of the vans lay on their sides. If another train had been approaching and had ploughed into the wrecked vans at speed there is no knowing how the ammunition might have reacted. According to the Army authorities that would have been the most serious risk.

There was no single clearly identifiable cause of the derailment. As was the case with so many of the frequent short-wheelbase vehicle derailments of the time, the cause was a combination of minor imperfections in the track, worn springs and tyres on the wagon, and the speed of the train. The defects in the track and the wagon were all within the prescribed engineering tolerances and the speed of the train was no higher than the permitted maximum of 45mph. Up to 1963 such vehicles had been permitted to travel at up to 60mph, but following a disturbing increase in the number of derailments the limit was reduced to 50mph. Following further derailments the speed limit was reduced to 45mph in 1966. If safety had been the only consideration a speed limit as low as 35mph would have been imposed, but even at 45mph the effect on transit times was disastrous for BR's competitive position. Not only did express freight trains have to travel more slowly, but they had to be shunted out of the way of passenger and parcels trains more frequently. This reduction in speed could hardly have happened at a worse time. The backbone of the railways' overnight express freight services had always been the movement of large numbers of vans of mixed merchandise (known as 'smalls' or 'sundries') between the large goods stations in main centres. Under the Labour Government's 1968 Transport Act, which was genuinely designed to help the railways, the sundries business was handed over to a new body known as National Carriers, part of the National Freight Corporation. This quickly proved itself to be no lover of railways, and with express freight trains limited to 45mph, and of dubious punctuality, National Carriers quickly transferred the sundries business to road. It really had no alternative if it was to survive in the market place. And so the railways' sundries traffic, now carried on behalf of National Carriers, disappeared almost overnight. Some railway managers were glad to see the end of the railways' sundries business. It had long been regarded as a loss-maker, and had been subjected to numerous reorganisations in an attempt to reduce the losses, but which had sometimes resulted in greater inefficiency. The work was often concentrated on fewer depots, which then found that they could not handle the influx of traffic owing to shortages of staff, whilst the recruitment of sufficient numbers of suitable staff was very difficult at this period. Dissatisfied customers took their business away. But without the nightly flow of sundries vans the network of express freight trains between main centres could no longer be supported, and this immediately struck at the railways' competitive position for its full

Left:
Freight train derailments were commonplace in the 1960s, each one resulting in a pile of wreckage, like the one seen here at St Devereux, between Hereford and Abergavenny, after a diesel-hauled train of empty vehicles became derailed in running, on plain track. This was a typical short-wheelbase vehicle mishap, with no specific cause, but where speed, and the condition of both the track and the vehicles all played a part. Derailments of this nature caused great concern to both the railway authorities and Railway Inspectorate alike.
D. H. Cape

wagonload merchandise traffic, which at the time was quite profitable. It quickly ceased to be so — costs increased and transit times worsened. The long, slow decline in wagonload carryings accelerated. It is sad, but ironic, that BR had just produced a goods vehicle that would have knocked spots off the competition — a long-wheelbase two-axle vehicle with modern suspension, capable of travelling safely at up to 75mph with a very substantial payload, and equipped with roller bearings and the air brake. But it was too late. BR was destined to become largely a passenger railway in less than 10 years — one of the most astonishing transformations of the railway scene ever. In 1970 one could still stand at the lineside and see streams of freight trains pass by. By 1980 one could stand at the same lineside and hardly see any on many routes.

However, to return to our story. By the 1970s freight train operation was becoming more and more complicated, and hence potentially unsafe. In the late 1960s a new and very complicated method had been introduced of calculating the loads which could be hauled by different classes of locomotive on freight trains. It was an attempt to ensure firstly that every locomotive was loaded up to its maximum hauling capacity, and secondly that the train had sufficient brake power to enable it to be stopped safely on any falling gradient it might encounter on its route. It required the optimum permutation of:

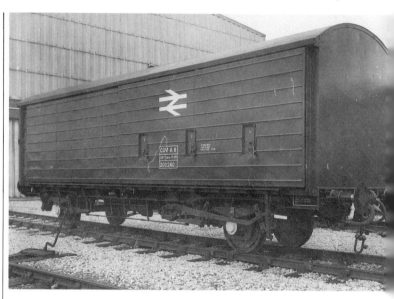

1. Restrictions on falling gradients on the route concerned.
2. The hauling and braking characteristics of the locomotive.
3. The weight of wagons to be conveyed.
4. The power brake force of those wagons.
5. A factor representing the fact that, ton for ton, it is easier to haul heavily-loaded vehicles than lightly-loaded ones (less friction, less wind resistance).

An alteration in any one factor affected the others, and to arrive at the optimum solution required both concentration and mathematical skill — not matters that were taken into account to any great extent when recruiting new guards or shunters. They were given training, of course, as were existing staff, but not enough. However, BR was so short of

Above:
A 75mph high-capacity van, equipped with roller bearing axleboxes, special suspension, and the airbrake, being loaded with cartons of Kellogg's Corn Flakes. *(Both) BR*

170

guards and shunters that to have released them for more training would have meant cancelling trains. In those difficult days training was low down the list of priorities.

To add to the staff's problems, new types of train were being introduced such as freightliners and merry-go-round (MGR) coal trains, each with its own book of instructions. The vacuum brake was giving way to the air brake. Then TOPS came on the scene. Entitled in full 'Total Operations Processing System', it was imported from the Southern Pacific Railroad, USA, in 1970 and modified over the next three years to make it suitable for BR. It is a computer-based system which requires a completely new approach to the assembly and preparation of a freight train. Initially it was yet another complication for hard-pressed and short-handed supervisors to have to deal with, although now it has settled down to become an indispensable tool for the more efficient handling of traffic operations. However, in the 1970s it was looked upon with suspicion, as being yet another burden for the long-suffering staff to have to carry. Older staff looked back nostalgically to the 1950s, when freight train operation was carried on in much the same way as it would have been 30, 40 or even 50 years earlier. Now the pace of change had quickened, and was about to exact its price.

On Wednesday 6 August 1975 train No 4068 set off from Coatbridge, near Glasgow, at 18.05 on its long overnight journey to Southampton. It was a Freightliner train, part of the new railway scene, and consisted of 15 vehicles, with a maximum speed of 75mph. On the first part of its journey it was electrically hauled, and it was well on its way when another train, No 6F52, left the sidings at Runcorn shortly before 22.00 on its journey to the ICI Works at Wallerscote, near Northwich. That train was hauled by a Class 40 diesel-electric locomotive No 40189 and conveyed 20 45-ton tank wagons, each one loaded with 30 tons of caustic soda liquor. The tanks had a maximum speed of 60mph but there was a particular complication that night, inasmuch as eight of the wagons were fitted with the vacuum brake, whilst the remaining 12 wagons had air brakes. The 1970s saw the transition from the vacuum to the air brake, and it had been the practice to equip air-braked wagons with a through vacuum pipe, so that they could run in a vacuum-braked train. The total weight of the train concerned and its locomotive was 1,033 tons and it had a vacuum brake force of 219 tons. The brake force available to the driver was insufficient, and either the load should have been reduced or the train should have been run at a lower speed. Neither was done, nor did the driver clearly understand that

Above and Below:
The scene of devastation at Weaver Junction after the sidelong collision between a freightliner train and a train of tank wagons on 6 August 1975.
(Both) Author's Collection

although his train was running as a fully-braked one, in that the brake pipe was connected up between every wagon, the power brake was only working on eight of the 20 wagons. Thus was the stage set for disaster.

The route of the train of tankers took it on to the West Coast main line at Weaver Junction, 16 miles north of Crewe, via a flyover with a falling gradient to the junction. In the signalbox there the signalman had been warned of the approach of both this train and the Freightliner train. He decided to give precedence to the latter and cleared all his signals for it. The train was approaching the junction at its maximum permitted speed of 75mph, when the driver glanced across at the Runcorn line and was alarmed to see a train approaching the junction on that line with sparks coming from its wheels. He immediately concluded that the tanker train would be unable to stop at the junction signal and would continue into sidelong collision with his own train at the junction. In a split second he decided to try to accelerate out of harm's way, a decision that may well have saved his life, but he was not completely successful, as the locomotive of the tanker train, running away at over 30mph, came into sideways collision with the fifth vehicle of the Freightliner train. It tossed aside the lighter Freightliner vehicles as though they were toys, whilst the heavy tank wagons piled up into each other. Caustic soda liquor began to gush out of the damaged tanks.

The signalman at Weaver Junction was a horrified spectator of all this. He had already cleared his Down main line signals for an express passenger train, the 16.39 from Poole to Liverpool, and when he realised that a collision between the two freight trains was likely he hurriedly put all his signals to Danger. He had a few anxious moments wondering whether he had acted in time to stop the express but luck was with him. The express had had to slow down to 20mph further back for track repairs and was able to stop well clear of the accident, thanks to the signalman's prompt action. If there had been no speed restriction . . . ! The consequences of an express crashing into the wreckage at 70mph with over 100 tons of caustic soda lying around in pools are too awful to contemplate. But accidents are full of 'ifs', and the fates were obviously satisfied with the extent of the existing wreckage.

The main line to Liverpool and the north was blocked for almost a week. The fire service attended and poured on millions of gallons of water to wash away the caustic soda liquor. Specialist teams from ICI also attended. They not only gave advice and provided protective clothing; they also arranged for unspilled caustic soda liquor to be syphoned off and transferred to empty tankers, and they tipped over 100 tons of sodium bicarbonate to neutralise the 250 tons of spilled liquor, which was causing the water authorities great concern. ICI maintains a number of emergency centres round the country, one of which is at Runcorn, and all tank wagons are labelled with the emergency telephone number. The procedure worked well, but the fact that Runcorn was only a few miles away was helpful.

In the Report into the accident, by Maj Olver, the Inspecting Officer, responsibility for the accident was put on the yard staff and local management at Runcorn, and on the driver and guard of the tanker train. After all, they had made the mistakes or been negligent. Local management had failed to ensure that the yard staff at Runcorn knew what to do and then actually did it. The yard staff had made mistakes in not reducing the load or the speed of the train; the guard had not done his job properly, but he had only been a guard for a year and was inexperienced; and the driver had failed to brake soon enough for the signal at Weaver Junction. This was the measure of blame as apportioned by the Inspecting Officer who took the public inquiry. But was it fair? All the men concerned had transgressed in one way or another. But did management bear no responsibility for introducing complicated systems and for not ensuring that staff were properly trained? Or for not paying sufficiently high wages to enable good quality staff to be recruited and, just as important, retained? It seems a little unfair to have blamed local management and supervisors, because ever since the war they were the people who had borne most of the burden in keeping the railway running despite crippling staff shortages. They have rarely received the credit due to them. And does the government bear no responsibility? It is the government which has created the conditions in which railways have to operate, and which has then made it difficult for them to do so efficiently, by imposing crippling financial burdens and unfairly favouring the competition. And if the railway trade unions have been difficult at times, is it really any wonder?

Turning now to another hazardous commodity, the railways have been carrying petroleum products in tank wagons for many years, almost always in complete safety. Traditionally the vehicles used were tank wagons of 14-ton capacity, not fitted with the automatic power brake, and they were quite satisfactory when hauled by steam engines with their plentiful brake power, and at the low speeds which applied in those days. However, in the more competitive conditions after the 1953 Transport Act there was a general trend not only to improve payloads but also to enable tank wagons to run at higher speeds by equipping them with power brakes. The late 1950s saw the introduction of the 35-ton gross tank wagon, which was quickly developed to allow 40 tons to be carried by 1961, 45 tons by 1965 and finally 50 tons, which represents the absolute maximum that the track can bear on two axles. The next logical step was the bogie tank — the 90 tonner in 1965, then the now very familiar 100-ton tank wagon, which first appeared in 1967. One of BR's successes of the period was the signing of long-term contracts with the oil companies for the carriage of their products by rail in 100-ton tank wagons, built privately and owned by the oil companies, or leased by them. The contracts were very keenly priced, but at least they gave BR a guaranteed traffic which has lasted to the present day, and should now be more profitable to BR with the trains being operated

Below:
A traditional oil train, headed by Class K1 2-6-0 No 62001, between Darlington and Aycliffe in August 1964. Note the two barrier wagons, intended to reduce the fire risk.
John E. Hoggarth

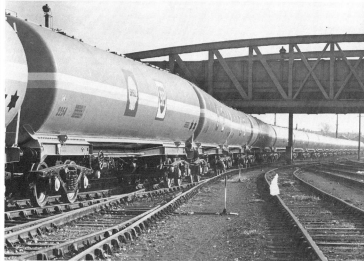

Stages in two-axle tank wagon design:

1. Shell-Mex Ltd 14-ton capacity, registered in 1929. Oil axleboxes, unbraked. *Ian Allan Library*

2. National Benzole Ltd 14-ton capacity, registered in 1954. Oil axleboxes, unbraked. One star (ie could be conveyed in partly-fitted trains). *Author*

3. Esso Petroleum Co Ltd 22-ton capacity, registered in 1957. Roller bearing axleboxes, vacuum-braked, screw couplings. Two stars (ie could be conveyed on express freight trains). *Charles Roberts & Co*

4. Esso Petroleum Co Ltd 45 tons gross laden weight, 1965. *Esso*

Below:
The final development — the 100-ton tanker, put into service in 1967. Many thousands are in use today. *Ian Allan Library*

wherever possible by just the driver — with no secondman and no guard.

BR has carried millions of tons of petroleum products under these contracts with a high degree of safety, and with only occasional accidents to mar the record. Derailments are not unknown, partly owing to the stresses which 25-ton axleloads impose on the track, but serious fires are uncommon. One of the early incidents of fire took place on New Year's Day 1969 at Crich Junction, near Ambergate, on the main line from St Pancras to Sheffield via Derby. The train concerned was No 4M66, the 01.17 Teesport Refinery to Washwood Heath, Birmingham, and consisted of 10 100-ton tank wagons owned by Shell Mex & BP Ltd, and hauled by a Type 4 diesel-electric locomotive. As the train came out of Wingfield Tunnel on the approach to Crich Junction at about 08.15 the driver noticed a glow in the cutting and, looking back, he saw that the train was on fire. Considerably alarmed, and knowing the volatile nature of the contents of the tanks (Light Distillate Feedstock, a highly inflammable light oil used at the time by gas boards for gas production), he immediately made an emergency stop. Driver and guard both descended on to the track and the guard called to a man in a factory alongside to telephone for the fire brigade. The man lost no time in doing so, and the fire services responded promptly, the first appliances arriving at 08.30. Spilt oil was burning on and around the seventh and ninth tanks, on both of which the forward loading hatches were open. Flames were shooting from these hatches to a height of 10ft.

The traincrew, reacting with the bravery which is customary in such circumstances, divided the train behind the sixth tank and drew the front portion clear. Meanwhile the firemen were directing jets of water on to the blazing tanks to keep them cool, and managed to extinguish the flames which were shooting from the loading hatches, by smothering them with foam. Whilst the burning tanks may have looked as though they might blow up at any moment, there is much less risk of that happening when a tank is full than when it is nearly empty, with space for an explosive mixture of air and oil vapour to form, but the traincrew did not know that at the time, and it is possible that the firemen did not know it either. In the event, the fires were extinguished without too much delay.

The cause of the fire was quite straightforward. The loading hatches on the seventh and ninth tanks had not been secured at Teesport after loading had been completed. Then, as the train was braking heavily from almost full speed for a signal stop at Crich Junction, because the line ahead was not clear, oil surged forward in the tanks and some escaped through the unsecured hatches, to become

Below:
The scene at Blyton, Lincolnshire, on the line between Gainsborough and Northorpe, after the 11.05 from Preston to Lindsey Oil Refinery became derailed on 18 September 1981. These two-axle tank wagons are prone to derailment when running empty at maximum permitted speed on track with minor imperfections. *John M. Capes*

ignited by sparks from the brake blocks. Subsequently, modifications were made to the hatches, and a certificate was introduced to be handed over to BR at the starting point, confirming that all hatches were closed and secured.

A rather more serious accident occurred three years later on 8 May 1972 at Chester General station, just before 21.00. There were, luckily, very few people about on that part of the station, and the refreshment room on Platforms 10/13, which was badly damaged in the crash, was empty apart from the staff. The train concerned was No 8D66, the 19.31 Ellesmere Port to Mold Junction (between Chester and Rhyl) and was marshalled as follows:

Class 24 diesel-electric locomotive No 5028
Brakevan, piped only
Esso 35-ton tank wagon, vacuum-braked, containing kerosene
Esso 45-ton tank wagon, vacuum-braked, containing petrol
Three Esso 35-ton tank wagons, vacuum-braked, containing gas oil.
31 other wagons and brakevan.

The total weight of the train and locomotive was 981 tons.

Approaching Chester station from the Warrington direction there is a steep falling gradient of 1 in 100 for just over a mile. When train 8D66 approached the top of this gradient, prior to descending to Chester, it was only travelling at about 15mph, then the driver closed the power controller and applied the locomotive's air brake to gather together the loose-coupled train (ie to let all the wagons buffer up to each other to avoid shocks and snatches during braking). As he approached the station he could see that the Outer Home signal for Chester No 1 signalbox was at Danger, and he made a full brake application. To his consternation it had no effect. The train ran on out of control, with the driver sounding a series of blasts on the locomotive's horn; past the Inner Home signal, then past No 1 signalbox and No 2 signalbox. The driver could see that the points were set for No 11 bay platform and as there was nothing else he could do he jumped out on to the platform with the train still travelling at 20mph. There was a diesel multiple-unit standing at the buffer stops. The locomotive hit it head on and completely demolished the first coach. The second coach was hurled on to the platform against the refreshment room wall. Luckily, both coaches were empty. As the DMU had taken the brunt of the impact, most of the force of the collision was spent and only the first three tanks were derailed. However, fire — fed from the ruptured fuel tanks of the DMU and the locomotive — broke out at once and threatened to engulf the tank wagons.

The alarm was raised immediately by the station staff, and three fire appliances arrived at the station within 2min. They concentrated at first on trying to keep cool the three tank wagons by spraying jets of water on them, the remainder of the train having been uncoupled and drawn away; but the fire grew in intensity. Foam was applied to subdue the ground fires but by this time petrol and kerosene were leaking out of the tank wagons, adding to the fierceness of the fire which had by now engulfed some DMUs standing in adjacent platforms. The dangerous stage of the fire was now being reached. Could the firemen damp down the flames before the tank wagon bodies split at the seams, leading to a serious explosion with blazing petrol being hurled in all directions? Railway officers and fire chiefs were both aware that such a thing had already happened in Canada and the USA and were apprehensive that it was about to happen here. The petrol in the second tank wagon was already boiling and was being forced out of the pressure relief valve, where it ignited like a flamethrower. With great courage the firemen pressed on with their task, and to everyone's intense relief were finally successful in overcoming the fire.

The cause of the accident was exasperatingly simple. The five tank wagons next to the locomotive were all equipped with the power brake and the brake pipes should have been coupled up by the guard so that the driver could safely control his train on the falling gradient into Chester. The guard overlooked the need to do so. He was relatively inexperienced, having been a guard for less than a year, but no such excuse can be offered for the driver, who had been in the grade for 12 years. He failed to ensure that the brakes were tested before the journey started, an oversight that is all the more astonishing when one realises how vulnerable a driver is in his driving cab in the event of a head-on collision of the sort that one might expect on a runaway train. Were the complexities of the relatively new freight train loads and brake power calculation system a factor in the reckoning, which might have been put right by more thorough training, or was it just carelessness, which no amount of training could have overcome? It was probably both. The Inspecting Officer, Maj Olver, who held a Public Inquiry into the accident, records in his report that he had been assured that checks had been carried out throughout BR to ensure that all drivers had received adequate training in the freight train loading scheme, and that where necessary additional training had been given. He was misled on both counts. Drivers did not receive adequate training in the scheme either before the Chester accident or after it. Some were not greatly interested — they had always relied upon the guard to form his train correctly, and they continued to do so. Very few drivers actually checked the details of load and brake power that the guard gave them, to see that it was within the limits for the route they were to work over. Old habits die hard, and nowhere more so than on railways.

The Warrington area is one that is no stranger to railway accidents, and we have already met one at Weaver Junction. Indeed, Chester is less than 20 miles away. During the early 1980s there were no fewer than 22 accidents in the Warrington area, eight of which involved the carriage of dangerous goods. One of the worst occurred at 07.10 on 3 March 1983. The train concerned was No 6Z97, a special from the Shell Oil Refinery at Stanlow, near Ellesmere Port, to Bishopbriggs, Glasgow. It consisted of 14 45-ton and 100-ton tank wagons loaded with gas oil, and an empty van which was marshalled immediately behind the locomotive (a Class 47 diesel-electric) to act as a 'reach' wagon so that the tankers could be shunted into the Bishopbriggs Oil Terminal without the locomotive itself having to enter the siding (a fire precaution). The train was air-braked throughout, and had a maximum permitted speed of 60mph.

The train approached Acton Grange Junction on the approach to Warrington from the Helsby line, running at about 40mph, and was signalled across the junction on to the Down West Coast main line. Just as the train approached the signal the driver felt a snatch, and he looked back down the train to see if anything was amiss. It certainly was. His train was derailed and on fire. When the wagons came to rest a major fire broke out engulfing all the wagons in the middle of the train. Burning oil ran down the Up side embankment and one of the 100-ton tankers rolled to the foot of the embankment.

The guard was riding in the front cab with the driver, as often used to happen. It was against the Rules but the Authorities largely turned a blind eye to the practice. It was against the Rules because, when the use of brakevans on fully-braked trains was dispensed with in the 1960s, it was thought that if the guard were in the rear cab he could keep

Above left and left:
Chester General station, after a freight train ran away approaching Chester and was diverted into bay platform No 11. The tank wagons caught fire, to add to the devastation. *Author's Collection*

Above:
The same location some years later, with a DMU waiting in bay platform No 11 on the left. The fire-damaged part of the station roof was removed. This photograph was taken on 1 September 1978. *Geoff Pinder*

an eye on his train just as well as he could from a brakevan, and raise the alarm if he saw anything wrong, for example a hot axlebox or a derailed wagon. The guard reported the derailment and fire to the signalman at Warrington power signalbox from a nearby railway telephone and the area supervisor telephoned the fire brigade. However, the fire service had already received a '999' call from a local resident and had already despatched four pumping appliances, a foam tender, an emergency tender and a Land Rover. Six more appliances were called, and later a further five. Clouds of dense black smoke blanketed the area. At first the firemen attacked the fire from the rear of the train to prevent those wagons not on fire from being engulfed, but they were driven back by a serious explosion, which they originally thought to have been a BLEVE, a Boiling Liquid Expanding Vapour Explosion, such as had been experienced in North America. It was later thought to have been due to the sudden release of inflammable vapour from a pressure relief valve, resulting in a fireball.

The fire was finally under control at 09.42. The fire service had responded very promptly to the '999' call and within 8min the initial fleet of appliances was already on site.

Reading through the reports of the fires mentioned in this chapter one cannot fail to be impressed by the speed of the fire service's response; by its courage in tackling dangerous fires and by its skill in dealing with them. The speed of response is undoubtedly helped by its foreknowledge of the contents of the tanks. All hazardous substances have a United Nations Substance Identification number of four digits — for example anhydrous ammonia is 1005. These numbers are shown on special labels on the tanks, but under the BR TOPS system of traffic reporting and control the description of all dangerous goods on a train is entered into a computer before the train starts its journey, and details can readily be ascertained by a simple computer enquiry process, available both in local area offices and also at the Regional Control Office. Details are also shown on the Train List carried by the traincrew. Fire services know whom they should approach on BR for such information, and this is far more satisfactory than having individual firemen asking questions of BR employees on site, who may not know the correct answer and may unwittingly give misleading information.

The TOPS computerised system contains all the requirements for the correct marshalling and conveyance of dangerous goods. For example, it will only allow different types of dangerous goods to be conveyed on the same train if this is specifically provided for in the Regulations, and it will check that the marshalling of such traffic in the train is correct, and that any necessary barrier wagons have been provided. The instructions to the staff are contained in a publication known to railwaymen as the 'Pink Pages', because they are printed on pink paper in the Working Manual.

According to Lt-Col Townsend-Rose, who held a Public Inquiry, the cause of the Warrington derailment was the

poor condition of the track. It had recently been relaid on a bed of new deep ballast, but some of the rail joints had become badly dipped, causing the empty van between the locomotive and the tanks to become derailed. It then ran on in derailed condition for several hundred yards before striking the points and crossings at Acton Grange Junction, whereupon it led almost the whole train into derailment. If the guard had been riding in the rear cab of the locomotive as he was supposed to, he could hardly have failed to see the van become derailed. He would then have had time to take action himself to have the train stopped. He could have done one of three things:

1. Apply the emergency brake in the rear cab (against the Rules but probably very sensible in the circumstances). The guard need not have made a full brake application himself but just enough to have drawn the driver's attention to the emergency, so that the driver could use his braking skills to bring the train safely to a stand without causing the remainder of the train to pile up into a general derailment.

2. He could have gone through the engine compartment

of the locomotive to the front cab, and warned the driver.

3. He could have given an unofficial code-ring on the firebell test button, which is one of those irregular but sensible practices used by traincrews to solve a problem in circumstances where railway management has failed to provide a solution. BR could quite easily have provided a buzzer connecting the two cabs, to be used in case of emergency, but chose not to do so.

However, the question of which locomotive cab a guard should ride in is now largely historical. Today most freight trains are worked without guards, and in any case the grade of guard has undergone a change. Where there is still a guard on a freight train he is likely to be called a trainman and can elect to enter the line of promotion to driver. His place now is in the front cab.

This accident is one of the first which we have discussed where the poor condition of the track was the primary cause. In the next chapter we will examine this question in more detail.

Above left:
Class 47 diesel-electric No 47163 leaving Redhill, Southern Region, with a train of Mobil two-axle tank wagons on 17 May 1980. *Les Bertram*

Below left:
On 8 April 1981, whilst negotiating a facing crossover at Hadfield on the former LNER electrified line from Manchester to Sheffield, five bogie tank wagons loaded with anhydrous ammonia became derailed, and one turned over on to its side. Because of the nature of the load a full alert, involving the emergency services, was called, but fortunately there was no escape of any of the liquefied gas. *David Maxey*

Above and Centre right:
Information panels on tank wagons:
Left-hand. TEA = Tank Type E, air-braked.
      72t = carrying capacity
      28t = tare weight
      PP 85209 = fleet number
Right-hand — Hazard identification panel.
  3YE is the Hazchem code for the information of the emergency services. 3 = foam fire-fighting equipment, Y = danger of violent reaction or explosion; use breathing apparatus for fire only. E = evacuation of people from the neighbourhood should be considered.
  1223 is the UN No for kerosene; 1270 is the UN No for petroleum fuel.
  Specialist advice can be obtained from the address given. *Author*

Right:
Dorman Traffic Products Ltd red flashing tail lamp, suitable for use on any type of wagon. The battery needs changing only once a year, and the light source is a light-emitting diode. *Dorman Traffic Products*

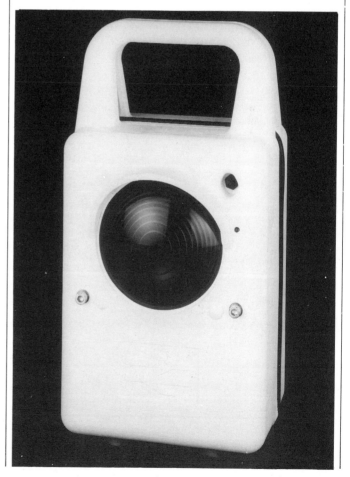

4
Buckled Track Derailments

When schoolteachers were introducing a new class to the subject of physics, one of the early lessons was sure to be devoted to the expansion of metals, and it became imprinted upon every student's mind that the purpose of the small gap at the end of each piece of rail was to allow for the expansion of the rail in hot weather. If the gap was not there, it was explained, the forces of expansion in the rail were so great that they would cause the track to distort — this distortion being known as a buckle (one wonders how today's schoolteachers explain away continuous-welded track, but that will be dealt with later in this chapter).

It is not uncommon to have fine hot days in the spring, and 18 May 1948 was just such a day. Indeed, in the afternoon the temperature reached 75°F. The 11.45am express from London St Pancras to Bradford Forster Square was loaded up to 12 coaches that day, being Whit Tuesday, and was therefore double-headed with two '5XP' 'Jubilee' class 4-6-0s, Nos 5605 *Cyprus* and 5609 *Gilbert and Ellice Islands*. As there was also a relief train running, the parent train was not heavily loaded with passengers, and when it left Sheffield on its journey north there were fewer than 200 of them. Perhaps if they had known what was in store, some of them would have elected to travel in the relief train. Such trains, however, were never as popular as the parent trains — mainly because they usually had no restaurant car and were formed of older coaches.

The line between Sheffield and Leeds by the former Midland route via Cudworth would never have won any prizes in a competition for Britain's most scenic railway, but it would certainly have been among the contenders in a 'Most collieries per mile' contest. As a result the route suffered severely from colliery subsidence, although the Civil Engineer had managed to maintain the overall line speed at 75mph, which was very creditable in the circumstances. However, the maintenance of the track was a great problem, not helped by frequent changes of staff. Platelayers' wages were very low, and although there was plenty of Sunday work, not many people were prepared to work at weekends if they could earn as much by working a five-day week in industry. This problem of staff shortage, and frequent changes resulting in an inexperienced workforce, placed a great strain and responsibility on supervisors and junior managers alike.

Near Wath Road Junction, about five miles north of Rotherham, the problem of subsidence was dealt with by the use of large quantities of ash to maintain the line as level as possible, but the permanent way was not up to the standards demanded by a high speed main line. Furthermore, insufficient attention had been paid to the oiling of the fishplates, which joined the rails together at their ends. If the bolts which held the fishplates to the rails were too tight, and if there were no oil between the fishplates and the rail, a certain amount of resistance to the forces of expansion would be created. If the rail could not expand lengthways it would eventually do so sideways in the form of a buckle, especially if there was little resistance from the ballast. Dry ashes gave very little resistance.

1

2

The 'Jubilees' involved in the Wath Road Junction derailment on 18 May 1948, seen in happier times:

1. No 45605 *Cyprus* (the pilot engine on 18 May 1948), shedded at Leeds Holbeck, heads north from Leeds City with the 4.55pm to Morecambe Promenade, the 'Residential Express'. The girder bridge in the background carried the lines to Leeds Central station.
   Eric Treacy/ Millbrook House Collection

2. No 45609 *Gilbert and Ellice Islands* in repose at its home shed, Sheffield Millhouses, on 11 April 1955. *D. Marriott*

3. No 5609 is seen in its earlier form in LMS days, with domeless boiler and straight-sided tender.
   L&GRP, courtesy David & Charles (814)

3

Right:

'Royal Scot' Class 4-6-0 No 46133 *The Green Howards* passes Wath on Dearne signalbox and Wath Main Colliery on 20 June 1959 with the 10.30am Bradford Forster Square to St Pancras, and approaches the site of the derailment at Wath Road Junction on 18 May 1948. *D. Hellewell*

Below right:

Not a picture for steam buffs, but enough to make present-day civil engineers green with envy, not to mention drivers. Such neat and tidy permanent way has not been seen for many years. There is not a particle of ballast visible on any of the sleepers, and the neatness of the cess in the 10ft way is astonishing, even if it were specially done for the photograph, which was taken on 15 June 1949 to show the first standard 109lb flat-bottom rail in the North Eastern Region at Alne, on the East Coast main line 10 miles north of York. Note also the two-hole fishplates on the far lines. *BR*

At 3.29pm the St Pancras to Bradford express left Sheffield on time for its nonstop run to Leeds City. After passing through Rotherham Masborough speed built up to 60/65mph then, near Wath Road Junction, the driver on No 5605, the pilot engine, was horrified to see a pronounced kink to the left on the track ahead of him. There was no time for him to do anything about it, other than shout a hurried warning to his fireman, and both men hung on to their engine for dear life. They had no idea what would happen when the engine hit that awful kink but they were running on a 30ft high embankment and they feared for their lives. The engine gave a tremendous lurch, there was the squeal of steel tyres on the rails, and the footplatemen felt their engine drop on to the sleepers. However, they were lucky. The engine ran forward as they hung on grimly, and eventually came to a stand, still upright. In the train behind them everything was suddenly chaotic. One moment complete normality — the next moment the train engine No 5609 hit the kink and turned over on to its side. The first five coaches all turned sideways across the track, almost side by side with each other, but by absorbing the train's momentum in this way they did not telescope into one another. Nonetheless, seven passengers and the driver of the train engine lost their lives, whilst 33 passengers and a dining car attendant were detained in hospital. It was remarkable that the death toll was not much higher. When looking at the pile of wreckage, one wonders how anyone could have survived. The first and second coaches were on their sides and the body of the fourth coach had been torn from its underframe.

The relief express had passed over the same spot only 8min beforehand. Its driver saw nothing, but the guard, who was riding in the last coach, felt a lurch. He later described it as severe but it did not alarm him enough to cause him to stop the train with his emergency brake and raise the alarm. The line would then have been examined before any more trains were allowed to pass over it at speed. Lurches on the track are part and parcel of every railway journey. Some are more severe than others but it is not an easy matter for a guard to decide at what point a lurch becomes so bad that the train should be stopped and the alarm raised. It is a matter of individual judgement and experience, and some guards may fear that they will be reprimanded for stopping their trains unnecessarily if no cause for the lurch can be found. Guards, and drivers too, are reluctant to stop their trains from full speed unless the lurch is so severe, or is so far out of the ordinary, as to cause real alarm. It is clear, however, that the guard's

failure to report the lurch preyed on his mind. On 30 July he committed suicide by coal gas poisoning, the verdict at the inquest being that 'the balance of his mind was disturbed'. Drivers and guards carry heavy responsibilities for other people's lives, which are not always recognised, and certainly not in the rates of pay of the time. These tended to reflect the security of tenure which a job on the railway afforded, an important factor in prewar days, but largely irrelevant in the booming postwar labour market.

By 1948 British Railways was beginning to change over from bullhead rail supported in chairs and held with wooden or spring-steel keys, to flatbottom rail standing on baseplates and secured directly to the sleepers by spring-steel spikes. Trials had begun as early as 1936, and by 1948, 260 miles had been laid by the former companies. The new Railway Executive, formed only at the beginning of 1948 following nationalisation, decided almost at once that flatbottom rail would be the future standard. The new rails, weighing 109lb/yd, were considered to be much stronger than the 95lb bullhead rails and more suitable for higher speeds and heavier axleloads. Thenceforth, flatbottom rail became increasingly common, but the mixture of the two was to cause problems.

On 8 August 1953 it was a particularly warm, sunny day in the Scottish lowlands. The Down 'Royal Scot' that day consisted of 13 coaches, hauled by Class 8P Pacific No 46231 *Duchess of Atholl*, and was coasting down easily

Left:
Class 8P Pacific No 46231 *Duchess of Atholl* pulls out of Carlisle with the Down 'Royal Scot'. This was the engine involved in the Abington derailment in 1953. *Ian Allan Library*

Below:
***Duchess of Atholl* in LMS days, in its original form without smoke deflectors.** *Wethersett Collection/ Ian Allan Library*

from Beattock when it became derailed near Abington. The engine and first six coaches passed safely, then a buckle developed underneath the train and the last seven coaches became derailed. The damage to the train was remarkably slight and there were no serious injuries. The train was formed throughout with the new BR standard Mk 1 coaches and it is probable that the buckeye couplings fitted to these coaches held them together and in line, whereas in the Wath Road Junction derailment the coaches had all been of the former LMS pattern with screw couplings.

The initial derailment at Abington occurred on bullhead track, but only 32yd beyond the end of a section of 113lb flatbottom rail. Owing to a lack of appreciation of the situation, action had not been taken to remedy the 'creep' of the heavier and stronger flatbottom rails against the lighter and weaker bullhead section, and this, coupled with the strong expansive forces developing during the hot afternoon, caused undue stresses to be set up, which became released in the form of a buckle as the express passed. There had already been a number of incidents of this nature, and indeed they continue to occur even now where different types of track join each other.

Rail creep, which has been mentioned, is a phenomenon which occurs when trains pass over a length of track and cause it to move fractionally lengthways. From time to time, therefore, the rails have to be pulled back to avoid undue stresses developing. In the worst places special anti-creep fittings, known as rail anchors, are attached to the rails next to a chair or baseplate to try to minimise the problem but they are only partially successful.

By the late 1960s the use of flatbottom rail on main lines had become commonplace, and the practice had developed of welding the ends together to form one continuous rail. The advantages of doing this are many:

1. It eliminates joints in the rails, which have always proved troublesome. Rail-ends are a source of weakness and prone to cracks radiating from the bolt holes. If not detected, breakage of the rail may ensue. Many derailments have resulted from this cause, as we shall see in the next chapter.

2. The track is less firm vertically at a joint, and this gives rise to pressures on the track formation and bed whenever a train passes over. In wet conditions it may even give rise to clay slurry being pumped to the surface by the frequent downwards pressure and subsequent release as the wheels of a train pass over. Such places are known as 'wet spots', and if not treated can lead to an empty space or void beneath the sleeper, leading to considerable stresses in the rail ends and possible breakage. The dip in the rail level at a bad joint as a train passes over it can lead to derailment.

3. Less maintenance is needed when there are no joints, for example there is no need to pull rails back to equalise expansion gaps, no oiling of fishplates, no checking the tightness of fishplate bolts. Apart from the obvious economy in manpower it helps to overcome the problem of recruitment and staff shortage.

4. Continuously welded rail (CWR) is stronger than jointed track, more suitable for high speeds and heavy axleloads.

5. Continuously welded rail gives a smoother, quieter ride.

However, it must not be thought that all these advantages are achieved without other problems arising. We are now back to our schoolteacher and the physics class. If there has to be a gap every 60ft to allow for expansion, how big does the gap have to be at the end of a piece of CWR half a mile long? Schoolboys might attempt to answer that, by working out how many 60ft rails there are in half a mile, then multiplying the result by a quarter of an inch. The end product would be a gap of nearly a foot, which no train could leap safely even at 125mph. The fact is that all the expansive forces are contained in the rail itself, except for short portions at the ends, which have special joints. To achieve this it is necessary for the stresses to be contained in the track, and this requires:

1. A greater depth of ballast under the sleepers.
2. A full ballast section up to the tops of the sleepers and extending sideways well beyond the sleeper ends.
3. Extra ballast being placed beyond the sleeper ends, creating a ballast 'shoulder'.
4. The use of tight-gripping rail fastenings.
5. Ensuring that the rails will be free from stress in the mid-temperature range.

Stressing is a technique which is applied to track when it is laid, and is intended to produce an absence of stress at a rail temperature of 27°C/81°F. When track is laid at a rail temperature below 27°C it will have shortened in length through natural contraction, and must be stretched to the length it would have been at 27°C. This stretching is done by hydraulic rams, and when the rail has been stretched to the required length it is welded to the adjacent rail. It is now under tension in a stressed condition and can safely contain the compressive forces of expansion up to a rail temperature of 27°C, at which temperature it will be stress-free. It should be noted that rail temperatures can be considerably higher than air temperatures — car drivers will know how hot the roof of a standing car can become when a bright sun is beating down on it.

By 1968, there were 4,000 miles of CWR and considerable experience had been gained of handling the problems involved, but two accidents that year showed that things could still go wrong. On 12 June, a fine, dry day, train No 3E46 the 12.40 Freightliner from Ardwick, Manchester, to Harwich Parkeston Quay, consisting of 15 wagons, became derailed on buckled track when running on the Up fast line at speed just before reaching Berkhamsted station.

The area had been relaid the previous December but had not been stressed. The actual work to be carried out had consisted of removing a redundant crossover, replacing it with new plain track, and stressing it. The work was planned to commence at 04.00 on Sunday morning, the quietest time of the week for closing the line, and needed two special cranes to work under the overhead electric wires. The works train was several hours late in arriving on site (not an uncommon occurrence when guards failed to turn up for duty, for example, and the source of innumerable acrimonious disputes between the operating and engineering departments) and as a result the work could not be completed in time. The general manager of the day was fed up with delays to the busy Sunday evening expresses caused by engineering work overrunning, and had laid it down that such work must end on time, being cut short if necessary. The problems that this caused to engineers can be imagined, especially if the cause was not of their making, but suffice it to say that the stressing work on the day was postponed. It was programmed to be done the following May but was somehow overlooked. And so the track eventually buckled and a train was derailed, although fortunately not an express passenger train.

The other derailment took place at Auchencastle on the descent from Beattock Summit, two days later on 14 June 1968. It was another hot and sunny day and the train, another Freightliner, was running down the bank at the maximum allowed speed of 75mph when the rear portion became derailed as the track buckled beneath it. The track had been relaid in 1965 and had been realigned and stressed in June 1967. Significantly, in the weeks preceding the derailment 170 sleepers had been changed, then on Sunday 9 June the section of line had been mechanically tamped by a new Plasser Duomatic lining and tamping machine (tamping is a process in which ballast is repacked under the sleepers to provide a firm trackbed). This derailment illustrated the dangers of disturbing a stressed section of line, especially when temperatures are higher than normal, because there is a possibility of inducing incorrect stresses. The whole question of stress is a complex one, and accidents were almost inevitable during the learning process.

If 1968 had not been a good year for the reputation of CWR, 1969 was to prove much worse and to demonstrate that the subject of track maintenance had progressed far beyond the school syllabus. It was now more appropriate to postgraduate research. On 13 June an express passenger train from Paignton to Paddington was derailed at nearly 80mph on CWR between Somerton and Castle Cary (Somerset), then 10 days later the 'Tees-Tyne Pullman'

Left:
Brush Type 4 No D1536 passing Marshmoor signalbox, near Hatfield with an Up East Coast Pullman express in March 1965.
P. Hocquard

185

express from King's Cross to Newcastle was derailed at over 90mph on CWR near Sandy. In each case the buckle in the track was seen by the driver as he approached. Although casualties were light in both cases a great deal of disquiet was aroused in the public mind, reinforced by two other CWR derailments — a train of empty carflats at Lichfield on 10 June and a Freightliner at Lamington, between Beattock and Motherwell.

Immediately a searching analysis of the forces set up in CWR was initiated. The Chief Civil Engineer quickly established an emergency programme to add extra ballast along the shoulders of the track. This was a very large-scale operation but it was given a high priority by both engineers and operators, so that by the onset of warm weather in 1970 virtually all the CWR lines had been strengthened, and there is no doubt that this relatively simple and unsophisticated measure played a major role in restricting the number of buckles the following year.

Simultaneously with the shoulder ballast programme a special exercise was launched in July 1969 to stress all lengths of CWR in which conditions were at all suspect. This was also a large-scale programme and the work continued until the summer of the following year. The Chief Civil Engineer incorporated all the lessons that had been learned, in a new Code of Practice issued in March 1970. This laid down strict conditions for the maintenance of CWR during hot weather. Arrangements were made with the Meteorological Office for weather forecasts to be supplied to local engineers during the hot weather months May to September. This enabled additional patrolling to be organised so that a special watch could be kept on rail temperatures during hot afternoons (especially when there had been a large temperature rise during the day). If there was any doubt about the safety of the track, speed reductions were imposed over the section of line concerned.

These measures in combination were highly successful. The number of track buckles on CWR (only a few of which resulted in derailment) went down from 48 in 1969 to nine in 1970. By comparison the number of buckles on ordinary jointed track was 55 in 1969 and 34 in 1970, for four times the mileage of track. It was found that almost half of the CWR buckles occurred on track less than a year old, and that almost half of all CWR buckles were caused by unsatisfactory ballast conditions.

By 1975 the mileage of CWR had doubled from 4,000 to 8,000, and the 'state of the art' regarding the maintenance of CWR had become very refined. However, on 28 July that year, another hot and sunny day, there was another derailment which re-emphasised the lessons previously learned, and the need to follow to the letter the instructions issued by the Chief Civil Engineer. The 08.20 Paddington to Fishguard express that day consisted of 12 coaches, hauled by a Class 47 diesel-electric locomotive No 47095. It had left Carmarthen and was on the last leg of its journey. Speed had risen to over 70mph by the time the train passed through Sarnau station, when the driver suddenly saw a bad buckle in the shape of an 'S' in the line ahead. He immediately threw on his brakes but there was insufficient

Above:
Sandy, on the East Coast main line, 23 July 1969. The last vehicle, a bogie van, of the Down Tees-Tyne Pullman has come to rest almost on its side after the train was derailed on buckled CWR whilst travelling at over 90mph. *P. R. Foster*

Centre right:
Yet another buckled-rail derailment in the Beattock-Carstairs area occurred at Lamington in 1969. English-Electric Type 4 No D301 is seen passing through Lamington station with the Up 'Royal Scot' on 8 April 1961, with a light load of eight coaches. *Derek Cross*

Below right:
Long-welded rail on concrete sleepers, secured by Mills clips. Photographed near Attleborough, Eastern Region, on 22 September 1960. *BR*

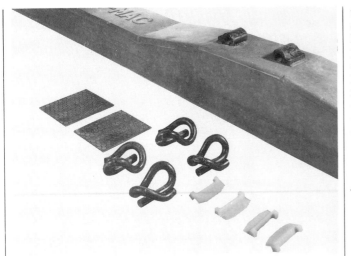

Above:
BR standard track components, showing Dow-Mac concrete sleeper and Pandrol clips. *Leslie Shipsides Ltd*

Below:
'Hall' Class 4-6-0 No 4962 *Ragley Hall* pauses at Clarbeston Road on 28 June 1962 with a train from Fishguard. *Rev T. R. Hughes*

time to prevent the whole of the train from passing over the distortion, resulting in the 8th, 10th, and 12th coaches being derailed. Casualties again were light, and only eight passengers were taken to Carmarthen hospital. They were all discharged the same day and continued their journey. Maj King, who held the Public Inquiry into the accident, found that there was no clear cause of the derailment, but only a number of minor discrepancies, the most significant of which were that the line had been tamped five weeks earlier and that ballast had not been heaped on the shoulders.

Since 1975 the mileage of CWR has continued to rise and is now over 12,000. By contrast the mileage of ordinary jointed track in 60ft lengths has gone down to 7,000. Whilst all attention was being focused on CWR problems in the early 1970s, there was a serious accident on jointed track as a reminder that CWR was potentially much safer. Smethwick is not one of the more favoured areas of the West Midlands, and certainly not as wealthy as Sutton Coldfield or Solihull. A special train had been organised to take parties of schoolchildren from the area to the seaside at Rhyl for a day's outing, and it pulled out of Smethwick Rolfe Street station early on the morning of Friday 2 July 1971 with 10 coaches, filled with 32 adults and 380 children. As the mothers stood on the platform and waved the train away, with just the odd tear, they said to themselves 'Aren't the children lucky to have such a lovely

sunny day'. They were indeed lucky. It turned out to be the hottest day of the year so far.

The children enjoyed themselves enormously in the sunshine, then, in the late afternoon, they all trooped back to the station, tired and sunburnt. The sun had shone all day, to the great delight of holidaymakers, and it bestowed its gifts far and wide, on railway lines as well. Engineers anxiously watched over their CWR, little thinking that danger may also be lurking elsewhere.

The train set off on its homeward journey at 17.25. It was still very hot, 75°F, and everyone settled down eventually for the journey home. The train passed through the busy junctions at Chester and headed for Crewe. In Tattenhall Junction signalbox the signalman received the 'Is Line Clear for an Express Passenger Train?' bell signal of four beats. So far as he was aware the line was clear, therefore when he had received permission from the next signalbox down the line for the train to proceed he cleared all his signals for it and waited for it to appear. Although the signalbox still bore the name Tattenhall Junction, there was no longer a junction there, the cross-country line to Whitchurch having closed in 1964.

The patrolman whose job it was to examine the stretch of line at Tattenhall Junction regularly had become concerned about an area of rail creep some months earlier. Rail creep has been mentioned before — it gradually closes up the gaps which are provided at the ends of the rails to allow for expansion in hot weather. By the beginning of July the gaps were becoming smaller and smaller and the weather was becoming hot. The patrolman was uneasy. If the gaps could not take all the expansion there was only one way it could go — sideways. The patrolman had already reported the matter to his superiors but it seemed to have got lost in the bureaucracy. About an hour before the schools special left Rhyl on its homeward journey, the patrolman was examining his length of track. Near a bridge, No 50, about ¼ mile on the Chester side of Tattenhall Junction signalbox, he noticed that the rail joints were completely closed up, but otherwise the track appeared to be in good order. However, any compression stresses that might have been in the process of being set up in the track were invisible to the naked eye. It was a very warm afternoon.

It was now 18.00 but the temperature was still in the mid-70s. In Smethwick housewives were washing up after the evening meal and thinking to themselves that they would soon have to be making their way to the station at Rolfe Street to collect their children. What a lovely day they must have had at the seaside.

Below:
Class 40 diesel-electric No 40028 pulls out of Chester past No 2 signalbox on 18 June 1983. *J. Checkley*

At 18.03 the signalman at Tattenhall Junction received the 'Train entering section' bell signal from Chester No 1 signalbox for the schools special. On the Class 47 locomotive the driver started to accelerate, after threading his way carefully through the maze of points, crossings and signals at Chester; and approaching Tattenhall Junction he had almost reached 70mph. The Distant signal had been pulled off for him and he was looking ahead through Bridge 50 to get his first view of the Home signal and signalbox when he suddenly saw the signalman standing on the little platform at the top of the signalbox steps, holding his arms above his head as a warning of danger. He immediately sounded his whistle in acknowledgement and threw on all his brakes. 'What on earth is wrong?' he thought to himself. What had the signalman seen?

In the signalbox the signalman had been watching for the train. He saw it approaching at normal speed then, when it had nearly cleared Bridge 50 he noticed dust and rubble being thrown into the air near the back of the train, and one of the rear coaches veering out of line. He realised that it was derailed.

In the train the guard was riding in the brake compartment of the last coach. The journey had been perfectly normal, then suddenly the coach seemed to jump in the air and sway violently. He caught hold of the handbrake wheel to steady himself as the coach struck Bridge 50 and turned over on its side. He managed to climb out and made his way to the nearby signalbox where the signalman assured him that the lines had been protected in both directions.

There was no doubt about the cause of the derailment. The track had buckled under the middle of the train when the forces of expansion could no longer be contained. The 8th, 9th and 10th coaches were flung sideways, crashing into the brickwork of Bridge 50, but the first seven coaches were undamaged and the passengers in them had no idea at first that death and disaster had struck the rear of the train.

The accident happened at 18.08 and the emergency services were called out at once. The police arrived at 18.21, ambulances at 18.24 and fire engines at 18.35. Eight adults and five children were taken to Chester Royal Infirmary, and one adult and 12 children were taken to Wrexham War Memorial Hospital. They had had an awful demonstration of the elementary laws of physics which they would never forget. There was no lack of helpers on site — the WRVS, the Salvation Army, Girl Guides, local shopowners, taxi and coach firms and teachers from other schools gave whatever assistance they could.

At Smethwick word quickly got around that disaster had struck the schools special. Anxious parents rushed to the station for news, and waited for the names of those who

Below:
Class 47 diesel-electric No 47541 hauls the 09.30 from Crewe to Holyhead on 24 April 1982. Half a mile away, in the distance, is the bridge at Tattenhall Junction where the derailment occurred in 1971. *Paul A. Biggs*

Top:
A view of the buckled track at Tattenhall Junction after the derailment on 2 July 1971. *Author's Collection*

Above:
Electric locomotive No 87002, which hauled the 07.10 express from Glasgow to Euston on 2 July 1977, and whose driver stopped specially to report a track defect near Bletchley which eventually derailed a later train. *B. J. Nicolle*

had suffered in the crash, or who had been spared. The anguish of the long wait can hardly be imagined. A special train was arranged to take relatives to Chester and Wrexham hospitals, whilst the uninjured adults and children went forward in the first seven, undamaged, coaches of the schools special. When it finally arrived at Smethwick the scene of joyful, tearful reunion would have melted the hardest heart. Two children, a little boy of 11 and a little girl of 10, never returned home. They paid the

price of a bureaucratic bungle, according to Maj Rose, who held a Public Inquiry into the accident. Repairs which ought to have been carried out to the track, were not. Local staff knew that the repairs were needed but somehow the urgency of the message was diluted as it passed up the organisational chain.

Six years exactly after the Tattenhall Junction derailment, Saturday 2 July 1977, was also a fine sunny day. By mid-afternoon the temperature was in the mid-70s, and it marked the start of a hot sunny spell.

The West Coast main line south of Rugby has always been very busy and its maintenance in tip-top condition has been a continuous preoccupation of the Civil Engineer, but the hammering it has received from a constant procession of trains passing at high speed and with heavy axleloads, to say nothing of the unsprung forces from the axle-hung electric motors on the Class 86 electric locomotives, has made it very difficult to achieve the desired standards; indeed, by 1977, 10 years into main line electrification, the quality of the ride was deteriorating and it was starting to become quite rough in places.

The 07.10 Glasgow to Euston express that day was hauled by a Class 87 electric locomotive, No 87002. About 11.40 the train passed through Wolverton and a couple of minutes later, when travelling at the maximum permitted speed of 100mph, the locomotive suddenly gave a severe jolt, bad enough almost to throw the secondman out of his seat. Drivers are accustomed to sudden lurches and know the bad places, but this was a jolt of unexpected severity and at a place where such jolts did not normally occur. Both driver and secondman looked back out of their cab windows to see if the train was safe, and were relieved to find that it was. However, the driver felt that the lurch was so severe that it could cause a train to be derailed, therefore he stopped his train and telephoned the signalman at Bletchley from an instrument at the foot of a signal post (all signals have a telephone in power signalbox areas). As far as he could remember he told the signalman that the bump had occurred at about 400yd on the approach side of signal No BY157.

The signalman at Bletchley immediately arranged to divert all Up trains from the fast line to the slow line, and sent for the local permanent way supervisor. However, he was on leave, so the signalman then called out the supervisor from the next section, who knew the area well. This supervisor immediately went to the site of the reported bump and found that there were dips in each rail of the CWR, voids under the sleepers, and signs of 'pumping', where wet clay slurry had been forced to the surface by the weight of passing trains. Satisfied in his own mind that these conditions were the cause of the reported bump, and that they were not sufficiently serious to cause any danger of derailment to trains passing over them, he asked the signalman to send one more train over the Up Fast line so that he could observe the behaviour of the track as the train passed over it. The next train happened to be an express from Llandudno to Euston. Its driver had not been warned and he came at full speed. His locomotive was No 85018, a rather rough-riding machine given to jerks and lurches, but about two miles south of Wolverton the driver felt a quite exceptional lurch. He was so alarmed by this that he made a full emergency brake application, and reported the facts to the signalman.

This information was relayed to the permanent way supervisor, who collected a gang of men to 'fettle up' the defective track. He asked the signalman to send one more train along the Up Fast line so that he could decide precisely what needed to be done. As it turned out, the next train was an express parcels train. South of Wolverton, travelling at 90mph, its driver was horrified to see a severe

191

Above:
A tamping and lining machine, seen at Midgham, near Newbury in 1980. *D. E. Canning*

distortion, like a snake, in the line ahead. He threw on his brakes, shut off power, and hung on as best he could. The lurch threw him first against the window, then right out of his seat on to the floor. The locomotive managed to cling to the rails but the entire train became derailed.

The permanent way supervisor had positioned himself to watch the train pass over the section of defective track which he had firmly fixed in his mind was the cause of the bumps that drivers had stopped to report. He saw the parcels train approaching in the distance, then it disappeared in a cloud of dust, and stopped. He was nonplussed. No wonder. He had been looking at the wrong track defect. There was a much worse section of defective track half a mile to the north. Had it been his regular section he would have known that men had been working on it there all week, dealing with a severe wet spot. They had left it with insufficient ballast, and the sun had done the rest. A serious distortion was just waiting to happen.
Maj Rose's Report, following his Public Inquiry, traced the derailment to a number of causes — bad management, poor supervision, wrong reporting of the location of the bump, people jumping to conclusions, and of course those two demons which are present at most accidents — coincidence and chance:

1. The signalman had not been told that the usual permanent way supervisor was on leave, and who his deputy was to be during that period.
2. The repair job carried out during the week had been left short of ballast.
3. The man in charge of the repair job was only a Leading Trackman. He had not been properly supervised.
4. Both drivers who stopped to report bumps had given wrong or vague locations.
5. The permanent way supervisor had been misled by the drivers' vague reports of location and he had found the wrong piece of bad track. He then jumped to the conclusion that that was the source of the trouble.
6. He should not have asked for a third train to pass over the bad piece of track. The fact that two drivers of express passenger trains had stopped specially to report a bump should have put him on his guard.

The signalman was in a difficult position. He was uneasy when the permanent way supervisor asked for a train to be sent over the suspect line at full speed. He was even more uneasy when he was asked to send another one, knowing that he had now had two reports from drivers of very bad bumps, and that drivers did not stop express passenger trains unless there was something really wrong. Yet what could he do? The technical expert on site had assessed it as being safe.

In a perfect world no work would have been done on CWR during hot weather, to avoid the dangers of setting up incorrect levels of stress in the rails. Yet, so far as the Civil Engineer was concerned he inhabited a very imperfect world. He was expected to maintain the track in fine condition suitable for 125mph speeds and 25-ton axle-loads, yet on the one hand the Operating Department would not give him enough opportunities to get to work on the track (known as 'possessions' or 'occupations'), and on the other hand mechanical engineers designed electric loco-motives that bashed his track to bits. Just to add to his troubles the General Manager told him to cut his staff numbers, so he took his cheque book to Plasser Theurer's and bought millions of poundsworth of shiny new track-maintenance machines only to find to his chagrin that they spent nine-tenths of their time standing idle because the Operating Department insisted on running trains instead of giving him possessions.

Was the operator, then, the stumbling block? Not at all. He had every sympathy with the Engineer. Nothing would have pleased him more than to have given the Engineer all the track possessions that he wanted. And why did he not do so? Because the railway would have lost half of its customers. If track maintenance work were to have been done during the daytime, the result would have been, on some lines at least, that streams of expresses would have had to be cancelled, or diverted with appalling delays. The train service would have deteriorated and the railway would have gained a reputation for unreliability — not a good selling point. The Passenger Manager would soon have been hammering on the operator's door to complain. Would it have been easier to have given possessions at night? Up to a point. But engineering gangs do not think it is much fun to work permanent nights. And some of the railway's freight and parcels customers would not have been very pleased if their trains had often been cancelled or delayed. The newspaper men valued punctuality and reliability very highly. So did the Post Office, which was often very critical of BR's unpunctuality, and threatened more than once to take its business elsewhere when it became weary of persistent train delays, often caused by possessions. Was weekend work the only answer? In many cases it was. The staff liked it, naturally, because of the extra pay, but even at weekends engineering work played havoc with the train service and BR was not really in the Sunday passenger market until after 4pm, thus denying themselves a wide range of business opportunities.

Was the situation of BR's own making? The answer has to be, partly, yes. Did the Civil Engineer make his needs sufficiently known? Did he emphasise the huge waste of money in having expensive machinery standing idle for much of the time? Did he protest loudly enough when alternative routes were closed, or additional running lines taken up, or sidings ripped out, making it more difficult for him to be given worthwhile possessions, or the facilities to make the most productive use of those possessions? Did he make his voice heard when remodelling and resignalling schemes were carried out, so that they incorporated the facilities that would allow the operators to give him more possessions, such as reversible working on both lines, or signalled high speed facing crossovers, or refuge sidings where he could temporarily shunt his machines clear of the main line?

Was the operator then to blame? Partly, yes. Certainly in the early days he did not appreciate the Engineer's needs,

Diverted West Coast main line expresses:

1. The Down 'Royal Scot' approaches Hellifield off the Blackburn line on 4 August 1968. *D. Cross*

2. English Electric Type 4 No D214 approaches Dent with the 11.30 from Glasgow Central to Manchester Victoria on 1 May 1966. *M. S. Welch*

and when he did start to appreciate them he found that the planners and accountants were very reluctant to allow him to provide them, because of the cost involved. Now that Sector Management has arrived things may improve, if it is not too late. At least we shall now have a corporate business approach, something which has been sadly lacking in the past.

The biggest mistake of all, so far as track maintenance is concerned, would have been the closure of the Settle to Carlisle line. How was the Engineer to maintain the line between Preston and Carlisle, 90 miles of heavily-used trunk route, nearly all double-track, without a reasonable diversionary route? And was it an indication of the diminishing degree of importance which BR seemed to attach to the West Coast main line north of Preston?

Sir Josiah Stamp, Sir William Wood, and Sir Ernest Lemon must be turning in their graves at the long, slow decline of the premier line that they bequeathed to British Railways on nationalisation in 1948. And to the decline of the former Midland route from St Pancras to Scotland via Leeds, Settle and Carlisle, which started with nationalisation when the route was split into no fewer than five sections under four different Regional managements, each already with its own favourite main line. How could any route prosper under such a cumbersome, negative organisation? Yet it could prosper under the new business organisation in BR, either as a Provincial route or an InterCity route. BR had already cut its marginal capacity so fine that it could hardly deal with any increase in traffic, and it was in danger of compounding the error with the proposal to close the Settle to Carlisle line. In 10 or 20 years' time BR may have regretted its actions, especially if the hoped-for increase in traffic resulting from the opening of the Channel Tunnel actually materialises.

And let not governments feel that they are free from criticism in this direction. During the whole lifetime of the railway they have interfered with its management. It is governments that have created the financial, legal, organisational and competitive conditions in which BR and its predecessors have had to operate.

The behaviour of CWR can still be unpredictable, even after all the studies that have been made, and all the experience that has been accumulated. The civil engineer is still often working at the boundary of his knowledge, as was demonstrated on Sunday 15 June 1986 when the 16.10 express from Glasgow to Euston became partly derailed as it was approaching Motherwell. The locomotive and first two coaches ran on and finally came to a halt half a mile beyond the station. The CWR had buckled as the train was passing over it. When the CWR had been laid, a section of points and crossings had been used as an 'anchor' when the CWR was stressed. During the winter some work had been carried out on those points and crossings and it is thought that incorrect stresses were then set up in the adjoining CWR, which finally buckled as the express was passing over. Fortunately there were no fatalities but it was an expensive lesson!

The Leeds-Settle-Carlisle line when it was still being properly used as a trunk route:

1. LMS Standard Compound No 41119 pilots a Stanier Class 5 4-6-0 into Skipton with the Down 'Waverley' on 10 September 1958. *R. H. Short*

2. 'Jubilee' No 45562 *Alberta* passes through Gargrave with the Up 'Waverley' Edinburgh to London St Pancras. *J. Davenport*

3. The 'Thames-Clyde Express' speeds through Kirkby Stephen in March 1973, on the long descent from Ais Gill.

5
Derailments on Broken Rails

When a child receives his first trainset he soon realises that the two essential components are the train and the track. He also discovers fairly quickly that unless he lays his track level and joins the ends of the rails accurately and firmly, derailments will occur. And he soon learns to examine the line frequently, so that any breaks are discovered *before* he runs his train. It is the same with the real railway.

Thirty years ago, there were about 200 broken rails per year, nearly all of which were discovered before derailment took place. By 1970, that figure had gone up to over 400, with a considerably reduced track mileage, and in addition there were well over 200 breaks at welded joints in continuously welded rail. In 1987 there were still over 350 broken rails, but the number of broken welds had risen to over 250, although with a much greater total number of welds in the track than in 1970.

One does not have to seek far for the reasons behind this rather alarming increase. Train speeds are higher — up to 125mph in the case of the IC125 units (HSTs) and up to 60/75mph for heavily loaded freight trains with 25-ton axle-loads. Locomotives and multiple-units with axle-hung nose-suspended electric motors severely punish the track, owing to their heavy unsprung weight.

There are three main types of rail break. On jointed track, which is the name for track laid in 60ft lengths joined together with fishplates, the most common break results from fatigue stresses at the fishbolt holes, resulting in cracks radiating from the hole in the form of a star, known appropriately as star cracks. If they are not detected and dealt with, the cracks will eventually extend until they reach the rail head, and at this stage a piece of the rail will become bodily detached from the rest of the rail.

Below:
On a misty Sunday morning in February 1975, breakdown cranes set to work to rerail several loaded 100-ton tank wagons which fell on to their sides following a derailment caused by a broken rail near Fosse Way, between Lichfield and Walsall. The operation is being watched with keen interest by Water Board officials, who had to intervene and stop the rerailing when oil started to gush out of one of the tanks whilst it was being turned to an upright position. *Author*

Below:
Very high standards of permanent way are required for IC125 units, one of which is seen passing through Newport with a Paddington train on 3 July 1977. *L. A. Nixon*

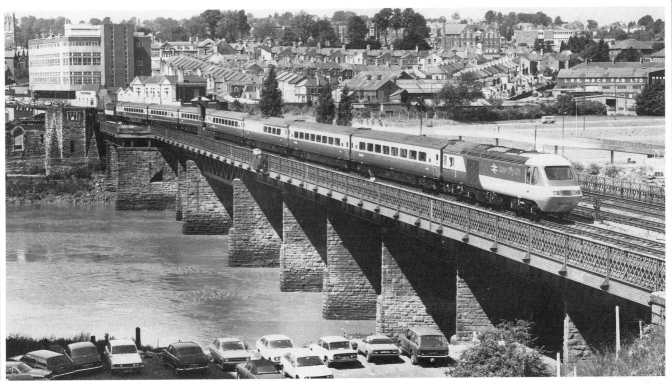

Right:
The permanent way needs to be strong to withstand 25-ton axleloads, imposed by trains such as the one seen here, at Langley, near Stevenage, on 31 January 1970, headed by Class 47 diesel-electric No 1872. *J. H. Cooper-Smith*

Below:
This derailment, at Stoulton near Pershore on 30 November 1984, was caused by a broken fishplate. The first six coaches of the train, the 07.05 Hereford to Paddington, which was travelling at about 75mph, remained coupled to the locomotive, Class 47 No 47500, but the last four became detached and were completely derailed. There were no serious injuries.
S. Widdowson

The second type of break occurs away from the rail end. Usually a fatigue crack develops, which will spread in time until either the rail breaks in two or a piece of the rail head breaks off. Sometimes the crack develops from a wheel burn, caused by a locomotive wheel spinning under power whilst the train is travelling at low speed. During a wheelspin, a portion of the rail head surface becomes heated very rapidly to a temperature as high as 700°C, and as soon as the spin ceases the area rapidly cools, causing a change in the nature of the steel, from which small cracks may grow. Sometimes the damage causes shelling of the surface, resulting in a shallow depression, which has to be restored to its former level by welding and grinding. In severe cases it may be necessary to replace the rail.

Sometimes rail breaks are caused by metallurgical faults arising during manufacture, and may be of the tache ovale type, which is a slowly growing internal flaw originating in an area of high stress concentration in the rail head, probably due to the presence of hydrogen trapped in the metal during the steelmaking process.

The third type of break is the defective weld, which has caused so much concern in recent years. The subject will be examined in detail when we look at the accident which

occurred at Bushey on the West Coast main line on 16 February 1980.

Each broken rail is a potential cause of derailment, which may have the most serious consequences. The highest death toll in an accident on British Railways in the last 30 years was caused by a broken rail at Hither Green, on the electrified South Eastern Division main line of the Southern Region, on Sunday 5 November 1967, when 49 passengers were killed. In view of such possible calamity the detection of defective rails is obviously a matter of great importance. There are two main systems for achieving this.

The first is the time-honoured system of visual examination by a track patrolman. All lines are patrolled regularly, either daily or every two days, so far as the busy lines are concerned. The patrolman is concerned with many aspects of track maintenance, particularly the security of track fastenings, but he is also looking for cracks and breakages. However, he can only really see cracks when they are so big that they are reaching the dangerous stage, and they need to be discovered before that if possible.

To enable cracks to be discovered before they have grown to the extent that they can be seen by the naked eye, a scientific apparatus was devised known as an Ultrasonic

Top:
A typical wheel burn. *BR*

Above:
A view of the wreckage in the Hither Green derailment on 5 November 1967. *Author*

current is fed through one of the running rails of a section of track, and then back along the other running rail. Adjoining sections of track are insulated from each other. At the opposite end of the section of track from the power source is a relay, held open by the current passing through it. When a pair of vehicle wheels enters the track-circuited section of line the electrical current takes the shortest way back, which is through the wheels and axles of the vehicle. There is then no current flowing through the relay, which closes and operates other equipment, such as placing signals to Danger or locking the movement of points. The track circuit in this state is referred to as 'occupied'. However, if an empty track circuit suddenly becomes occupied when there is no train in the vicinity, the signalman will become aware of this from his indications panel, but he will not yet know the cause. It may be due to an obstruction on the line short-circuiting the current (for example a lorry may have fallen on to the track from an overbridge), or it may be due to a failure of the apparatus, or it may be due to a broken rail. If the rail is completely broken and there is a gap between the two pieces, the electric current will not be able to flow and the relay will close, putting the protecting signal in rear to Danger and alerting the signalman. Unfortunately on some lines the track circuit only uses one rail, therefore the equipment will not detect a break in the other rail. To convert all track circuits to two-rail operation would be a costly process, especially in skilled man-hours, which BR is not prepared to undertake.

It might be appropriate at this stage to examine the actions of the signalman when he notices that a track circuit is showing 'occupied' when there is no train nearby. At this stage he does not know the cause, and one of his first acts will be to ask the signal technician to find out if there is a fault in the equipment which can quickly be put right. If not, the signalman must arrange for the section of line to be examined. This is normally done by using a train, and the driver will be told what has happened, and that he is to proceed cautiously through the affected section and to report at the next signal ahead. The driver must pass the protecting signal even though it is showing Danger, and travel at a speed low enough to enable him to see what is wrong and to stop before hitting any obstruction. In the great majority of cases the cause will be either an equipment failure or a broken rail. If the driver travels through the section and notices nothing, subsequent trains may be allowed to pass through at low speed after the drivers have been cautioned by the signalman, and this procedure will continue until the cause has been found and remedied. However, if the driver notices a broken rail, or feels what he suspects is one as his locomotive travels over it, it will be necessary to call out the civil engineering staff to deal with the defect. In the meantime, trains may be allowed to pass over the break at walking pace under certain safety conditions, among which are:

1. The break must be in CWR.
2. The break must be nearly vertical.
3. The gap must be not more than an inch.
4. A supervisor or other authorised member of staff must watch the train pass over the break, so that it can be stopped instantly if necessary.

When the engineering staff arrive on site they will put a clamp on the rails at the break, rather like a pair of fishplates, so that trains can pass over safely, then at a convenient time they will cut the rails a few feet to each side of the break, and weld in a new piece of rail cut to the precise length of the gap. When that has been done trains may be allowed to proceed normally.

Flaw Detector. This is a hand-held apparatus which sends ultrasonic waves into the rail, and the operator can distinguish, for example by a variation in the pitch of an audible signal, whether the waves are being reflected from the base of the rail or from a bolt hole or hidden flaw. The use of hand-held equipment is slow and laborious, and to overcome this disadvantage BR brought into service in 1971 an ultrasonic rail flaw detection train, which is a converted two-car diesel multiple-unit and travels at 20mph whilst testing.

A third way of discovering a broken rail arises quite fortuitously through the use of track circuits. As has already been explained, a track circuit is an electrically-operated train detection device in which a weak electric

There is yet another way in which broken rails are detected. Drivers are accustomed to lurches and bumps and bounces as part and parcel of everyday life on the footplate. They also know the rough spots on any particular route and can quite easily distinguish anything out of the ordinary. In the latter case they should stop at the next signalbox or telephone and inform the signalman, so that he can call out the civil engineering staff and arrange for other drivers to be cautioned. The cause of the unusual bump felt by the driver need not be a broken rail. It might be a bad wet spot or a buckle in the track, as we saw in the last chapter. It might be an obstruction on the line, or a body on the track.

There is of course the ultimate way in which a broken rail is discovered, and that is when it derails a train. History is littered with such cases, and some of them have interesting features, or have happened to famous trains. The 'Royal Scot' has had quite an eventful career and it was destined to add another page on 3 February 1954. The Up 'Royal Scot', 10.0am Glasgow to Euston express, that day consisted of 10 coaches, and was hauled by a Class 8P Pacific locomotive No 46250 *City of Lichfield*. It was travelling through Watford Tunnel at about 65mph when a broken rail derailed the last pair of wheels of the eighth coach. The train travelled on like this for a mile and a half until the derailed wheels hit the points and crossings at Watford No 2 signalbox, whereupon the last two coaches became completely derailed. They broke away from the remainder of the train and came to rest leaning against the platform at the station. The 4.37pm Euston to Wolverhampton express was just leaving the station on the next line when its driver saw the derailed vehicles approaching him. He immediately

stopped his train but the sides of some of its coaches were grazed as the two derailed coaches scraped past them. The first eight coaches of the 'Royal Scot' were brought to a stand when the brakes were automatically applied by the parting of the train. No one was seriously injured.

An interesting feature in this accident is that the communication cord was pulled by a passenger in the ninth coach as soon as he realised something was wrong, and although the brakes were partly applied and speed was reduced slightly the driver was unaware that the cord had been pulled, and had no idea that anything was wrong until the brakes went on fully when the train broke in two. The passengers at the rear of the train were terror-stricken. They suddenly heard a banging and clattering underneath the coach and their hearts momentarily stood still. Anyone who has travelled on a train when it has thrown up pieces of ballast on to the underside of the coach will recognise the sudden feeling of alarm at the unusual noise, then the relief when the noise subsides. On the 'Royal Scot' that day the noise did not subside, and the pulling of the communication cord did not seem to have worked. The apparatus is designed so that the pulling of the cord (on the coaches then in use it was actually a chain) causes a rod, mounted transversely at the end of the coach, to rotate and lift a valve to allow air into the vacuum brake pipe, thus causing a partial application of the brakes. The amount of vacuum

Above:
A scene of track maintenance in years gone by, when labour costs were lower and recruitment easier. *LMS*

in the pipe is shown on a gauge in the locomotive cab. When the brakes are fully off it will register 21in and a normal brake application will reduce it to 12 or 13in. When the communication cord is pulled and air is allowed into the brake pipe the gauge on the locomotive will start to fall, and when the driver notices this he is told to infer that the cord has been pulled and that he must stop the train with as little delay as possible, but that he must use his discretion in stopping, it being undesirable to bring the train to a stand on a bridge or viaduct, or in a tunnel. In order that he can exercise such discretion most effectively a driver will normally look back down the train to see what is wrong. If he sees smoke he will stop as quickly as possible, but if he sees that part of his train is derailed he will apply the brake more gently to keep the train upright and in line as far as possible. The guard also has a responsibility — if he has reason to think that the cord has been pulled but has not been noticed by the driver he must apply the brake from his van. In the case of air-braked trains the method of operation is very similar. When the brake is off, the brake pipe pressure gauge reads 72lb/sq in of air pressure. A normal brake application will reduce the pressure to 48lb/sq in, and an emergency application will reduce it to zero.

The equipping of trains with an apparatus which the passenger can use to stop the train, or to have it stopped by the driver, is a legal requirement under the Regulation of Railways Act of 1868. Section 22 states that 'All trains travelling a distance of more than 20 miles without stopping are to be provided with a means of communication between the passengers and the servants of the company in charge of the train. The apparatus provided is to be approved by the Board of Trade'. The duties of the Board of Trade have now been taken over by the Ministry (or Department) of Transport. It will be noticed that the Act does not specify that the passenger must be able to stop the train, but merely to 'communicate', and that was precisely what was done at first. A cord ran down the length of the train at roof level outside the carriages, and pulling it rang a bell on the locomotive. The modern form of apparatus was introduced later in the century when the use of the automatic vacuum brake became standard (the continuous brake itself became a legal requirement under the

Regulation of Railways Act 1889), but the name 'communication cord' has survived until the present day.

On older coaches the actuating rod referred to above was fitted with a red disc at each end. The disc is horizontal when the equipment is normal, but when the rod rotates upon the cord being pulled, the disc turns to the vertical position. The guard can then tell in which coach the cord has been pulled.

At the Public Inquiry into the accident Lt-Col Wilson, the Inspecting Officer, commented upon the failure of the passenger communication apparatus (the cord) to alert the driver, and there were discussions with the British Transport Commission as to whether the brake application when the cord is pulled should be made automatic and outside the control of the driver, but the railway authorities felt that this was an isolated case and that discretion should remain with the driver. The Inspecting Officer also commented upon the difficulty of maintaining the track in tunnels and mentioned, significantly, that the quality and quantity of labour had been insufficient for a long time to maintain the track to the standard required. This was a problem that was to dog the London end of the West Coast main line for many years; indeed it affected the standard of performance in both the civil engineering and operating departments throughout most of Britain until the labour market eased in the late 1970s. It is easy to forget how difficult those days were for local managers, with the constant daily struggle just to keep the job going in the face of staff shortages, the poor quality of some of the new recruits, and the rapid turnover of staff.

Further north on the West Coast main line there is a delightful spot where the line descends from the bleak moorlands of Shap to the fields and pastures of Morecambe Bay, where on a clear day the mountains of the Lake District provide an attractive scenic backdrop, and it is possible to pick out the shipyard cranes at Barrow-in-Furness 20 miles away. At Hest Bank the line actually runs along the coast for a few hundred yards, the only place on the West Coast main line where it does so. There was a small station here, half a dozen camping coaches, and a junction to Morecambe

Below:
Hest Bank, on the West Coast main line between Lancaster and Carnforth, and the site of the derailment of the 22.10 sleeper from Glasgow to London on the night of 19/20 May 1965. The photograph shows a Fowler Class 4P 2-6-4T on an excursion from Barrow to Morecambe on 18 September 1954. The sleeping car express was derailed when passing over the water troughs, just beyond the tail lamp of the excursion train. *H. Armitage*

Euston Road station. There were also water troughs just to the north of the station level crossing. During the winter at high tide tens of thousands of birds can be seen from the train, feeding on the shore line.

Not long after midnight on 19/20 May 1965 the 22.10 sleeping car express from Glasgow to London (Kensington Olympia) set off from Carlisle on the next stage of its long journey south. It consisted of 12 vehicles, including seven sleeping cars, and carried 114 passengers. The locomotive was No D1633, a Type 4 diesel-electric. After running down easily from Shap and Grayrigg the driver was passing through Hest Bank station at about 70mph and was just closing the power controller to slow down for Lancaster when he felt a pull and saw that the needle on his vacuum brake gauge had fallen to zero. When the train stopped he sent his secondman forward to protect the other line and warn the drivers of any approaching trains to stop whilst he himself went back. He could hardly believe his eyes. There were only three coaches attached to his locomotive, then nothing for 250yd. He hurried along in the darkness with mounting apprehension and then came upon the next four vehicles, three of which were sleeping cars, lying on their sides between the platforms. Reaching the signalbox, he was assured by the signalman that both lines had been protected and that the emergency services had been sent for. He could dimly make out to the north the shape of two more sleeping cars on their sides. Ambulances arrived quickly at the level crossing and the injured were taken to hospital. There were only 11 of them, all with minor injuries or shock, and only two were detained for a few days. There were no fatalities, the reason being partly that five of the six overturned vehicles were sleeping cars, whose occupants were cushioned to some extent from the effects of the derailment. A very rude awakening was all that most of them suffered, apart from the memory of those awful moments when the derailed train bounced along then turned over onto its side, which will stay with them for ever.

The cause of the derailment was a broken rail. The line had been relaid 10 years earlier, using 60ft flatbottom rail welded into 300ft lengths. The rails had been wheelburnt in a number of places and a transverse crack had started from one of them, spreading horizontally for a length of several feet, leading eventually to a whole section of rail head breaking off. Wheelburns were a problem at this location, wheelspin being aided by water spilt from the troughs, and salt spray from the sea, borne on the prevailing westerly wind. The rail had been examined for cracks six months previously but fatigue cracks underneath wheelburns are almost impossible to detect with an ultrasonic flaw detector.

Across on the other side of northern England the East Coast main line also runs close to the sea at places north of Newcastle. Given the present flourishing state of Anglo-Scottish traffic on the East Coast main line and its relative stagnation on the rival West Coast route it is odd to recollect that in the 1960s it was intended to downgrade the line north of Newcastle, and actually to single it from Alnmouth to Dunbar. Anglo-Scottish passenger traffic would have been concentrated on the West Coast main line and freight traffic would have been routed via Newcastle and Carlisle. Planning for the future has been a notoriously difficult exercise on BR ever since it was created and the record is not a good one, in fact some of the planning assumptions and decisions that were made with apparent great confidence now appear to us quite astonishing. The fact is that it is quite impossible to plan with any degree of accuracy 20 years ahead or to forecast the changes that might take place. All the more foolish, therefore, would it have been to jettison the Settle to Carlisle line, just as it

Above:
The scene at Amble Junction after the Up 'North Briton' was derailed by a broken rail on 15 July 1967. *Author*

Below:
The pieces of broken rail reassembled afterwards. The star crack can be seen running from the bolt hole. *Author*

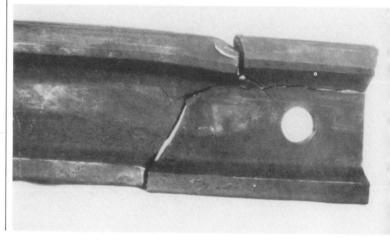

would have been reckless to have singled and downgraded the Newcastle to Edinburgh line.

These difficulties of long-term planning are the background to the next accident to be examined. On the evening of 15 July 1967 the 'North Briton' express from Edinburgh to Leeds was running at about 75mph between Acklington and Chevington when it became derailed on a broken rail. Fortunately all 12 coaches remained upright and fairly well in line, and only nine of the 160 passengers required hospital treatment. All were discharged within a few days. Prompt action was taken to summon assistance but as the site was not easily accessible by road the ambulances were sent to the nearby RAF station at Acklington and the injured passengers were airlifted by helicopter; perhaps an additional fright for some of them but a good example of initiative, and certainly an effective way of getting them to hospital with the least possible delay.

The rails in the line were of the 95lb bullhead type and had been laid as long ago as 1941. Their weight had been reduced over the years to 84/88lb/yd and that section of line was programmed to be relaid in the following October. The rails were drilled with only one fishbolt hole, a common practice at one time. A star crack had developed from the bolt hole at the running-on end of a rail, and eventually a piece of the rail had broken off, leaving a gap which caused the derailment. The LNER had adopted the two-hole fishplate in some areas because it allowed the sleepers at each side of the rail joint to be brought closer together, thus providing better support for the joint, but the practice was not thought to yield sufficient benefits and it was later abandoned.

The incidence of rail breakages at joints was causing concern both to the Railways Board and to the Railway Inspectorate, even though the derailments that were occurring were not causing fatalities. However, that was to change dramatically a few months later, and the concern felt was seen to be well founded.

Trains on the Southern Region's electrified lines often seemed to give a rougher ride than trains on other Regions' lines, although it was difficult to tell whether it was the rolling stock or the track which was at fault, or indeed a combination of the two. It would be easy to understand why the track may have been less than perfect — the punishing effect of electric multiple-units, the frequency and the speed of trains, the lack of opportunity to carry out maintenance, and the difficulty in obtaining a sufficient quantity of good quality labour, are reasons which spring readily to mind. Couple all those with restrictions on staff numbers and expenditure imposed by the Railways Board and it becomes easy to understand why the quality of the ride from Paris to Calais on what was not one of SNCF's front-rank main lines was so vastly superior to the ride from Dover to Victoria.

The Chislehurst to Hither Green section of line was considered by passengers to be fairly rough in the 1960s, especially after the Southern Region raised the speed limit from 75mph to 90mph in July 1967. Local permanent way staff had some misgivings about this, firstly as to whether the track was in a good enough condition for 90mph running and secondly whether they had sufficient resources to maintain it to the standard required for such speeds. However, they certainly did not imagine how quickly defects in the standard of the track would lead to one of Britain's worst postwar railway disasters.

On Sunday, 5 November 1967, the 19.43 from Hastings to Charing Cross, composed of two of the six-coach diesel-electric 'Hastings' multiple-units was approaching Hither Green under clear signals on the Up fast line, running at about 70mph, when the leading pair of wheels of the third coach struck a small wedge-shaped piece of rail that had broken away from the end of the running rail, and became derailed. The train ran on in this condition for about a quarter of a mile, to the mounting alarm of the passengers in the coach, an open second-class, until the derailed wheels struck some points and crossings. The impact caused the coach, together with the one in front and the two behind, to fall over and slide along for 250yd; the sides of two of the coaches being torn off as they did so, precipitating the passengers on to the rails, sleepers and ballast below to be mangled or crushed to death, or to suffer severe injuries, as the disintegrating coaches grated

Below:
Hither Green, on Monday morning 6 November 1967, showing the wreckage of the 19.43 Hastings to Charing Cross, which had been derailed by a broken rail the previous evening. The ease of accessibility to the site, for the emergency services, was fortunately very good. *Author*

over them. The train was well filled, with some passengers having to stand, and altogether 49 of them were killed and 27 seriously injured. It is significant that the number of serious casualties in an accident in which coaches overturn is almost always related to the extent to which the coach bodies retain their integrity, even though the bogies may be torn off and the ends battered. Provided the coach body sides remain intact and the body remains whole, so that passengers are not thrown out or dropped on to the ballast, the number and severity of casualties remains low, but as soon as the coach body is breached or torn open the number of casualties rises considerably. This is a lesson which has not been lost on coach designers, and it is rare to see modern coaches being breached, even when thrown on to their sides at high speed. The passengers inside may be bounced around, and suffer bruises and broken bones, but they rarely receive the serious injuries which occur to passengers thrown out of a coach, who are harmed not only by the impact with the ground but also from the mauling they receive bodily as the train or wreckage passes over them.

The emergency services reacted very promptly indeed. The accident happened at 21.16 and the Metropolitan Police were on the scene within 5min, just a minute before the first ambulances. The first casualty reached hospital only 18min after the accident. Fortunately, road access to the site was good.

One of the features of this accident was the behaviour of the first coach. The driver was just preparing to apply the brake lightly for the 60mph restriction in the inner suburban area beyond Hither Green, when he felt a drag on the train, which became progressively more severe with much snatching. The brakes came hard on and the coach stopped in a short distance. The driver concluded that his train had become divided, and he opened the cab door and prepared to climb down on to the track. As he looked back along his train he could scarcely believe his eyes. His coach was standing alone on the rails, undamaged, but the other coaches were scattered in all directions. It is a situation that we have met before, where a derailment occurs part of the way along a train.

Col McMullen, the Inspecting Officer who held the Public Inquiry into the accident, found that the rail end had broken off owing to stresses which had been set up in it by the unsatisfactory manner in which it was supported by the sleeper and track bed. He considered that the general standard of maintenance of the section on which the derailment occurred was inadequate for the speed at which trains were being run, and he attached the responsibility for this to the entire permanent way organisation, all the way up from the local staff to the Chief Civil Engineer.

One of the 'Hastings' units was tested on the East Coast main line to see how its 'ride' compared with that on its home ground. It was markedly better, to no one's surprise. Passengers on the East Coast main line are accustomed to having a comfortable ride, although a Great Western supporter might maintain that the ride from Paddington is superior. He may well be right — the Western Region seems to have been rather more adept than the other Regions at squeezing money out of the British Railways Board. The London & North Western Railway (LNWR) used to pride itself on the condition of its main line from Euston, and it was widely regarded as being among the best in the country. That was long before the days of main line electrification, and by 1980 the ride on the West Coast main line at its southern end was definitely lively. It was almost unbelievable that a line could have deteriorated so much in such a short time. Part of the reason was the hammering it received from electric locomotives, but when the effect became apparent remedial action should have been taken.

Below:
High Speed Trains have been a major commercial success on the East Coast main line. The 07.45 King's Cross to Edinburgh is seen passing Ouston Junction, north of Chester-le-Street, on 5 April 1978. *I. S. Carr*

The fact that it was not is surely a criticism of the management of the London Midland Region, and not just of the civil engineering function but of general management as well. It is also surely a criticism of the Railways Board, which changed the General Manager frequently. Between 1970 and 1977 there were no fewer than four changes of General Manager at Euston. There were also no fewer than five Chief Operating Managers at Crewe! In such circumstances, how could any proper control and direction be exercised or any continuity be given? And this on BR's biggest Region!

The London Midland Region's attitude to its most important line seemed to be that as long as it was not unsafe the passenger would just have to put up with a rough ride, and an uncharitable observer might remark that that more or less encapsulated the Region's attitude to its passengers, as though they were a nuisance to be tolerated. How else can one explain the declining popularity of the West Coast main line, compared with King's Cross and Paddington? In 1989 for example, the express service from King's Cross to Edinburgh has become so popular that the hourly service has had to be augmented to half-hourly at certain times of the day, and the average journey time is down to about 4½hr. By contrast, the rival West Coast service to Glasgow has declined to two-hourly, with an average journey time an hour longer than the East Coast.

It seems incredible that there are more trains from London to Plymouth than there are from London to Glasgow, which is three times bigger. Part of the West Coast malaise can be attributed to the long-drawn-out Advanced Passenger Train fiasco, but its roots go back much further. The fact is that the East Coast companies always fostered and nurtured their passenger traffic. So did the Great Western, which was held in immense esteem by its passengers. The LNWR and its successor, the London Midland and Scottish Railway, were quite content to pay lip service to the passenger business but the main interest of these two companies was in the freight business, which provided much more of the revenue and the profits. From a business point of view, that was a perfectly proper attitude, and any other would have led to the bankruptcy courts, but today the relative size of the passenger and freight businesses has been completely reversed. The passenger business is absolutely dominant, yet the old attitudes seem to have persisted to this day at Euston, which is incredible 40 years after nationalisation. It is almost as though the Eastern and Western Regions were determined to prove

Below:

The East Coast companies always fostered their passenger traffic. They were the first to use Pacifics on their expresses, the first to use streamlining, and they ran crack high speed services such as the 'Elizabethan', pictured here behind Class A4 Pacific No 60024 *Kingfisher* at Grantshouse, on its 6½hr run from King's Cross to Edinburgh. *Eric Treacy/Millbrook House Collection*

Right:

Class 86/2 Electric No 86247 approaches Bushey with the 09.00 Euston to Carlisle on 30 June 1976. *Brian Morrison*

Below right:

Bushey station, on the West Coast main line just south of Watford, showing one of the derailed coaches of the 20.25 Euston to Manchester on 16 February 1980, caused by a broken weld in the rail. The strength of the coach bodies helped to prevent any fatalities. This photograph was taken from the Up Fast platform, looking north. The coach body is lying across the Watford dc lines. *Daily Telegraph*

that they could be better than the London Midland when the latter was favoured to be the first long-distance electrified main line. The other Regions were put on their mettle and were determined to prove that they could do better even without electrification. The LMR was content to rest on its laurels.

The West Coast main line, especially its southern end, has seen many accidents, and it was to be the scene of yet another on the evening of Saturday 16 February 1980. A regular passenger on the 19.40 express from Euston to Birmingham was relaxing in the first coach of the train as it settled down on its 100mph run to the first stop at Rugby. Approaching Bushey, just south of Watford, he was startled by a bad bump underneath the coach. Other people felt it too, but none of them thought that they ought to tell the guard, or do anything about it, and they felt reassured when the train immediately resumed its normal progress. Perhaps they thought that if there was anything wrong the driver or guard would have taken the necessary action. However, the driver felt nothing.

Just as the train was slowing down for the Rugby stop, and the passengers had put the bump near Bushey out of their minds, another express was approaching Bushey. This second train was the 20.25 Euston to Manchester, consisting of nine coaches hauled by a Class 87 electric locomotive No 87007 *City of Manchester*. It carried about 150 passengers. The driver was sitting quietly at the

Top and above:
Site welding in progress, and the finished weld. *BR*

controls watching the succession of green signals ahead, and keeping his eye on the speedometer needle, which was hovering around the 100mph mark, the maximum speed allowed. At this speed even the excellent Class 87s bounce around a little, and when he felt an irregularity in the ride approaching Bushey he dismissed it from his mind as just another wet spot. It was to prove nothing of the sort.

Above:
The last two coaches of the 13.50 from York to Liverpool rolled down an embankment into a field near Ulleskelf after the train was derailed by a broken weld on 8 December 1981.
Yorkshire Post

Almost immediately the driver felt the brake go on, and he noticed the 'line light' go out, indicating that the locomotive was no longer receiving power from the overhead electric wires. He lowered the pantograph to save any damage, then got down on to the cab floor to avoid any bits and pieces of the overhead equipment that might be flying around. When the locomotive stopped he sent his secondman forward to telephone the signalman from the next signal, whilst he himself placed track-circuit operating clips on the next line, the Up fast, to put the signals on that line to Danger. In the darkness and mist he could only see two coaches, but the second was leaning at an angle of 45°. He could not see the rest of his train and he would have been horrified if he could have done. The next three coaches were strewn on their sides across the track, and torn from their bogies, but the coach bodies remained structurally intact and very few of the windows, all of which were double-glazed, were broken. The passengers inside those Mk 3 coaches owe their lives to the integrity of the coach bodies, and there were no fatalities, although 19 passengers suffered serious injuries. The Inspecting Officer Lt-Col Townsend-Rose, commented that the derailment had had a more serious effect on the behaviour of the coaches when they were running along derailed because the buckeye couplers became disengaged vertically. He felt that if the couplers had been so constructed as to prevent vertical disengagement the coaches might have been held together

and in line, instead of becoming uncoupled and falling over on to their sides. It seems an excellent idea, and yet eight years later a solution has not been found by BR, which might indicate that very little effort has been applied to find one.

The track in the area of the derailment was originally laid in 1965 using flatbottom rail but in October 1979 the cess-side rail was found to be worn and contain serious flaws. It was therefore replaced on 16 October 1979 by two 720ft lengths of CWR, which were welded in, and it was the site weld between this new rail and the old rail which failed. The weld was not up to the required standard and there was little supervision of the work. The organisation was faulty — the welding supervisor was almost fully occupied in the office doing administrative and clerical work, and could rarely get out to exercise supervision. After the accident more welding supervisors were appointed, and were relieved of some of their office duties.

Broken welds are not a rare occurrence. Several had been found in the Watford area previously by patrolmen, and some had been reported by drivers or brought to light by track circuit 'failures'. However, to keep the matter in

Above:
**The rear coach of the 13.50 from Aberdeen to Inverness on
3 February 1983, lying on its side near Elgin after the train had
been derailed by a broken rail-end.** *Northern Photos*

perspective, there were at this time approximately 150,000 welds of this type in track on the LM Region and the failure rate was no greater than on the other Regions. At the end of 1979 there were very nearly 10,000 miles of CWR and there were 550 broken welds that year, a rate of 5.5 every 100 miles. In the Watford area the rate was almost the same at 5.4. By the end of 1987 there were 12,000 miles of CWR and the failure rate had gone down to 2.18 every 100 miles, a welcome improvement.

However, defective track continues to cause derailments, which are invariably expensive and occasionally cause fatalities. On 8 December 1981 the 13.50 York to Liverpool express, consisting of seven coaches hauled by Class 47 diesel-electric No 47409, was derailed by a broken weld near Ulleskelf, between York and Church Fenton. The locomotive remained on the track as usual but all the coaches were derailed and the last two rolled on to their sides down a steep embankment. Twenty-four passengers were taken to hospital, nine of whom were seriously injured, and one subsequently died. The weld which broke was situated between the first two sleepers following the ends of the waybeams over a steel girder bridge spanning the River Wharfe, and was thus subjected to additional stress.

A broken rail-end caused another fatality when the 13.50 train from Aberdeen to Inverness, consisting of a Class 27 diesel-electric locomotive No 27007 and five coaches, was derailed at Llanbryde, two miles east of Elgin, on Thursday 3 February 1983 when travelling at 60mph. The last three coaches were derailed, and the rearmost one turned on to its side and slid for 100yd. Three other passengers were seriously injured. The break in the rail started as a fatigue crack from a fishbolt hole and developed into a brittle fracture.

Derailments continued to occur but year by year the situation improves, which must give the Chief Civil Engineer and his staff much satisfaction. It is also worthy of comment that in none of the derailments we have looked at in this chapter was a second train involved. It is partly a matter of luck, but is also partly due to the widespread use of track circuiting, which allows protecting signals to be put to Danger instantly either because derailed wreckage short-circuits the track circuit or it is done by the traincrew using a track circuit operating clip. The Engineer deserves a bit of luck. He has had to cope with the demands for heavier and faster trains, the pounding of electric-motored traction units, shortages of staff and a tight purse. He also has other responsibilities, such as thousands of bridges; a subject which we will look at in the next chapter.

6
Bridges Under Attack

The River Towy in South Wales is not a long and mighty river. It rises in the bleak moorlands to the north of the pleasant market town of Llandovery and is joined by many tributaries, then it flows down the peaceful and pastoral Vale of Towy to Llandeilo and Carmarthen, gaining in strength and size all the time. In dry spells of weather the flow of water is very much reduced, but even at such times a glance at the nature of the river bed and the banks, together with the width of the watercourse, betrays the fact that the river is not always benign and somnolent. When storms break, up in the mountains and moorlands, and the rain lashes down hour after hour, the tiny tributaries become torrents and the river becomes a raging brown flood, strong enough to uproot fully-grown trees and carry them miles downstream. Such storms are not unknown in South Wales, in fact they are quite common, and to be told that the Towy is in flood would excite no special interest, except among the fishermen, who regularly line its banks.

There is also a railway in the Vale of Towy, just a single track, which sticks fairly close to the river and changes sides every now and then. It is a railway with an interesting history. The line was opened on 1 April 1858 by the Vale of Towy Railway, but it was worked from the outset and leased by a neighbouring railway company known as the Llanelli Railway & Docks Co, which had reached Llandeilo the previous year. Meanwhile, the mighty LNWR had its eyes on the lucrative traffic in the Swansea district and Southwest Wales and pondered upon how it might obtain access to the area. It had already reached Shrewsbury and owned jointly with the Great Western the railway which joined that town to Hereford via Craven Arms. It therefore resolved to project lines through central Wales via Knighton and Llandrindod Wells to Llandovery, which it reached in 1868 and where it joined the Vale of Towy Railway. The LNWR then took over a share of the Llanelli Co's lease of the Vale of Towy Railway, and a few years later gained the lines from Llandeilo to Carmarthen, and from Pontarddulais to Swansea Victoria. The LNWR had

achieved its objective, and for the next century or so the line saw a fair amount of long-distance freight traffic and some passenger traffic, including the legendary York to Swansea mail, which ran nightly in both directions. The Great Western also ran a local service from Llanelli to Llandovery over the Vale of Towy line, which it jointly owned as successor to the Llanelli company. For many years after World War 2, the former LNWR services were worked mainly by standard Fowler parallel boiler 2-6-4 tanks and Stanier '8F' 2-8-0s, which came to epitomise the line.

Between Llandeilo and Llandovery the line crosses the river three times — near Glanrhyd, five miles from Llandeilo; between Llangadog and Llanwrda, about seven miles from Llandeilo; and at Llwyn Jack, 10 miles from Llandeilo and a mile or so from Llandovery. The maintenance responsibilities of the Vale of Towy Railway were divided between the LNWR and the Great Western, the boundary point being Milepost 24.

Sunday 18 October 1987 was a very wet day in South Wales. The driver of a light locomotive returning from Craven Arms to Pantyffynnon after weekend engineering work on the Central Wales line noticed that floodwater was near the track at Milepost 26 between Llandovery and Llanwrda. He resolved to report it to the signalman at the first opportunity and continued on his way. At the Glanrhyd Bridge he stopped for a short while out of curiosity to see how high the river was and how fast it was flowing. It was quite an unnerving sight even in the darkness, being almost up to bridge level. He set off again, but at Milepost 21 he found that the track was flooded and some of the ballast had been displaced. After that he proceeded even more cautiously, not knowing what he might find, then just

Below:
Fowler LMS Standard 2-6-4T Class 4P, of the type used on the Central Wales line. Side cab windows were fitted to the last 30 of the class, Nos 2395-2424.

outside Llandeilo he saw that the floodwaters were actually above rail level. He reported the facts to the signalman by telephone and thought to himself that he had never seen such bad flooding on the Vale of Towy line.

The situation was reported to various 'on-call' staff and it was decided that the first train the next morning, the 05.27 Swansea to Shrewsbury, should be accompanied by the local permanent way supervisor so that he could look at the places where flooding had been reported and examine the track to make sure that it was safe for the train to pass over, and to assess any necessary repairs. He made his way by road to Llandeilo with some difficulty as the road also was flooded, then met the train there, having already examined the line just outside the station and decided that it was safe for the train to proceed over it at 5mph. The permanent way supervisor then joined the train and they set off towards the next reported trouble spot at Milepost 21. This also was negotiated safely at about 5mph; and the train went on its way towards the last of the three places where the driver of the previous night's light locomotive had reported flooding. En route they passed over the level crossing at the old Glanrhyd station, which was closed about 30 years ago, at the required speed of 10mph and headed towards the bridge. In the driving cab were the driver, the permanent way supervisor and an operations manager. They saw the grey steel girders of the bridge end-on, then just as they reached them they noticed that the twin ribbons of the rails did not stretch in a straight line across the bridge, but they dipped somewhat and were out of alignment to the right. The driver shouted 'Hang on', and pushed his brake handle straight through to the 'emergency' position. It was too late. Even though they were only travelling at 10 to 15mph the front coach dipped and plunged into the swollen, raging torrent. It righted itself and settled down horizontally, with water up to chest level inside. The second coach came to rest on the sloping bridge deck.

To add to the sudden terror and confusion the lights in the first coach went out, although they remained on in the second. Dawn was just breaking and, when it was discovered that it was possible to clamber through the gangway connection into the second coach, and into relative safety, the few passengers and the railwaymen started to make good their escape. It was not at all easy; the two coach-ends were at an angle to each other and a torrent of water was surging through the gap. Three of the passengers and two railwaymen had crossed through safely to the second coach, and they were struggling to pull through an elderly lady when, with a loud crack the coupling between the two coaches snapped and the stricken coach swung away to become almost totally submerged. It became a tomb for the 58-year-old driver and a 14-year-old

Above left:
Llwyn Jack Bridge, between Glanrhyd and Llandovery. The width and strength of the River Towy can be gauged from this photograph. The bridge is supported by metal tubes, unlike the Glanrhyd bridge, which was supported on masonry piers. *Author*

Left:
End view of Llwyn Jack Bridge over the River Towy. *Author*

Below:
The Glanrhyd bridge over the River Towy on 19 October 1987. The first coach of the two-car DMU is almost completely submerged at this stage. *South West News*

schoolboy who had bravely stayed behind in the front coach to try to help everyone out. The elderly lady and her husband also lost their lives. Mr Alan Cooksey, Deputy Chief Inspecting Officer, subsequently held a Public Inquiry into the accident.

The bridge piers, of which there were four, all of the masonry type, dated from the opening of the railway, but in the 1950s the original box girders of the bridge itself were found to require replacement, and a new steel girder bridge was constructed, resting on the old piers. The bridge had been examined regularly, and from time to time repairs had been carried out to the piers and to remedy the effects of scouring round the foot of the piers. So far as everyone knew, the bridge was perfectly sound and none of the railwaymen involved had the slightest qualms about travelling over it, as indeed they had had no fears about travelling over another bridge over the same river at Ffair-fach, about a mile on the far side of Llandeilo. No one locally had had any experience of bridge collapses, nor ever heard of one except for the Tay Bridge disaster over a century ago.

If four people are killed on the roads it excites little interest, but four people killed in a railway accident by drowning, in a train which has plunged off a railway bridge damaged by a fast-flowing river running at flood level, is a matter of great public interest. All the dramatic elements were there — the darkness, tinged with the first glimmer of daylight, the fear of being trapped in a coach with water rising over your head, the noise of the river in full spate, the terror that the coaches might be swept away at any

Above left and left:
Two views of the 05.27 Swansea to Shrewsbury after the river level had fallen by several feet. The ordeal of the passengers and train crew can be imagined from these photographs.
Tom Clift

Below:
Another bridge over the River Towy, near Carmarthen. Great Western 0-6-0 No 2200 is seen on the 3.20pm to Aberystwyth on 20 June 1951. *J. N. Westwood*

moment, and the sheer uniqueness of the situation. Questions began to be asked about the wisdom of running a train in such conditions, and particularly a passenger train. The Railway Authorities were severely criticised, as though they ought to have known that the Glanrhyd Bridge would collapse. And yet such an eventuality was totally outside anyone's experience or knowledge. There was absolutely no reason for any of the local BR staff to suspect the integrity of the bridge at Glanrhyd, nor of any of the other bridges on the line, even though conditions were described by some people as the worst they had ever seen. After all, bridges are always built with a wide margin of safety, and those four bridges over the Towy had easily withstood the worst that the weather had thrown at them for 130 years. Anyone saying that a train should not have crossed the Glanrhyd Bridge that morning was surely being wise after the event. But great emotions had been stirred, and passions roused. BR was negligent, people said; as though the local staff should have been able to divine the future. The inquest jury agreed and returned a verdict of 'unlawful killing'. They did not specify who had done the unlawful killing, and it is difficult to escape the feeling that it was simply an emotional swipe at BR; an easy target. What no one seems to have considered is the sequence of events that would have unfolded if the light locomotive had not run on the Sunday evening. It was purely fortuitous that it did run. It was purely fortuitous that the three areas of flooding were noticed and reported. It was purely fortuitous that the 05.27 Swansea to Shrewsbury was accompanied by a permanent way supervisor and an operations manager. Without all that, the train would have set off normally as on any other day. The driver would have noticed the flooding just beyond Llandeilo and he would have slowed down. Being an experienced man he would have known where he might expect flooding and he would have driven accordingly at what he considered to be an appropriate speed. He might well have gone on to the Glanrhyd Bridge a little faster — is there any reason why he should not have done? — and the result might have been even more serious. He would have had no reason to have doubted the stability of the bridge. Would the inquest jury then have found 'unlawful killing'? Perhaps not. It would not have wanted to have blamed a dead man. Was the inquest jury aware that the last time anyone was killed in a bridge collapse was over 70 years ago? That was at Carr Bridge on the Highland Railway, between Aviemore and Inverness, on 15 June 1914, when the 10.00am express from Glasgow Buchanan Street to Inverness became derailed as the train was crossing a flood-damaged bridge. The driver stopped the train with some coaches still on the bridge, and a few minutes later it collapsed. One of the coaches fell into the swollen river and five passengers were killed.

It was absolutely right that there should have been searching inquiries into the circumstances of the Glanrhyd Bridge collapse in order to see what went wrong and to ensure as far as possible that such an accident does not happen again. And yet, our views on road and rail accidents are quite unbalanced. Some time after the Glanrhyd accident the following note appeared in one of the daily newspapers:

'Four men were killed last night on a country bypass, the A350, near Chippenham, Wiltshire, during the rush hour. A mother and child were among five injured cut from the wreckage and were rushed to hospital with serious injuries.'

Was there a great outcry? No. Were the four men who were killed any less dead than the four people who died at Glanrhyd? No. Did their relatives grieve any the less? No.

Was there a full-scale public inquiry lasting four days and headed by a senior inspector from the Department of Transport? There was none. Did the inquest jury return a verdict of unlawful killing against the operators of the road system and the drivers of the road vehicles? Were stringent measures taken to ensure that it could not happen again? No, in all cases. Why do we apply such double standards to road and rail safety? Either we are over-reacting when there is a railway accident, or under-reacting when there is one on the roads. We cannot have it both ways.

There have been rare instances of other trains being involved in bridge collapses but without any casualties to passengers. An LMS Compound 4-4-0 was involved in one on an early morning local train to Skipton on 12 April 1947 after the severest winter in living memory in those parts. The bridge over a tributary of the River Aire at Eastburn near Keighley had been damaged by floods a year earlier and was being repaired. Single-line working was in operation over the double-track bridge and the traffic inspector on pilotman's duties was anxiously watching the river, which was in spate. He decided, in conjunction with the Engineering Department watchman, that no further trains should be allowed to pass over the bridge, but the District Control Office 'persuaded' him to allow the early morning train to pass, as it conveyed the mails, newspapers and parcels. It was therefore allowed to proceed, but the bridge collapsed under the engine and tender.

During the enquiries into the Glanrhyd disaster it was suggested that trains ought not to run over river bridges during flood conditions, but that seems to overlook a number of points. The damage is likely to be to the foundations of the piers or abutments, and may not be apparent except to divers. The damage may still be hidden when the flood waters recede and the river level goes down, except to divers. Is it seriously being suggested that BR should stop running trains for several days every time a river is in spate, and employ an army of divers? The point is that bridges are designed and built to withstand the worst possible flood conditions, and provided that there are adequate inspection and maintenance procedures, those whose job it is to run the trains are entitled to do so whatever the weather conditions, so far as bridges are concerned, unless the Civil Engineer advises to the contrary. Flooding of the track is a different matter, because it can damage the trackbed, hidden beneath the water. In such circumstances it is necessary to take the special precautions that were adopted for the passage of the 05.27 DMU from Swansea to Shrewsbury. The train was accompanied by a permanent way supervisor to advise the driver about track conditions, and the driver was warned by the signalman to proceed cautiously. The actual instructions to the signalman are contained in Regulation No 9 of the Regulations for Train Signalling, as follows:

'When it is required . . . to ascertain whether a line is clear, the signalman may allow a train to enter a section, subject to the following conditions: [among which the relevant ones are]

A train conveying passengers must not be used during fog or falling snow (the reason being the reduced visibility).

During darkness the driver must be accompanied by a competent person (for example the guard, another driver, or any railwayman with enough railway experience of a relevant nature. The purpose of this instruction is to assist the driver in keeping a sharp lookout in the darkness).

The driver must be informed of the circumstances, instructed to pass the section signal at Danger, and proceed cautiously through the section prepared to stop short of any obstruction.

(There are special instructions regarding tunnels.)

The text in brackets does not form part of the Regulation.'

These are the instructions to the signalman, and tell him what to do. So far as the driver is concerned, he is told by the signalman what he is to do, and he is informed of the circumstances. He is not issued with a copy of the signalling regulations but is guided by what the signalman tells him, and the instructions in the Rule Book (of which he does have a copy). The following are the relevant ones:

The driver must not pass a signal at Danger except . . . when the line is to be examined to ascertain whether it is clear (there are several other exceptions).
The driver must ensure that he clearly understands what is required and how far the movement may proceed.
The driver must proceed at such reduced speed throughout the section of line concerned as will ensure that he can stop safely and well clear of any train or obstruction on the line ahead. In determining the safe speed at which the train may proceed, the driver must be guided by the braking capability of his train and the distance ahead which he can see to be clear. He must take account of darkness, fog or falling snow, curvature of the line or any other feature affecting his view of the line ahead. THE DRIVER MUST ALWAYS BE ABLE TO STOP WITHIN THE DISTANCE HE CAN SEE THE LINE TO BE CLEAR.

The Railway Rules and Regulations use ordinary English words in a special way at times, for example, the words 'obstruction', and 'clear'. In the quotations from the Rules and Regulations just mentioned, the word 'obstruction' is considered to mean a physical obstruction, such as another train, a vehicle, or some wreckage or fallen rocks, literally something which would impede the free passage of the examining train. In that context, 'clear' means unobstructed. However, the examination procedure can also be used if there is a suspected track defect, in which case the word 'obstructed' takes on a new meaning and the staff concerned would proceed accordingly. This examination procedure would never be used if the structure of a bridge were suspected of being unsafe. In such circumstances no trains would be allowed to pass until the Civil Engineer had decided that it was safe for them do do so.

This special use of 'Railway English', that is the attaching of a specific meaning to a general word, can be confusing to the lay person. It can be particularly confusing to members of the legal profession, who of course use words as the tools of their trade and find themselves puzzled when a word or expression does not mean what they think it means.

Having mentioned lawyers, this might be an appropriate place to comment on what appears to be an undesirable trend in the conduct of public inquiries into railway accidents held by Railway Inspecting Officers of the Department of Transport under the provisions of the Regulation of Railways Act 1871. Section 3 of that Act states that:

'The Board of Trade (now the Department of Transport) may . . . appoint any person to be an inspector for the purpose of . . . making any inquiry . . . into the cause of any railway accident.'

It is customary for such inquiries to be held in public, but it should be noted that the public have no legal right to be present, and the Inspecting Officer may at his discretion hold part of the inquiry in private. The Inspecting Officer conducts the inquiry and hears the evidence, being assisted in this by the report of the railway internal inquiry conducted by a panel of railway officers. The Inspecting Officer has the following powers under Section 4 of the 1871 Act:

'He may by summons under his hand, require the attendance of any person who is engaged in the management, service or employment of (the railway undertaking) and whom he thinks fit to call before him and examine, and may require answers . . . as he thinks fit . . . (It should be noted that the Inspecting Officer has no powers to summon members of the public to give evidence, but he may invite them to do so, and they usually accept the invitation).
He may require and enforce the production of all books, papers and documents (of a railway undertaking) which he considers important (for the purpose of the inquiry).'

The Inspecting Officer's task is to establish the cause of an accident and to make recommendations to prevent a recurrence. The inquiry is not a court of law and it is not concerned with legal or criminal responsibility. He, and he alone, is entitled to ask questions, but it is customary to allow the senior railway officers who are present, to put questions to witnesses, but they will only do so where it will clarify points and aid him. The trade union representatives are also allowed, solely at the Inspecting Officer's discretion, to put questions to witnesses, but they are accustomed to public inquiries and do not normally abuse the courtesy extended to them. What is more, they are *au fait* with railway terminology and practice. A particular problem arises in that respect with counsel and solicitors attending the inquiry on behalf of clients, because members of the legal profession may have little or no knowledge of either railway terminology or practice. The Inspecting Officer may sometimes extend to them the courtesy of asking questions, which should be put through him, but the practice is growing of allowing them to put questions directly to witnesses. Because lawyers may not understand railway working they may ask questions which confuse the witnesses, and they may misunderstand the answers. They may have to waste the inquiry's time by seeking clarification to help them to understand. None of this assists the Inspecting Officer in any way in the task for which he has been appointed. Finally, under Section 7 of the 1871 Act, the Department of Transport is required to make the Inspecting Officer's report public.

The catalogue of bridge collapses caused by the action of flooded rivers is not a long one, despite the fact that there are thousands of such bridges. Starting about 50 years ago, the ones not already mentioned include:

21 June 1936   River Dulais
Between Newtown and Caersws, GWR Shrewsbury to Aberystwyth line (graphically described in O. S. Nock's book *Historic Railway Disasters*).

March 1947   River Wye Strangford Viaduct.
Near Fawley. GWR Hereford to Gloucester line.

August 1948   Several bridges
East Coast main line north of Berwick.

19 Nov 1951
Between Cocking and Midhurst, Southern Region. Engine of freight train fell into the gap.

Early 1960s   River Ystwyth
Near Aberystwyth, on the line to Carmarthen.

Sept 1968   River Wey
Godalming, on the Woking to Portsmouth line, Southern Region.

Sept 1968   River Mole
Cobham, on the Guildford New Line, Southern Region.

Sept 1968   River Kennett
Between Kennett and Higham, Eastern Region, near Newmarket.

Sept 1968   Bridge 317
Between Diss and Burston, Norwich main line.

Bridge collapses are rare, but not unknown. However, none of the following involved a passenger train:

1. **Strangford Viaduct over the River Wye, Great Western Railway between Hereford and Gloucester, March 1947.** *GWR*
2. **East Coast main line Bridge No 133 between Grantshouse and Reston on 15 August 1948, with the rails suspended in mid-air over the gap.** *BR*
3. **East Coast main line Bridge No 133 after temporary repairs, being tested by Class D49 4-4-0 No 62706** *Forfarshire* **and Class A4 Pacific No 60012** *Commonwealth of Australia.* *BR*

215

4. **Cobham Bridge, September 1968,** *BR*
5. **Bridge No 1122 over the River Kennett, Eastern Region, September 1968.** *BR*
6. **Bridge No 317, between Diss and Burston, September 1968.** *BR*

Of all these incidents, the most spectacular must have been the East Coast floods of 1948, which were caused by torrential rain during 11 and 12 August. Between Reston and Grantshouse, over a distance of five miles, the Eye Water normally meanders along, being crossed repeatedly by the East Coast main line. It is generally little more than a stream, but following the unrelenting downpour it became a torrent with sufficient force to demolish no fewer than seven bridges. On the next section of line between Grantshouse and Cockburnspath long lengths of track and ballast were washed away. Five of the seven bridges which collapsed were of the masonry arch type and two had wrought-iron girders. The line was reopened for passengers on 1 November 1948, using military-type bridges as a temporary measure, with severe speed restrictions. Some of the branch lines inland also suffered damage.

Railway bridges over rivers are designed to be able to withstand the most severe weather conditions, and generally speaking the weather is no worse now than it was 100 to 150 years ago when most of them were built. Railway bridges over roads were designed for the road traffic of the period — perhaps high enough for the driver of a stagecoach to pass under safely, without having his hat or his head knocked off. Today those bridges are under relentless attack from lorries, the speed and weight of which are sometimes sufficient to cause physical damage to the bridges. The building of motorways and bypasses, with higher overbridges, has eased the problem somewhat, but it is still a matter of concern to BR, as two recent items in its house magazine *Rail News* show. The October 1987 issue

Right and below:
The bridge over the A5 London to Holyhead trunk road at Hinckley, on the Leicester-Nuneaton line, has regularly been attacked by lorries. These two photographs show the result of one of the more severe impacts from an overheight lorry or load. *Raymonds Photographers/Author*

Above:
A view of the bridge over the A465 Hereford to Abergavenny road, just south of Pontrilas, as seen in July 1988. The bridge, which carries the Shrewsbury-Hereford-Newport main line, has been shored up to allow trains to pass over, pending permanent repairs. Single line working is in operation for road traffic. *Author*

tells how the Anglesey town of Llangefni narrowly escaped disaster when a juggernaut lorry rammed a railway overbridge shortly after a train conveying dangerous chemicals had passed over it. The main girder of the bridge was pushed off the abutment on to the top of the trailer, making a kink in the line which was so severe that it would almost certainly have derailed a passing train. Local police reported seeing the driver make two attempts to drive his 14ft 1in vehicle beneath the bridge, which was clearly marked 13ft 8in, and one wonders why they did not stop him before he made his second attempt. Perhaps they thought that an apparently flimsy trailer could not possibly damage a big, strong bridge. Maybe the driver thought so too, but at least he was caught in the act, unlike the lorry driver who attacked the bridge over the A465 Hereford to Abergavenny road, just south of Pontrilas, on 6 March 1988. The impact was so great that it damaged the bridge, so the driver can hardly have been unaware of the fact, but he did not bother to report it to BR. Either he did not imagine that his lorry could actually have damaged the bridge and endangered trains, or he did not care. Fortunately, a BR inspector driving his car under the bridge noticed the damage and raised the alarm. Single line working had to be introduced, with a severe speed restriction, until the bridge was shored up.

The second *Rail News* item tells of a low-loader type of lorry, carrying an excavator, becoming jammed under a railway bridge near Westbury (Wilts). The force of the impact lifted the bridge girders by 8in. Some 24hr later engineers were dealing with two more incidents in which container lorries had become wedged under bridges in Bristol. Low-loaders carrying plant and machinery are probably the greatest hazard. In 1975 one hit and almost completely demolished an overbridge at Gorey in Ireland. A CIE express train attempted to jump the gap but failed, and scattered itself all over the area, several lives being lost. It is feared that one day the same thing will happen in Britain. Already there have been derailments.

Bridges are not only at risk on trunk roads, but also on minor and local roads, as was demonstrated on 12 May 1978 in the quiet Scottish countryside about 25 miles inland from Aberdeen, on the line to Inverness. The train concerned was the 07.43 three-car diesel multiple-unit (DMU) from Aberdeen, and it set off from Inverurie at 08.12, with 54 passengers on board, on its way to the next station, Insch. About two miles before reaching Insch the railway line crosses the B9002 road, a quiet country road which connects Insch with the A96 Aberdeen to Inverness trunk road. The bridge bears a sign showing its height — 15ft 3in. There is a plant hire firm in Insch, and that morning one of the drivers, on reporting for work at 07.30, was told to take an excavator on an articulated low-loader type of lorry to Peterhead. His route lay along the B9002 road. He had driven this vehicle, loaded with the excavator, on several occasions and he knew that the overall height of the lorry and the excavator, when properly loaded, was just 15ft. The total weight was 30 tons. Being a careful driver he had checked on the first occasion when he had driven under the

1

The results of bridge-bashing at Oyne, between Aberdeen and Keith, on 12 May 1978

1. The excavator on the low-loader, which caused the damage. The trailer has broken in two. *Author*
2. The distorted track and the derailed train. *Author*

2

railway bridge on the B9002 that there was adequate clearance, and he had actually stopped close to the bridge to check.

The driver had loaded the excavator on to the low-loader himself the previous evening, so he knew that it was safe to pass under the bridge. Having received his orders for the day he went to get ready for the journey and whilst he was away the excavator operator started up the machine to remove the blade from the bucket, leaving it with the boom vertical. It was now 16ft high. Just after 08.00 the driver set off on his journey and at about 08.15, 3min after the DMU had left the last station before the bridge, the lorry with its 16ft high load approached the 15ft 3in high bridge, at a speed of about 20mph. The boom of the excavator hit one of the bridge girders with a resounding crack and knocked it out of alignment by over 3ft, distorting the railway track as it did so.

The passenger train was still five miles away. Was there sufficient time to warn its driver, so that the imminent disaster could be averted? When the lorry collided with the bridge, its driver was momentarily stunned. A moment or two later, a passing motorist helped him from the cab and then went off to telephone for assistance. The lorry driver, upon seeing the damage to the bridge, realised that if there was a train coming it had to be stopped. Not knowing from which direction a train was due, and in an awful quandary, he started to run towards Insch. He had taken the wrong decision. After a few moments he turned and saw the train approaching from the other direction. It was now too late to do anything.

Below:
The bridge over the A68 road, on the Danderhall to Bilston branch, near Edinburgh, completely demolished by a lorry on 24 September 1977. *The Scotsman*

Below right:
It is feared that this scene will one day be repeated in Britain. This accident happened at Gorey on the Coras Iompair Eireann in 1975 and several passengers were killed. The remains of the bridge can be seen in the top right-hand corner of the photograph. *Author*

On board the train, the driver was sitting at the controls, quite relaxed as he coasted down the gently falling gradient at about 55mph. He could see the bridge clearly from some distance away, but the curvature of the line prevented him from having a good view of the track over the bridge until he was quite close to it. With a start he realised that the track was terribly distorted and he immediately pushed the brake handle straight through to the emergency position. It seemed like an eternity before the brakes started to bite but they had reduced the speed of the train to about 40mph when it hit the buckle in the track. The driver clung on grimly as the train bucked and reared, then his coach plunged down the embankment and rolled over on to its side. The second coach followed but remained upright, whilst astonishingly the last coach was not even derailed. There was comparatively little damage to the coach bodies, and most of the passengers were able to climb out with no more than cuts and bruises, thankful to be still alive and in one piece. Only five passengers received minor injuries.

Could the accident have been prevented in any way, or was it just the consequence of an unfortunate set of circumstances? The lorry driver knew the bridge and believed that his load would safely pass under it. There are then only three ways of protecting bridges in such circumstances:

1. To erect a massive steel beam across the road on both sides, set at about 3in below the bridge height. This would effectively prevent any overheight vehicle from reaching the bridge, but the consequences of the collision of the lorry or its load with the beam might endanger other road users, although no more so than a collision with the bridge. The Department of Transport has assessed the cost at £100,000 per bridge, because the beams would have to be of very robust construction. A cheaper and less robust beam might suffice because even though it would not physically prevent the lorry from reaching the bridge the shock of the collision would alert the driver. This solution is not favoured by the Department of Transport (DTp) because the dislodged beam might injure pedestrians or other road users, which might suggest that the DTp

considers the lives of road users to be more important than the lives of railway passengers. This is the classic 'horse and stable door' situation. No loss of life has yet resulted from a damaged bridge derailment in Britain, although each year there are several bridge-strikes which could have resulted in railway passengers being killed, and it is generally accepted that sooner or later such a fatal accident will occur.

2. To raise the height of the bridge, either by increasing the height of the bridge abutments or by lowering the road surface. This would certainly be effective, but would be very expensive and could only be justified at the few bridges considered to be most at risk. The B9002 bridge would certainly not fall into that category.

3. To install infra-red detectors and automatic signs. High vehicles passing through the detector beam would activate a sign with amber flashing lights to indicate to a driver that his vehicle was over-height. It is the most effective signing measure available, and would cost about £35,000 per bridge. Whilst the equipment would not physically protect the bridge, only a very reckless and foolhardy driver would proceed after such a warning.

For various reasons the scale of the problem has reduced in recent years, thanks partly to the measures which have already been taken, such as improved bridge marking and signing; improved road signing; marking the height in the cab; and various other measures designed to increase driver awareness; although new road construction, with bridges at a minimum height of 16ft 6in has probably had most effect. As long ago as 1972 Col Robertson, the Chief Inspecting Officer, was drawing attention to the problem in his Annual Report. He mentioned that there were about 500 cases a year of damage to railway bridges over roads, and gave his prophetic view that the most damaging type of road vehicle was the low-loader conveying a heavy piece of engineering plant. However, by 1987 the number of potentially serious 'strikes' at the 4,640 bridges considered to be vulnerable had gone down to just over 200, but it is still regarded as a serious hazard and the Minister asked the Bridge-bashing Working Party, which had been in existence since the 1970s, to suggest a strategy to reduce substantially the number of 'strikes' over the next five years. The Working Party produced its Report in 1988 with a comprehensive list of options and a proposed programme, so the prospects are good, but the accident on the B9002 road seems to make it likely that the danger will never be completely eradicated. However, if it can be substantially reduced it will be another step forward in the long quest to improve railway safety.

7
Death on the Line

Hellifield is a station of ghosts. It is impossible to stand on its dilapidated platforms, parts of which are roped off so that the few waiting passengers or curious visitors will not be decapitated by panes of glass falling from the platform roof, and not sense the hustle and bustle that was once a part of everyday life there. The Scotch expresses used to call, not for the convenience of Hellifield's small community, but for the Lancashire connections. There was a sizeable engine shed here too with the noise of engines clanking on and off the shed, or the rattle and clatter of the tubs on the coaling stage as they were wheeled out to tip their contents into waiting tenders. Little knots of locomen and guards would hang around waiting to relieve through trains in order to work them over the 'Long Drag' to Carlisle, or into Lancashire. One can still hear in the imagination the voice of the foreman calling out 'The Brindle Heath's just passed Settle Junction'. Few passengers use the station nowadays, and there are no longer any staff there. It is a station of ghosts. And now there are two more.

Snow is not uncommon at Hellifield, situated as it is almost in the shadow of the Pennine giants — Penyghent and Ingleborough. When the winter wind blows from the north or the east it often brings snow with it; then Hellifield lies under a white mantle. Railwaymen in those parts learned long ago how to cope with snow and it became part of the railway tradition that 'the trains must get through'. The winter of 1978/79 has gone down in history as the winter of discontent. Not only were there industrial relations problems, but the weather was more severe than usual. At Hellifield on 15 February 1979 it was bitterly cold and a keen northeaster was blowing the lying snow about. In the signalbox at Hellifield South the signalman was trying to keep himself warm as the wind whistled through every nook and cranny whilst he waited for the late-running express from Nottingham to Carlisle. It should have passed through Hellifield just after lunch but here he was, after eight o'clock at night and still no sign of it. The weather must be bad further south, he thought to himself,

Below:
Hellifield — scene of former splendours. Now a station of ghosts.

when finally, at 20.46, his signalbox block bell rang to announce that the train had just left Skipton, 10 miles to the south and the next signalbox open. He sent the bell signal 'Is the line clear for an express passenger train?' to the signalman at Settle Junction and when he received an affirmative answer he tried to clear his signals for the express. However, when he tried to pull the lever of his Down Home signal he found that it was still 'locked' in the lever-frame, and he noticed that the indication light for some points beyond the signal had gone out. The points were electrically operated because they were at the far end of the station, and when they were in their normal position for trains to travel along the Down main line this fact was indicated to the signalman by a small light on an instrument in the signalbox.

The signalman had had some difficulty with these points earlier in the day when he wanted to run a train from the Down loop on to the Down main line, because snow had blown into them; and when he moved the points the snow became squeezed and compacted into ice, preventing the points from fitting correctly. He had then sent for the Signal Department technicians, who had put the matter right. They had now gone home, therefore he telephoned the permanent way cabin nearby and asked the platelayers to attend to the points. A few minutes later he saw his points indicator light up, telling him that the points were now in their correct position and that the electrical lock on his Down Home signal lever should now be free, so he pulled the lever over and cleared the signal together with all the other signals, for the express to pass.

The express no longer called at Hellifield — the Lancashire connections had long since been withdrawn — and the train approached the station at about 60mph as it swung round the approach curve on the falling gradient from Otterburn and roared past the signalbox. At the far end of the platform the driver suddenly saw the shadowy outline of a man crouched over the points leading from the Down Loop, and directly in the path of the train. He sounded the horn and threw the brakes on. It was much too late. Almost immediately the driver heard the stomach-churning thud and realised that the man had not managed to get clear.

When the call to clear the points had been received in the permanent way cabin two men had gone out to do it. They had donned all their cold weather clothing and muffled themselves up, then they picked up their tools and, heads down, they went out into the howling wind, with the flakes of snow stinging their faces. They cleared the snow and ice from the points (which allowed the signalman to obtain a 'points correct' indication, and clear his signals), then started to put a clamp on the points (a clamp is a metal appliance, rather like a vice, which is screwed up to hold the points firmly in position), oblivious of the fact that death was approaching them at 60mph. With the wind whistling round their ears, and bent over their task, they heard nothing of the train's approach until the last second. They looked up startled but it was too late. A 60mph train is a very effective killer.

Perhaps the two unfortunate platelayers had not expected the signalman to clear his signals, nor expected the train to arrive so soon nor travel so quickly. However, the signalman was fully entitled to clear his signals, and there were no instructions in the Rule Book or elsewhere to tell him not to. Platelayers had always cleared the points during snowy weather and were accustomed to look after their own safety. If necessary, one of the men would act as a lookoutman whilst the other got on with the work. The Rules stated that:

'When work is to be carried out on or near lines in use for traffic and danger is likely to arise, the man-in-charge must appoint one or more men . . . expressly to maintain a good lookout and to give warning of approaching trains. Where, of necessity, men are working during fog or falling snow, the man-in-charge must post a lookout-man . . .'

The question to be considered was whether one of the two men should have acted as a lookoutman. They were both qualified to do so. The Rule says that a lookoutman must be appointed if danger is likely to arise. With the line still open to trains, it was evident that danger was likely to arise, especially in the wind and darkness. On the other hand, until the points were cleared of ice and snow danger was unlikely to arise, because the signalman was unable to clear his signals. This risk of danger then became active at the moment the 'points normal' indication appeared in the signalbox. The platelayers may not have known the precise moment when this took place, but they would know that it was likely to occur as soon as the points were fitting correctly, and from that moment on there should have been a lookoutman. What we do not know, of course, is whether one of the two men was already acting as a lookoutman but if he was, such action was ineffective. There is another point too. The Rule says that during falling snow there must be a lookoutman. At the time of the accident, snow was not actually falling but it was being blown about and the effect on visibility may have been the same.

Below:
Hellifield — freight trunk route. LMS 'Crab' 2-6-0 No 42899 of Carlisle Kingmoor shed draws slowly along the Goods line to wait a path, passing Midland Class 3F 0-6-0 No 43756 as it does so, on 3 September 1962. *L. Sandler*

Bottom:
On the same afternoon, sister engine 42798 of Holbeck shed hurries through on the Up main line with an express freight. Another reminder of the past are the cattle wagons next to the engine. *L. Sandler*

As has already been mentioned, there was nothing in the Rules to prevent the signalman from clearing his signals for the express. He had no means of knowing whether or not the platelayers were relying on him for their protection, indeed for their very lives, but to place such a responsibility on the signalman would have been grossly unfair. Supposing that the signalman had misunderstood an arrangement he had made with the platelayers to protect them, or had momentarily overlooked it, might he not then have found himself in the dock facing a manslaughter charge?

And yet, was it enough to have left it to the platelayers themselves to look after their own safety on such a night? The circumstances of the tragic accident at Hellifield focussed attention once more on the subject. If there was going to be a system of protection involving the signalman it had to be cast-iron. BR pondered hard over this. There were two main considerations — the avoidance of the possibility of any misunderstanding between the signalman and the platelayers, and the avoidance of a situation whereby the signalman might be loaded with an unreasonable and haphazard responsibility for other men's lives. BR's solution was essentially simple. It issued a new Regulation designed to remove any doubts or misunderstandings. It stated that when a signalman sent for platelayers or technicians, etc to repair or make workable some piece of equipment on the track the men concerned must come to an understanding as to whether trains were still running or not, and if not, when they could be allowed to resume running. Alternatively, if the work could not be carried out safely with trains running, they were to be stopped. Where trains were stopped the signalman would give an assurance that this was so and that he would not allow train running to resume until the platelayers agreed. The signalman would also place a metal lever collar over the appropriate signal lever, to physically prevent him from pulling the lever in a moment of forgetfulness, and he would record all the facts in his Train Register Book.

Hellifield was not the only railway location to be affected by snow and tragedy that winter. The following morning, at Rowley Regis on the former Great Western line from Stourbridge Junction to Birmingham, two platelayers were clearing snow from points when they were taken unawares by the 07.42 DMU from Worcester to Birmingham. One of them managed to jump clear when the driver of the approaching DMU sounded an urgent warning on his horn but the other one was knocked down and killed. They had no lookoutman, but at least it was daylight and not snowing. They had merely carried out the former practice of looking out for their own safety when engaged in snow clearance.

Fatal accidents to men working on the line have been occurring ever since railways began and still do so today, despite all the Rule changes, explanatory booklets and changes in procedures, etc. BR is very concerned that such tragedies still occur, as the front page headlines in the September 1988 issue of *Rail News* show — 'Board alarm as track death figures mount'. The article goes on to say that of 83 railwaymen killed on duty since January 1984 more than half have been struck by trains while crossing, walking or working on the line. The table below nevertheless illustrates the tremendous improvement which has taken place since steam days. 1986 was the best year ever.

	1957	1971	1980	1985	1986	1987
Total No of staff	597,000	261,000	232,000	181,000	178,000	179,000
Killed whilst working on the line	33	14	6	10	3	7
Killed whilst on the line, eg standing or walking	70	18	9	4	1	1
Total killed (all causes)	176	60	32	25	16	16

(The above figures are for all railways in Britain)

The figures for 1985 were inflated by a particularly appalling accident which occurred at Severn Tunnel Junction on 11 February. Once again there was snow and men were on duty specially to keep the points clear. There were no fewer than six men employed in a gang that night, keeping the points clear of snow and ice on the main line from Paddington to South Wales, to the west of Severn Tunnel Junction station. It had stopped snowing but there was a strong, cold easterly wind, which was blowing loose snow into the points. All the points and signals were operated from Newport power signalbox 10 miles away, and the points themselves were equipped with gas heaters to prevent them from freezing up, but heaters are prone to being blown out in strong winds and require periodic checking and relighting. There were 42 sets of gas point heaters in the area.

Two teams of men were used at Severn Tunnel Junction for snow clearance duties and each team worked a 12hr shift, changing over at 19.00. The night shift men on 11 February worked for a while then had a break, during which some of them went to a local public house. On their return the six-man gang set to work again. It was now approaching midnight. They worked progressively on the points comprising the 'ladder' at the Newport end of the yards, but they had no lookoutman, nor had they come to any understanding with the signalman; errors that were to prove fatal. Perhaps, being Sunday night, they thought (incorrectly) that there would be very few trains about. They had perhaps forgotten about one insignificant little train, the 00.25 DMU from Cardiff, which terminated at Severn Tunnel Junction. Approaching the station its driver had reduced his speed to about 45mph, when he suddenly caught a fleeting glimpse of a high-visibility vest and almost immediately heard an impact. He knew instinctively what it was, but he had no idea that that slight noise had signified the deaths of no fewer than four men. It was one of the worst accidents of its type which had ever happened. All six men had received training and had passed a skill test for carrying out lookoutmen's duties. In addition four of them had attended a special course on lookoutmen arrangements and had passed out as qualified to decide whether or not lookoutmen should be appointed.

Above:
In 1965 Standard Class 9F 2-10-0 No 92208 draws slowly along the Down Goods line at Hellifield with the empty anhydrite hopper wagons in circuit working between Long Meg Sidings, near Langwathby, and Widnes. *N. Gascoine*

At the inquest the Coroner said that the cause of the accident was the failure to appoint a lookoutman. He did not consider that consumption of alcohol played a prominent part and thought it was probably a case of familiarity breeding contempt. The jury's verdict was 'Accidental Death'. The accident was also investigated by Mr A. W. Froud, a Railway Employment Inspector of the Department of Transport, who recommended that the

Below:
A Class 45 diesel-electric heads through Severn Tunnel Junction station with the 06.14 Sheffield to Cardiff Central on 13 August 1977. *D. Kimber*

Above:
'Planlite' gas-operated point heaters. *BR*

provision of lookout protection during the hours of darkness for men working on lines open to trafffic should be made compulsory. This recommendation was accepted by BR and is now incorporated in the Rules. He also reiterated the Railway Inspectorate's oft-repeated recommendation that headlights should be fitted to all traction units, so that men working on the track could identify the approach of a train sooner and more easily. BR is working on this, but slowly, because of the cost involved. All new traction units are so equipped but BR have been reluctant to spend money on slower traction units which are approaching the ends of their lives.

The problem of the appointment of lookoutmen is a very long-running story. An official group, known by the somewhat cumbersome title of 'The Railway Industry Advisory Committee Working Group on Safety of Staff on the Track' (a joint body representing the DTp, BR and the trade unions — chaired by an Inspecting Officer) has spent many years deliberating this issue and gradually pushing BR into extending and improving the lookout arrangements. The question might reasonably be asked as to why BR apparently had to be pushed, when lives were at stake, and there are two main reasons — the difficulty in fixing a precise dividing line between those situations where a lookoutman was essential for safety and those where men could reasonably be expected to look out for their own safety; and the fact that every additional lookoutman employed means another man on the line and another life at risk. Lookoutmen themselves have been knocked down and killed by the very trains they were supposed to be looking out for. And whilst cost ought not to be a factor in the

Below:
The effectiveness of point heaters in keeping the points free from snow. *BR*

reckoning where men's lives are concerned, it must be. It has to be. Cost is a factor in the reckoning of any safety precaution.

The main difficulty has been the fixing of the dividing line between those cases where a lookoutman was necessary and those where he was not. It would obviously be nonsense to provide a lookoutman for someone who merely needed to cross a quiet branch line in broad daylight, or who needed to do a little work on such a line where trains approached at low speed and could be seen a mile away. Equally it would be nonsense not to provide one, or even two, on a high speed multi-track main line, when a gang of men had to work on the track. Between those two extremes there is a judgement area where the decision is left to the man in charge. He was given some guidance — the time-honoured phrase being 'where danger is likely to arise a lookoutman must be appointed'. That sufficed for many years. It was embraced within the Board of Trade's 'Prevention of Accidents Rules 1902', made under The Railway Employment (Prevention of Accidents) Act, 1900, and was still in the Rule Book, though amplified somewhat in 1988. The Rule has been the subject of many court cases. In a 1942 case the Court of Appeal held that a lookout might not be necessary in the case of a branch line with only two or three trains a day. In 1958 Viscount Kilmuir said that the words 'any danger is likely to arise' must be given their ordinary meaning and import an estimate of likelihood not of what might possibly be foreseen, but of what should be expected to occur. The estimate must be made according to ordinary principles of common sense and experience in the light of all the relevant circumstances known.

The Health and Safety at Work Act 1974 gave a fresh impetus to the question of safety of men on the line and since then BR has found its Rules and methods and procedures under closer scrutiny. It has responded by issuing reams of instructions in an attempt to cover every contingency and situation, lest it should find itself in the dock facing a criminal charge under the Act; but the men who work on the track are employed for their manual skills rather than their intellectual capacity and there is a danger that, finding themselves bemused by floods of literature and continuous exhortation, they will revert to first principles. It is, of course, absolutely right and proper that BR should do all it sensibly can to protect the lives of its staff, regarding equipment, methods, Rules, procedures and training, but in the ultimate reckoning some regard has to be paid to the nature of the men concerned and how they will respond. There is a law of behaviour which states that 'the degree of observance of a rule is in inverse proportion to its complexity'. 'Keep it simple' should be every rule-maker's motto, and some regard must be paid to the common sense and experience of the men whose job it is to interpret and carry out Rules and instructions. After all, the volumes of Rules and instructions and the thousands of hours spent in learned discussion by eminent committees did not save the lives of four men at Severn Tunnel Junction on the night of 10/11 February 1985. Perhaps there is

another law in operation here — 'the bigger the committee, the less it achieves'.

The provision of a lookoutman does not in itself automatically guarantee the safety of the men at work. In an accident at Pear Tree public footpath crossing near Salfords station on the Brighton main line on 2 October 1983 two men, a father and son, were killed when they were knocked down by the 08.00 train from London Victoria to Three Bridges. The lookoutman himself was also hit by the train, which cut off his left leg. The men were part of a gang repairing the timber crossing and they appear to have been taken unawares by a train on the Down slow line. There are four tracks at this location and the line is busy, with train speeds up to 90mph. The accident happened in clear weather and daylight and the fact that the lookoutman himself was injured seemed to indicate to the investigating Inspector that he had failed to see the approaching train until the last few seconds, and in consequence had failed to warn those whose lives were in his hands. This underlines the heavy responsibility which lookoutmen carry.

In another case, on 7 May 1984, near Bushey, on the West Coast main line from Euston, a lookoutman was knocked down and killed by the very train for which he had already given a warning to the men he was protecting. They were unharmed.

Perhaps this would be an appropriate place to say a few words about the 1974 Health and Safety at Work Act. Its title sounds harmless enough, indeed it sounds entirely beneficial and a credit to a responsible and progressive society. In reality it is a burden and an encumbrance so far as the railways are concerned, BR being an innocent victim. It may well have been a necessary measure so far as certain industries were concerned, but it was almost entirely superfluous so far as BR were concerned, because the railways already had a very extensive safety organisation, in which the local staff representatives were already involved; and the Department of Transport already had extensive powers under the 1900 Railway Employment (Prevention of Accidents) Act. The 1974 Act was quickly discovered to be something of a bureaucratic nightmare, and it has absorbed enormous quantities of management time in its procedural complexities; time which would have been more usefully devoted to the practicalities of achieving a safer railway. It did not prevent the accidents at Polmont, or Severn Tunnel Junction, or Methley Junction, described in this chapter. In the view of many people the Act was ill-conceived, inadequately thought-out and badly drafted.

As train speeds rise and the use of noisy machinery increases, the difficulty of giving timely and effective warning to men working on the line becomes more pronounced. In an accident at Polmont, on the Edinburgh-Glasgow main line on 5 August 1983, inquired into by John Seager, the Principal Railway Employment Inspector, both these factors were present. The line at the site of the accident was sharply curved, and the maximum permitted speed was 90mph (100mph for IC125 units). A gang of men was employed in repacking the ballast under a dipped welded rail joint on the Down line, using Kango electric tamping hammers. Owing to the restricted visibility the man in charge had appointed an extra lookoutman to give advance warning of the approach of trains on the Down line before they could be seen by the normal lookoutman, who was posted at the site of work. When the advance lookoutman saw a train approaching he would wave a blue and white chequered flag, and upon seeing this the site lookoutman would switch off the electric power to the Kango hammers and sound a siren. These combined actions were sufficient to warn the workmen to stand clear of the tracks. Whilst the provision of an advance lookoutman enabled the men to be given an earlier warning than would otherwise have been the case (and without whom it would have been unsafe to have carried out the work at all without trains being stopped), the procedure suffered from an

Below:
One of the high speed push-pull services in use between Edinburgh and Glasgow. Class 47 diesel-electric No 47702 is seen near Linlithgow with the 08.30 from Glasgow on 20 September 1986. *W. A. Sharman*

inherent and dangerous defect — it was not fail-safe. If the site lookoutman for any reason did not notice the advance warning, the men at work would not receive a warning to stand clear until the train came into view from the work site, if then. That could be too late.

After the men had taken their breakfast they resumed work on the track. Then, according to the evidence given in Mr Seager's Report on the accident, a Down train approached and the advance lookoutman waved his blue and white flag. The site lookoutman saw this, switched off the Kango hammers and sounded the siren. The gang moved clear, and then restarted work after the train had passed. A few minutes later an IC125 unit came along the Up line. The warning was given and the men stood clear. They had very little time to do so because of the curvature of the line and the speed of the train, and the site lookoutman felt uneasy about this. He called across to the man in charge to discuss the problem with him, taking his eyes off the advance lookoutman as he did so. It was a fatal mistake. The advance lookoutman saw another train approach on the Down line and turned to wave his flag. To his consternation the site lookoutman did not respond. He waved his flag frantically and shouted, but got no response. The men on the Down line, directly in the path of the approaching train, carried on with their work, quite oblivious of the fact that they were living their last few seconds. The train struck them with appalling suddenness, and they probably never knew what hit them. Two men were thrown clear and killed, whilst the body of a third man became lodged below the nearside guard iron of the power car and was carried forward to where the train stopped. The fatal flaw in the system had been exposed. It is expecting a lot of human nature to rely implicitly for the safety of men's lives upon one man never taking his eyes off another for hours on end. There was, in fact, a better warning system available, known as the 'Pee Wee' system. This is a transportable electrical advance warning set of equipment which is used by the advance lookoutman to sound the siren at the worksite, and is a safer method of giving warning. Two sets of this equipment had been supplied to the local depot, but one had been unserviceable for some time prior to the accident and the other was missing, presumed stolen.

It might be thought that the only certain way to prevent men from being killed whilst working on the track would be to stop trains from running altogether. Such arrangements already exist when major items of work have to be undertaken, but even then misunderstandings can have fatal results. On Saturday night 6 November 1982 some work was programmed to be carried out at Denham station on the Bicester to Marylebone line. Accordingly, the Civil Engineer closed the Down line at 01.15 on Sunday morning and told a gang of painters that they could erect scaffolding on the Down line in order to paint the bridge at Denham station. He could not at that moment close the Up line because he had to wait until an empty DMU from Bicester to Marylebone had gone by. Through some misunderstanding the painters erected their scaffolding on the Up line instead of the Down line, before the empty DMU had passed. It ran into the scaffolding and three painters were killed.

One might imagine that an accident such as the one at Polmont on 5 August 1983 could not happen again; that steps would be taken, training improved, supervision intensified, new equipment devised and maintained in proper working order, and everything reasonable be done to ensure safety. And yet there was an accident at Methley Junction, near Leeds, on the former Midland Railway main line to Sheffield on 8 December 1987 that had many similarities with the Polmont tragedy. Once again a gang of men was working on the track with Kango hammers, which make so much noise that the machine operators cannot hear the approach of a train. Indeed, the equipment makes so much noise that the operators have to wear protective ear muffs, thus ensuring that they cannot hear trains approaching. In such circumstances, with the men so completely exposed to mortal danger, it is essential that the

Below:
The 13.17 Edinburgh to Dunblane train brakes for the Polmont stop on 20 February 1982. *D. M. May*

Left:
Men at work on the track using hand-held machinery. They are wearing ear protectors, which prevent their hearing from being damaged, but make them totally dependent on the lookoutman for their safety. The lookoutman is holding the switch which cuts off the power to the equipment and sounds a siren on the approach of a train.
John Rose Associates

warning system is foolproof and fail-safe. We have seen how the system in use at Polmont had a fatal flaw, but in fact the system in use at Methley was the same one, with the advance lookoutman with his same blue and white chequered flag, and the safety of the gang entirely dependent on the site lookoutman never taking his eyes off the advance lookout.

On the morning of the accident two trains had passed without incident. Each time, the site lookoutman had seen the chequered flag and had switched off power to the Kango hammers, which automatically sounded a siren. Each time, the gang had stood clear until the train passed and had then resumed work. Each time, whilst the men were standing clear, the site lookoutman had walked down the line about 60yd to move a marker board. It was not his job to do so; he should have had no other duties but it seemed safe enough at the time. However, and here was the fatal flaw, in order to stop the siren from sounding, the site lookoutman had to switch on the power to the Kango hammers. The consequences were revealed in the following evidence given at the Official Inquiry and at the Coroner's Inquest.

A little later, the 10.43 DMU from Leeds to Sheffield approached at 60/65mph. The advance lookoutman waved his flag. The site lookoutman acknowledged and gave his usual warning. The gang stopped work, then the site lookoutman walked down the line a little way to move the marker board. Power to the tools was now back on again. Suddenly he heard the Kango hammers working. Through some misunderstanding the gang had gone back on to the track and restarted work, but the train had not yet gone by. The site lookoutman ran back towards the gang shouting and waving his arms in desperation but they did not hear him. The noise of the hammers, and the protection of the ear muffs, ensured that they did not.

The DMU had just got into its stride after the Woodlesford stop when the driver saw the gang of men on the track with their backs to him. 'I was shocked when I saw what was in front of me,' he said at the Inquiry. 'It was unusual that they were still on the track as I approached. I blew the horn to warn them but I got no response. The men didn't appear to move so I started blowing the horn again and putting the brake on. There was no reaction from the

men whatsoever. There was no movement from them before the impact. I hadn't a chance to stop. It was terrible. I was just transfixed.' Four men were killed.

The foreman of the Inquest jury criticised BR, saying that the warning systems were inadequate, the men lacked training, and there was insufficient supervision. The Coroner commented 'It seems inconceivable that in this day and age we still rely on 18th century methods of using flags to warn men on the track.' What would he have said, one wonders, if he had known that the flag system was of quite recent vintage, and introduced to enable the workmen to be given earlier warning of the approach of trains? A foolproof portable, fail-safe system, which relies as little as possible on human intervention, has still to be introduced for one-off use. On high speed lines there is a permanent automatic system which gives an audible warning, initiated when an approaching train occupies a track circuit. The system can be switched off when not required, because the noise it makes is not popular with local residents, but there is a danger that one gang could switch off the system, unaware that another was still depending on it. Work is therefore in progress to see whether an Inductive Loop Warning System can be devised for use on such lines. In this system, cables would be laid along each side of the track to form a loop which would transmit warnings to portable units carried by lookoutmen and others who need them. It would also be able to give warnings inside protective ear muffs when noisy equipment such as Kango hammers are in use. However, as long as human beings are capable of error or misunderstanding it seems likely that death on the line will continue to occur.

Almost as a postscript to this chapter it is sad to have to relate the death of yet another lookoutman, on 13 October 1988, near Attleborough on the line between Norwich and Peterborough. A 61-year-old leading trackman, with 31 years' railway experience, was acting as a lookoutman for a track maintenance gang of four men when he was knocked down and killed by the 13.43 Sprinter from Norwich to Blackpool. His was the 10th death on the line in 1988, emphasising that the problem of the safety of men working on the track is particularly intractable. The train is a most effective killer.

8
Trespassers and Suicides

In 1987 three passengers were killed in train accidents. Sixteen railway staff were killed in all types of accident. By contrast, in the same year 144 trespassers were killed, and there were 173 suicides. Ten years earlier the figures were:

Passengers killed in train accidents	Nil
Railway staff killed in all types of accident	34
Trespassers killed	101
Suicides	219

The distinction between trespassers and suicides depends on the findings of the Coroner, but the annual total of trespassers killed is running at a very high level, and in part it represents the increasing tendency of people to trespass on the railway by using it as a short cut, instead of going a longer way round by public road or footpath. But whatever the reasons are, trespass is much commoner than it used to be.

However, the problems of trespass were recognised at a very early stage in the development of railways, and it was considered such a dangerous practice that it was legislated against in the Railway Regulation Act of 1840. Section 16 of that Act imposed a fine not exceeding £5 (a hefty sum in those days) upon any person who wilfully trespassed upon the railway, or any of the stations or other works or premises connected therewith, and who refused to quit the same upon request by an official or agent of the company. Section 16 also provided a power of arrest to any officer or agent or any person called to his assistance. It will be noted from this that the offence of trespass arises anywhere on railway premises and not just on the railway line (which is where the danger arises), but only if the trespasser refuses to leave. The penalty is now £200.

The Regulation of Railways Acts of 1868 and 1871 laid down that 'if any person shall be or pass upon any railway, except for the purpose of crossing the same at any authorised crossing, after having once received warning not to go or pass thereon' such person would be liable to a fine of 40 shillings.

The individual railway companies made similar provisions under their own Acts, thus giving rise to those well known and wordy cast-iron signs to be found at stations and crossings, the wording of which many youthful train spotters could recite by heart, having read it many hundreds of times in the intervals between trains. Here is a typical one:

Midland Railway
7 Vict Cap 18 Sec 238 enacts "That if any person shall be or travel or pass upon foot upon the Midland Railway without the licence and consent of the Midland Railway Company, every person so offending shall forfeit and pay any sum not exceeding Ten Pounds for every such offence."
Notice is therefore hereby given that all persons found trespassing upon this railway or the Works thereof will be prosecuted.

Alexis L. Charles
Secretary

June 1899

In the general sense, ordinary trespass, as is now well known, is not a criminal offence, and those notices which say 'Trespassers will be Prosecuted' are misleading. This is not to say, of course, that a landowner has no rights against a trespasser. He can, for example, claim damages in a civil court if he thinks he can prove that damage has been caused, and in general he owes a trespasser no duty of care, other than not to injure him intentionally or recklessly, but the legal position today is rather more complicated, particularly regarding children.

To understand the relatively new situation regarding children it would be as well to describe the legal position regarding fencing, which is largely governed by the Railway Clauses Consolidation Act of 1845. Section 68 lays down that:

'The company shall make and at all times thereafter maintain the following works for the accommodation of the owners and occupiers of lands adjoining the railway: Sufficient posts, rails, hedges, ditches, mounds or other fences . . . to protect from trespass land not taken for the use of the railway, and to protect cattle of the owners or occupiers of such land from straying thereout by reason of the railway . . .'

It will be seen, therefore, that the railway's requirement to fence is to protect adjoining land from trespass from the railway, and to prevent cattle from straying on to the railway. There is no duty on the railway to prevent the public at large from straying on to the railway, and the fences which are erected are not intended to keep people out, nor are they intended to be unclimbable. They are merely required to comply with the Act. First time travellers on the Continent are always astonished by the absence of fences, but those countries have no 1845 Act. (Note that there is a separate requirement to provide a 6ft unclimbable fence on lines electrified on the third-rail system.)

BR has tens of thousands of miles of fencing, and its maintenance is very expensive and labour-intensive. Local civil engineers, whose job it is, have customarily concentrated their resources on those locations which appeared to them to be the most important, but a legal action in 1970, known as the Herrington Case, altered the position substantially. The facts of the case are that a six-year-old child was playing in a meadow next to the railway line, a meadow which was sometimes used by children as a playground. Part of the railway fence was dilapidated and offered no barrier, and there was a hole in the fence opposite. People were using it as a short cut across the line. The child walked over the broken-down fence on to the line and was injured. About six weeks earlier the stationmaster had been notified that children had been seen on that stretch of line, but there was no evidence of any inspection of the fence. The judge awarded damages against the BR Board because he held that it was negligent for, among other things, permitting the fence to remain in a dilapidated condition. The BR Board appealed to the House of Lords on the grounds that since the child was a trespasser it owed him no duty in law to take any care for his safety, but the Lords dismissed the appeal, mainly on

SOUTH EASTERN & CHATHAM RAILWAY COMPANIES' MANAGING COMMITTEE.

WARNING TRESPASSING

THE PUBLIC ARE HEREBY CAUTIONED NOT TO TRESPASS UPON THE RAILWAY. ANY PERSON SO OFFENDING WILL BE PROCEEDED AGAINST, AND WILL, ON CONVICTION, BE LIABLE UNDER THE SOUTH EASTERN & LONDON, CHATHAM & DOVER RAILWAYS ACT 1901, TO A PENALTY NOT EXCEEDING 40/-.

C. SHEATH
SECRETARY.

LONDON BRIDGE STATION,
S.E.

L.D.& E.C.R
TRESPASSERS
WILL BE PROSECUTED
BY ORDER

Pre-Grouping railways' notice boards warning against trespass.
R. E. Vincent/
J. A. Cupit/C. R. L. Coles

GREAT WESTERN AND GREAT CENTRAL RAILWAYS JOINT COMMITTEE.

NOTICE.

ALL PERSONS ARE WARNED NOT TO TRESPASS UPON THE LINES OF RAILWAY OF THE COMPANY, AND NOTICE IS HEREBY GIVEN THAT PURSUANT TO THE PROVISIONS OF THE COMPANY'S ACTS EVERY PERSON WHO TRESPASSES UPON ANY OF THE LINES OF RAILWAY RENDERS HIMSELF LIABLE TO A PENALTY OF FORTY SHILLINGS, AND IN DEFAULT OF PAYMENT TO ONE MONTH'S IMPRISONMENT FOR EVERY SUCH OFFENCE.

BY ORDER.

the grounds that if railway operators foresaw or ought to have foreseen the likelihood of such trespassers, common humanity should require them to take some reasonable steps for their safety.

This decision increased the Civil Engineer's burden considerably. He now had to maintain fences in good repair wherever children might be expected to play, no matter how frequently those fences were damaged or broken down, either by the children themselves or by adults seeking a short cut. However, he is not expected by the Courts to erect childproof fencing. Infants are expected to be under the control of an adult, whilst there are few fences which cannot be climbed by a determined child.

Local authorities and other developers often do not help the situation. For example they construct housing estates next to the railway line and leave an open area adjacent to the fence, which is an invitation to children to play there. Sometimes the school is on the opposite side of the line, which encourages children to take a short cut across the railway line. Often shops and public houses are on the other side of the line, so that adults are tempted to break down the fence so that they can use the railway line as a short cut. A few years ago one of the large metropolitan authorities in the north of England mounted a campaign against BR on the question of deaths to child trespassers. Discussions followed at national level with the Association of Metropolitan Authorities and when their own sins were pointed out to them by BR they quickly retreated. As a result of these discussions local authorities have a much better appreciation of BR's problems, whilst BR in return is able to demand the provision of a much sturdier fence when land alongside the railway is developed.

Coupled with the need to maintain fences is the need to take more positive steps to discourage child trespass. This takes two forms — education and deterrence. Specially selected drivers regularly visit schools to talk to children about the dangers of trespass, both from trains and from the electrified third rail or overhead wires. Police officers do the same, at least in those areas where there are sensible local authorities. So far as deterrence is concerned the practice started in the 1970s of running 'Q' trains in the worst affected areas. These carried a number of police officers and stopped wherever trespassers were seen. In some cases the officers were in radio contact with nearby patrol cars, who could be summoned if necessary. In the West Midlands, where the idea is thought to have originated, diesel parcels railcars were used. Elsewhere DMUs and EMUs have been used. The practice is very effective, but needs to be repeated at fairly frequent intervals. The desire is not to prosecute, but to educate and deter.

Suicides are a different matter altogether. Thirty years ago there were 123 cases in a year. In 1987 there were 173. The railway has always been and still is, a favourite place for committing suicide, as this recent newspaper extract shows:

'John Smith (not his real name), 18, jumped to his death in front of an express train near Reading after a row with his parents.'

It is quick and effective. In 1987 only 19 people failed in the attempt, receiving serious injuries instead of death. One of the worst effects of a person committing suicide is upon the innocent train driver. One moment he is quietly and happily sitting at the controls of his locomotive; the next moment he suddenly sees a figure step out from behind a bridge abutment and stand directly in front of the train. There is rarely time for the driver to do anything other than blow his horn and avert his eyes, then wait for the awful thud as the locomotive hits the person. It is far too late for the brakes to have any effect — even a suicide has enough presence of mind not to give the driver time to stop. Some drivers are able to shrug off the experience, but it haunts others for months or even years, to such an extent that ASLEF, the drivers' trade union is trying to obtain compensation for them. There are, however, certain areas, usually near mental hospitals, where suicides are not uncommon and railway staff in the area become hardened to them. On one occasion two railway officers had been visiting a stationmaster and as the three of them came out of his office they saw a terminating DMU arrive in the platform opposite, four tracks away. Whilst standing on the platform talking they noticed without much interest a man whom they took to be a carriage examiner crouch down and apparently look underneath the coach just behind the first bogie. They were interested only to the extent that if the DMU had some defect which could not be quickly rectified it would be necessary to make alternative arrangements for its next journey. As they stood there mildly interested, the DMU set off gently in the opposite direction in order to cross to the other platform, and as it did so the person who had mistakenly been thought to be a carriage examiner calmly laid his neck across the rail and his head was cleanly and noiselessly severed, without any fuss. The DMU continued on its way, because its driver had no idea of what had happened, but the three railway officers were momentarily stunned. Quickly recovering themselves they sent for a large sack in which to put the remains, partly to hide them from the horrified gaze of passengers on the platform which the DMU had just vacated, who were suddenly confronted with a severed head and a headless body, and partly to allow the London-bound express, already standing at the signal, to enter the platform. They were a hard-bitten trio, who had experienced too many suicides and knew how seriously trains could be delayed if the police arrived on the scene before the body was moved clear. Some police officers are under the impression that a body must not be moved until it has been photographed by the police photographer, which may mean the line being closed for up to 2hr, but this is not so. The instructions to staff as to what to do in the case of fatalities on the line, either from accident or suicide, are contained in the General Appendix and were revised some years ago in consultation with chief constables after several cases of serious delays to trains. The revision was done to clarify the situation and to explain to staff exactly what they were entitled to do.

The instructions say that the body should be moved clear of the rails immediately in order to prevent delay to trains, but the position in which it was found must always be carefully noted and marked out. After this has been done the police must be informed as quickly as possible, and normal train running must be resumed. Decisions on the running of trains are matters for BR staff and not the police. If the police arrive on the site before BR staff do so, as often happens, and have reasonable grounds for suspecting foul play they may request that the body remain on the line for a short time, and this should be agreed to, but such occasions are comparatively rare.

So far as the locomotive is concerned, it does not normally need to be taken out of service immediately, but the maintenance depot concerned must be asked to test various items of equipment. The police have to make a report to the Coroner and need evidence about the locomotive.

It might be mentioned at this stage that British Railways has its own police force, whose status is unique. In the early days of railways, when construction was proceeding apace, Justices of the Peace sometimes found it necessary to appoint special constables to keep the peace amongst the unruly navvies, and in due course railway companies obtained powers under statute to appoint their own constables. Upon nationalisation in 1948 these separate police forces were combined in the new force, the British Transport Police, which is a properly constituted police force the same as any other police force, and at one time was the largest police force in the country after the London Metropolitan Police Force. However, by virtue of the layout of the railway system BT police tend to be concentrated in the larger centres, therefore if an emergency arises in other areas it is likely that a member of a local police force will be on the scene first. Such constables may only enter railway property or land upon invitation or in certain specific circumstances of crime, and when they do so unaccompanied, difficulties can arise, particularly if they attempt to interfere with railway operations. They may also put their lives at risk if they stray upon the railway line. After some particularly unfortunate incidents following an accident at Luton on 25 June 1976, when staff were obstructed by police officers when carrying out protection procedures, Lt-Col Townsend-Rose, who inquired into the accident, gave the following views and guidance in his Report, and suggested that when the local police force is called to a railway accident it is mainly for the following reasons:

1. To escort and help passengers to safety.
2. To take charge of personal belongings left behind.
3. To note the names and addresses of killed or injured passengers, so that the next of kin, etc may be informed.

4. To control crowds of onlookers who may interfere with rescue operations.
5. To provide radio communication.
6. To evacuate surrounding property if dangerous chemicals have been spilt, or if there are other hazards, eg fire or explosion.
7. To co-ordinate rescue and restoration activities being carried out by the emergency services and voluntary bodies.
8. To retrieve, identify and remove bodies on behalf of HM Coroner.

Lt-Col Townsend-Rose also attempted to give some guidance as to what police officers should not do. He said that they should not delay traincrews in the protection of the lines after an accident; they should not interfere with a signalman's duties, and without good reason should not enter a signalbox unless accompanied by a competent railway officer, and should not interfere with any signalling equipment either in the signalbox or on the ground. One might go further and suggest that they should not interfere with any equipment, eg on the locomotive or in the train, or parts of the permanent way, because to do so might impede both the railway authorities and the Railway Inspectorate in the investigation into the cause of the accident.

Below:
The problem of maintaining fencing in good condition is well illustrated here. The fence had been erected at a cost of £9,000, only six weeks before this photograph was taken. *BR*

This timely warning has generally proved sufficient, but a railway employee going about his ordinary duties may feel intimidated when faced by a uniformed police officer making what appear to be urgent demands, as happened quite recently at Shippea Hill station on the Norwich to Ely line. The county police were following a suspect car, but after it went over the station level crossing the signalman closed his gates for a locomotive and brakevan. When the police car arrived at the level crossing and found the gates barring the way, a police officer insisted that the signalman reopen the crossing, despite being told that a locomotive was approaching. The signalman thereupon swung his gates across the railway to allow the police car to cross. Unfortunately the locomotive was too near the crossing to stop clear when the protecting signal was put back to Danger and it smashed its way through the gates.

One final case might be quoted, which emphasises some of the points already made. On 17 April 1969 a little girl of two years and two months, who lived on a housing estate next to a railway line, toddled off whilst her mother was hanging out the washing and obtained access to the railway through a gap in a broken-down stile leading to a level crossing, where she promptly sat down on one of the rails. When the driver of a single coach diesel railcar came round the bend he saw something on the line ahead which he took to be a piece of paper or litter. He sounded his horn as a precaution, and reduced speed, but then he saw some movement and he applied his brakes fully. He waved frantically at the little girl and hoped desperately that he would be able to stop in time. It was not to be. The front wheels of the railcar just ran over the little girl's legs.

When the railway was built in 1860, the railway company had bought a stretch of pasture land on which to construct its line, and there was a footpath across the pasture and across the railway line. In 1969 the local council developed a housing estate of nearly 200 houses on the pasture and it bought a strip of land along the railway, on which it erected a fence, and a new stile for people using the footpath. The stile was completed 16 days before the accident but it was not suitable for old or small people, or small children, and it was soon demolished, probably by vandalism, leaving an open gap.

The Court of Appeal allowed an appeal on the child's behalf in a claim for damages for negligence and breach of statutory duty against the British Railways Board for failing to maintain the stile. Fortunately the Board was entitled to recover the damages from the local council, because when the housing estate was built the council had entered into an agreement to maintain the fence and stile.

The points of interest to us in this case are:

1. When the housing estate was being developed the local council agreed to erect, and to be responsible for, a fence and a stile. This absolved BR from the responsibility for its maintenance and from the consequences of any negligence to do so.
2. The new stile was broken down within a week or so. The problem of maintaining gates and stiles in good condition in places where children play, or where adults find the gates or stile a nuisance, is a serious one.
3. The path was a well-used one. It linked the housing estate on one side of the line with shops and a school on the other, creating much more pedestrian traffic over the crossing. It is possible that the stile was broken down so that mothers with prams could use the crossing to reach the shops. If there had not been a footpath already in existence it is quite possible that the fence would have been broken down in order to make an unofficial one. This often happens in such circumstances, but it then allows small children to get on to the line, as happened in the Herrington case.

Trespassers and suicides represent by far the most common cause of death on the railway. In 1987 there were 317 of them, compared with 73 from all other causes (excluding the King's Cross fire), including railway staff and road users at level crossings. It is a figure which seems unlikely to decline.

Below:
Today's fast, silent motive power means that children playing on the line often do not have time to get clear. Nos 87024 and 87001 (the latter having failed) speed through Berkswell with the diverted 09.38 Liverpool-Euston on 14 October 1987.
John Chalcraft

9
Rush-hour Disaster at Clapham Junction

On Monday 12 December 1988 the 07.18 from Basingstoke to Waterloo, packed with commuters, came to an unscheduled stop at signal WF47, only a few hundred yards short of the platform at Clapham Junction station. It was not quite 8.10am.

The train was formed of 3×4-car VEP electric multiple-units, and had a seating capacity of 840. There were known to have been at least 700 passengers on board, but the actual figure may have been as high as 900. Certainly, some passengers were standing at the front of the train, but they often do so from choice, even though there may be vacant seats further back along the train, so that they can be among the first through the ticket barriers at Waterloo and so avoid the crush.

It is unlikely that any of the passengers felt uneasy that the train should be stationary on the line in the middle of the rush-hour. They may have been irritated at the delay, but they would hardly have felt unsafe. However, barely had they begun to wonder about how long the delay was going to last when their thoughts were shattered by a tremendous impact. The unthinkable had happened. Another train had come along and had crashed headlong into the standing train. The second train was the 06.14 Poole-Waterloo, also a 12-coach EMU, formed of a four-coach REP set, plus two sets of four unpowered vehicles. Its seating capacity was 610 and it was known to have carried at least 519 passengers, but undoubtedly there

were more. (That morning it had started from Bournemouth at 06.30 owing to a previous accident, but that had no bearing on subsequent events.)

At this precise moment an empty EMU train was passing the other way on the next line. The Poole train tossed the last coach of the Basingstoke train up the bank, cannoned off, and hurled itself into the ever-narrowing gap between the two other trains, utterly destroying its first two coaches in the process. Some 35 people were killed in British Rail's worst disaster since the Hither Green derailment in 1967, described in Chapter 5, and 46 were injured sufficiently seriously to be detained in hospital. Altogether 130 people were treated in hospital, and it must be said at once that the response of the emergency services was rapid, efficient, and beyond praise.

Below:
The scene on the approach to Clapham Junction on 12 December 1988. On the left is the empty EMU which was travelling away from the camera. In the centre is the 06.14 from Poole (running towards the camera) which crashed into the rear of the stationary 07.18 from Basingstoke (right), tossing the last coach of the Basingstoke train up the bank. The first two coaches of the Poole train plunged into the narrow gap between the two other trains and were utterly destroyed. *Times Newspapers Ltd*

A fourth train narrowly avoided running into the rear of the Poole train. The driver of this train, a Waterloo to Waterloo circular via Weybridge, found that his train was losing power near Earlswood, about a mile from the wrecked trains, and as he coasted along hoping to reach Clapham Junction station he saw signal WF138 showing Yellow. Then, as he came round the corner he saw ahead of him, to his consternation, the rear of the Poole train. He threw on his brakes, hung on grimly, and screeched to a stop only 20yd clear. It was particularly fortunate that the collision between the Poole and the Basingstoke trains had caused the electric traction current to the third rail to be cut off otherwise the Waterloo circular via Weybridge train would have been travelling at the normal speed of a train preparing to stop at the next signal, WF47, and that may have been too fast for its driver to have stopped clear of the rear of the wrecked Poole train standing ahead of him.

There were now three trains in the 800yd section between signals WF138 and WF47, and signal WF138 was still showing Yellow.

The question to be asked immediately was how such an incredible series of events could take place on a busy suburban line. The safety of trains throughout the length and breadth of the country depends on the integrity of the signalling system; and on the simple principle of ensuring that the first signal behind a train is at Danger. In modern systems such as the one at Clapham this is achieved by a train detection device known as a track circuit. When a track circuit detects the presence of a train it reacts by switching to Danger the signal protecting that train. It is a simple device, and virtually foolproof. It has been in existence for a century or more. The track circuit between signals WF138 and WF47 should have detected the presence of the Basingstoke train and switched signal WF138 to Red. It did not do so. It should also have detected the presence of the Poole train and the Waterloo circular, and in due course we shall see why it did not do so, but first we must see why the driver of the Basingstoke train stopped at signal WF47.

As he approached signal WF138 (which was an automatic signal operated only by the passage of trains occupying track circuits and by the aspect being displayed by the next signal beyond it, and not capable of being operated by the signalman), it was showing Green, but when he was very near to it the signal suddenly changed to Red. That meant only one thing to the driver. Stop. He did so at the next signal WF47, which was showing Red when he first saw it, but then changed to Yellow.

The driver climbed down from his cab and telephoned the signalman at Clapham Junction 'A' signalbox from a nearby phone to find out what was going on. Sometimes, a malfunctioning track circuit will cause a signal to switch to Red, but the signalman replied that there was nothing wrong so far as he could tell. Perplexed, the driver turned to rejoin his train, but hardly had he gone two steps when he heard a tremendous crash and saw his train suddenly leap forward several feet.

The Poole train had been travelling at normal speed, but then it slowed down to about 50mph near signal WF138 (which was probably showing two Yellows — preliminary caution — but may even have switched to Green), in readiness for the 40mph speed restriction through Clapham Junction station. A driver who was travelling in the train saw the brake pipe pressure gauge suddenly go to zero and felt the brakes come on seconds before the crash. He estimated that the impact speed was about 35mph.

Nearly all the deaths occurred in the first coach of the Poole train, where 29 people died including the innocent driver. Sixteen passengers in it suffered only minor injuries or shock, and one incredibly fortunate passenger survived the crash quite unharmed. The other six passengers who died were in the seating portion of the second coach of the Poole train, which was a buffet car. The buffet was out of use but passengers who were standing in the buffet area were protected by the longitudinal bulkhead, which remained largely intact and saved their lives. The pattern of deaths did not seem to have been affected by whether people were sitting or standing.

We must now see why signal WF138 did not return to Danger behind any of the three trains which passed it, and which was still showing Yellow when the driver of one of the trains went back to look at it. Track circuits are designed in such a manner that if a malfunction occurs the equipment will react by switching signals to Danger, thus causing trains to stop, and ensuring safety. This is known as the 'fail-safe' principle, and is referred to as a right-side failure. What railwaymen fear most is the wrong-side failure which, though rare, has caused accidents in the past. However, it is almost unknown for a wrong-side failure to allow a signal protecting a standing train to show anything other than Red — Danger. Yet that almost unknown failure is what happened at Clapham Junction.

An examination of the signalling equipment in the Relay Room at Clapham Junction 'A' signalbox soon revealed the cause of the failure. In the signalbox a piece of wire, which should have been removed during signalling modernisation work, and which connected a power source to a piece of equipment known as a relay, was still in place, and was still connected to the power source. The other end was free, but continuously live. As long as the loose end did not touch any other terminal there was no danger, but it was a potential time-bomb.

The wiring was being renewed on a piecemeal basis over many weekends, and on 27 November 1988 a new wiring circuit was installed to control signal WF138, which was a new signal. The old wire already mentioned should have been removed at that time, but only one end (the relay end) was disconnected and moved away from its previous terminal. There it stayed, and as it was not at the time making any electrical contact its presence was not discovered during subsequent testing.

Two weeks later, the day before the accident, more work was being carried out in the signalbox relay room, this time on the adjacent relay. It is thought that this work may have disturbed the old piece of wire, which may then have resumed its previous shape and come into contact with its previous terminal, thus feeding current to the relay.

Track circuit equipment is designed so that when current is flowing, the track circuit is considered to be clear (ie unoccupied) and the signal approaching the track circuit will show 'Proceed'. (This may be one Yellow, two Yellows, or Green, depending on the indication being shown by the next signal.) When the Basingstoke train occupied the track circuit between signals WF138 and WF47 it had the planned effect of short-circuiting the electric current to the relay through the new wiring, which should then have caused signal WF138 to switch to Red, but the 'rogue' wire was still feeding current to the relay, therefore so far as that relay was concerned the track circuit was still unoccupied and signal WF138 did not revert to Red. The system 'lost' the train.

We must now consider why signal WF138 suddenly went to Red as the Basingstoke train approached it, and which caused its driver to stop at the next signal WF47. The standard signalling arrangements for the control of signals provide not only that a signal shall switch to Red when the track circuit beyond that signal is occupied by a train, but also that the signal shall remain at Red until the train has cleared a safety margin (known as an overlap and usually 200yd long) beyond the next signal. The safety margin had

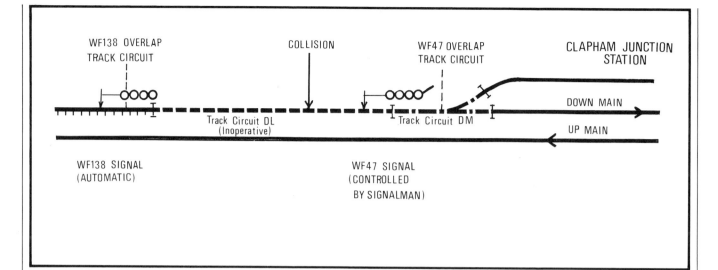

WF138 OVERLAP
TRACK CIRCUIT

COLLISION

WF47 OVERLAP
TRACK CIRCUIT

CLAPHAM JUNCTION
STATION

DOWN MAIN

Track Circuit DL
(Inoperative)

Track Circuit DM

UP MAIN

WF138 SIGNAL
(AUTOMATIC)

WF47 SIGNAL
(CONTROLLED
BY SIGNALMAN)

Above:
Approaching Clapham Junction from Woking (local lines not shown)

its own separate track circuit and the effect of this on WF138, with the 'rogue' wire feeding current, would be as follows:

As a train passed signal WF138 on to the bridged-out track circuit the signal would continue to show 'Proceed', and the train would disappear from the signalling system, but as soon as the train passed signal WF47 and occupied the 'overlap' track circuit it would be rediscovered by the signalling system and signal WF138 would immediately switch to Red. That is what the driver of the Basingstoke train saw, and that means that the train in front of him was not far ahead.

We may ask why the signal technician left the rogue wire in place. Was it tiredness, forgetfulness, carelessness, pressure of work? Human beings make mistakes. This sort of mistake was extremely rare. Almost unknown. Could any checking system or any amount of supervision guarantee to detect with 100% certainty such a rare error, year in and year out? There is no doubt that checking systems will be tightened up. Supervision will probably be intensified. Technicians' hours may be reduced (if BR manages to recruit more). But let us not delude ourselves. The Court of Inquiry may make a sacrificial lamb of the unfortunate technician, or the supervisor, or BR management, but errors of this nature by their very rarity may occasionally slip through the net. And let us not fall into the trap of believing that more supervision is necessarily the answer. We would do well to remember the old Latin tag *'Sed quis custodiet ipsos custodes'* which might be broadly translated as 'But who supervises the supervisors?' The causes of the Purley and Glasgow Bellgrove accidents, which occurred a few months later, were far more significant in safety terms, as we shall see in the next chapter.

The Court of Inquiry under Mr Anthony Hidden QC commenced in public on 20 February 1989, and the information given so far in this chapter is based on the evidence given at the inquiry. It would be inappropriate to make further comment until the inquiry report is published.

The Clapham accident was exceptional in its severity. Since the Hither Green derailment in 1967 there have been only three accidents on BR in which 10 or more passengers were killed. These accidents were:

1. West Ealing, 19 December 1973
   Ten passengers on the 17.18 locomotive-hauled train from Paddington to Oxford lost their lives when it was derailed at 70mph by points moving under the train. An unlocked battery box cover on the locomotive fell open soon after the train had left Paddington. It hit the platform at Ealing Broadway, breaking the chains supporting it and allowing it to swing down and smash into some lineside equipment which operated facing points in the line the train was travelling on. The points moved as the rear of the locomotive passed over them, turning the locomotive on to its side and derailing the coaches, which concertinaed together almost side by side. The locomotive had spent the previous night at Old Oak Common depot, where it had gone for repairs to a diesel engine, and the opportunity had been taken to recharge the battery. The battery box cover should have been locked when the locomotive left the depot, but it was not.

2. Taunton, 6 July 1978
   Twelve passengers were killed in a sleeping car fire. This accident is described in detail in Chapter 1.

3. Polmont, 30 July 1984
   Thirteen passengers were killed when the 17.30 Edinburgh-Glasgow push-pull express, being propelled, collided with a cow at 85mph and became derailed.

No pattern emerges from the causes of these three accidents and the Clapham accident, although simple human error is present in three of them. It is also significant that in those three cases the human errors involved people who had nothing to do with the actual operation of the train, and that in no case was either the driver or the signalman involved.

Wrong-side failures caused by errors of Signal Engineering Department technical staff have caused a number of accidents in recent years, some of which have occurred during signalling modernisation work, but none of them has resulted in passenger fatalities. All except one involved points operation irregularities, the exception being one of those very rare cases where a signal did not protect a standing train. This occurred on 7 March 1984 between Nuneaton and Water Orton (Birmingham) and is described in the Report for that year by the Chief Inspecting Officer of Railways. A freight train was brought to a stand at signal No SY326, which was showing Green, after the guard saw sparks coming from one of the wagons. A few minutes later a diesel locomotive running light (ie without a train) ran into the back of the standing train, causing considerable damage. The driver of the light locomotive had seen the signal in rear of the freight train at Green, and saw the train's tail lamp too late to avoid a collision. Investigation revealed that a Signal Engineering Department technician had attended a failure of the signal in rear of the freight train some months previously. He carried out repairs but failed to test the signal properly afterwards. Unfortunately a track circuit was omitted from the control of the signal, which consequently showed a clear aspect (Green) behind the standing train. This condition had existed undetected during those several months, because it was rare for a train to be stopped at signal No SY326, and the train in question was probably the first one which had done so since the wrong-side failure was built into the system by the technician.

Some of the other wrong-side failures which have caused accidents in recent years are shown in the appendix to this chapter. None of them has a direct parallel with the Clapham accident, although it is noteworthy that two of them occurred during the stage works of major resignalling schemes.

There were suggestions in the media after the Clapham accident that many lives might have been saved if the Poole train had been composed of more modern coaches of greater strength. This raises two questions. Were the coaches that were used on the Poole train that day unacceptably weak, and should they have been replaced by stronger ones? An examination of the behaviour of Southern Region coaches in accidents over the last 20 years shows that they have a very good safety record indeed. In that period there were 11 derailments and 21 collisions of sufficient severity to justify the holding of a public inquiry by the Railway Inspectorate. Six passengers were killed in those 32 accidents, but none of them were commuters. Before the Clapham accident, not a single commuter had been killed in a train accident on the Southern Region in the last 20 years — an almost unbelievably good record when one considers the intensity of the Southern Region commuter service, and the amount of resignalling work which has been done to commission the modern power signalboxes at London Bridge, Victoria and Three Bridges.

The second question, concerning the replacement of Southern Region coaches by more modern stock is really superfluous, because Southern Region stock has such a good behavioural record in accidents and its strength has been practically demonstrated. And even though the modern Mk 3 coach has a superb safety record it is impossible to say how it would have behaved in the Clapham crash. To put the proposition bluntly, should one replace all existing coaches or equipment immediately something safer is designed? Such a move could only be justified if the existing coaches were demonstrably unsafe and the new ones considerably better, which is not the situation in this case. It is not a new problem, but is as old as the railways themselves, as they progressed from four-wheeled coaches to six-wheelers and then to bogie vehicles; from wooden frames to steel frames; from wooden bodies to steel bodies; and from gas lighting to electric lighting. As is the case in so many other activities, the speed at which older designs of coaches are replaced by more modern and safer designs has to be set against the estimated degree of risk in allowing those older coaches to remain in service. In the case of Southern Region coaches, the experience of the last 20 years shows that it has been a very low level of risk.

We now come to the question of radio, and whether the provision of a radio link between the driver and the signalman would have avoided the accident, or at least have reduced its severity. On the morning of the accident the driver of the train from Basingstoke observed a signal behaving in an irregular manner, therefore he stopped his train at the next signal to report the fact to the signalman, using the telephone at the signal. He had no reason to suppose that the signal protecting his train would have done anything other than revert to Red. Nor had the signalman. The defective signal would have been dealt with in accordance with the Rules, and the drivers of all the following trains would have been stopped and warned about it by the signalman. If a train had already passed the point at which it could be stopped by the signalman, the driver of the train would have acted in the same way as the driver of the Basingstoke train, provided that the signal appeared to the driver to be acting irregularly. The Rules tell the driver that 'a signal imperfectly shown' must be treated as a Danger signal and reported to the signalman, which is what the driver of the Basingstoke train did. If radio had been provided he would probably have stopped his train and then reported the facts to the signalman by radio, it being undesirable, except in an emergency, for the driver to carry out radio conversations when his train is running at speed, owing to the obvious danger that his concentration on signals, etc, may be impaired. On the other hand, if an emergency arose the driver would make a special emergency contact with the signalman at once, but a defective signal would hardly be considered an emergency in those terms because it would be regarded as a Danger signal and could safely be dealt with under the normal procedures. When the signalman received such a report by radio he would put into operation the procedures designed to deal with it, and the radio would merely take the place of the telephone as a quicker and more convenient means of passing messages. However, if the next train had already passed the last signal at which it could be stopped, the signalman would send a radio message to that driver warning him of the defective signal ahead and giving him any necessary instructions. The vital point, so far as the Clapham accident is concerned, is whether there would have been sufficient time for the driver of the Poole train to have been warned about the defective signal and to apply his brakes before he saw the Basingstoke train standing on the same line ahead of him. It is at least possible that the Poole train might have been slowing down more than it did, when it hit the Basingstoke train. The driver of the Waterloo via Weybridge train could also have been forewarned.

The provision of radio communication between drivers and signalmen on BR did not start until comparatively recently, and then mainly as a by-product of other schemes, particularly in connection with a new signalling system on single lines, known as Radio Electronic Token Block signalling. However, radio communication between drivers and signalmen is also required if trains are to be operated without guards on suburban services. This already applies on lines from St Pancras, King's Cross and Glasgow, and is expected to be introduced on the Southern Region soon, but some years are bound to elapse before all the Southern Region commuter services are equipped.

The reasons for BR's dilatoriness in providing radio communication were not entirely financial, although the poverty-induced inertia of the late 1970s/early 1980s is a factor. Compared with the cost of electrification, or new power signalboxes, or new fleets of locomotives or rolling stock, the cost of a nationwide radio system is quite small. The fact is, that in order to survive, BR has had to concentrate on essentials, and radio was not considered to be essential. Also, BR had to cut its staff numbers to the bone, whilst the planning and installation of a national radio system is very labour-intensive in the use of planning and technical staff.

Serious accidents, especially where accompanied by loss of life, are normally followed by public inquiries held by an Inspecting Officer of the Railway Inspectorate of the Department of Transport. The legal authority for such inquiries, and the procedures for holding them, have already been discussed in detail in Chapter 6, but there is an additional provision in the 1871 Regulation of Railways Act, under Section 7, for the holding of a more formal investigation. Section 7 gives the Secretary of State for Transport the power:

1. To direct that a more formal type of investigation be held.
2. To appoint particular persons to assist the Inspecting Officer.
3. To appoint someone else to hold the investigation, assisted by an Inspecting Officer.
4. To hold the investigation in open court.

The court has all the powers of a court of summary jurisdiction and all the powers of an Inspecting Officer, plus:

1. They may enter and inspect any place or building which appears requisite (ie not confined to railway premises).
2. They may call any witnesses they think fit (ie, not just railway staff).
3. They may take evidence on oath.

So far as BR and its predecessors are concerned, this more formal type of inquiry has only twice been conducted by someone other than an Inspecting Officer since 1871 — once in connection with the Tay Bridge collapse in 1879 and once in connection with a collision between an express train and an abnormal load on a road trailer at Hixon level crossing (Staffordshire) in 1968. In each case the Railway Inspectorate had been previously involved; in passing as fit for use the Tay Bridge, and in drawing up in conjunction with BR the requirements for the installation and operation of automatic half-barriers at level crossings. In each of those cases it was necessary for the person holding the inquiry to be seen to be independent, and it was clearly an advantage to be able to call non-railway staff as witnesses, ie the designers and builders of the Tay Bridge on the one hand, and Department of Transport officials, road haulage people and the police on the other. In each of those cases, therefore, it was appropriate to hold the more formal type of investigation. It was also appropriate to do so following the fire at London Transport's King's Cross station on 18 November 1987, because it was expedient to consider the actions, responsibilities, and organisation of the emergency services. The King's Cross fire was not a train accident and there were many questions to be asked about materials used in the construction of the station, which involved calling non-railway staff as witnesses. These three accidents were exceptional in that they were not train accidents of a conventional nature, ie they were not collisions between trains, or derailments, or train fires. By contrast, the collision at Clapham was entirely conventional. One train running into the back of another has been a common occurrence throughout railway history. It happened at Harrow & Wealdstone in 1952, when 108 passengers were killed. It happened at Lewisham St Johns in 1957, when 89 passengers were killed. It happened at Winsford, near Crewe in 1962, when 18 passengers were killed. In each case the subsequent inquiry was held by an Inspecting Officer in the entirely satisfactory, thorough and competent manner which always has been the hallmark of the Railway Inspectorate.

Why, then, did the Secretary of State for Transport choose to order the more formal type of investigation for the Clapham accident, which was not in any way exceptional except for the death toll, and why did he appoint a QC, Anthony Hidden, to hold it? Is the Secretary of State suggesting that his Railway Inspectorate is no longer competent, or not independent? There can be no valid questioning of its competence or experience — one Inspecting Officer has served for over 20 years and two have served for between 10 and 20 years. Between them they have carried out dozens of inquiries. Any one of them could have carried out the Clapham inquiry without difficulty. Is it therefore the Railway Inspectorate's independence (presumably from BR's influence) which is in question? If so, the Secretary of State clearly does not know his Inspectorate. Even though it works closely with BR there has never been the slightest suggestion that it might favour BR in any way. The whole issue bears all the marks of a hasty reaction by the Secretary of State under political pressure on the question of the provision of public transport in the London area, and its financing. His ill-advised decision will provide a field day for the legal profession, but will not enable the cause and circumstances of the accident to be established any more clearly or accurately. It will certainly take a lot longer. But by far the worst feature is that it undermines the status and reputation of the Railway Inspectorate, which has been built up and enhanced over a continuous period of 150 years, and sets a lamentable precedent for the future. This dedicated body of men, never more than five or six strong, has performed services for railway passengers of a value quite out of proportion to its size; and it deserved better treatment.

Details of Accidents Caused by Wrong-Side Failures

1. Bletchley, 10 July 1974
   A special excursion train from Wigan to Euston was passing along a crossover from the Up Slow line to the Up Fast line opposite Bletchley signalbox at about 15mph, and just as the last coach was astride the facing points of the crossover they moved across, causing the trailing bogie to continue to run along the Up Slow line. The coach was eventually dragged into derailment and broke loose from the train. Lt-Col Townsend-Rose, who inquired into the accident, concluded that it was probably an irregular action by a Signal Engineering Department technician in the Bletchley power signalbox Relay Room that caused the points to move.
2. Hither Green, 6 November 1976
   As the 17.12 Margate-Charing Cross passenger train was approaching Hither Green on the Up Fast line, the driver observed two signals ahead of him revert from Green to Red. On telephoning the signalman he was instructed to pass them at Danger and to proceed at Caution. He had just passed the second signal at Danger and was travelling at about 25mph when his train was diverted at a facing connection, becoming derailed at switch diamonds in the adjacent Down Fast line, along which his train travelled until it came to rest some 20yd short of the Down Fast platform at Hither Green station. Control of the signalling in the Hither Green area had only just been transferred to the new London Bridge signalbox, and final testing had not yet been completed. Lt-Col Townsend-Rose also inquired into this accident, and found that the derailment occurred because of an error in the electrical connections to the points, which had remained undetected in spite of very thorough testing.

3. Farnley Junction, near Leeds, 5 September 1977

Both a Down train and an Up train were stopped by signals near Farnley Junction, on the line between Leeds and Huddersfield. There were a number of failures in the signalling equipment, which had their roots in industrial action threatened by electricity power station workers, and Signal Engineering Department technicians were on the spot attempting to put things right. The 20.40 locomotive-hauled passenger train from Liverpool to Hull was standing on the Down line, and the 21.50 Mail from York to Shrewsbury, also locomotive-hauled, was standing on the Up line, with a facing crossover between them connecting the Up and Down lines. Maj Rose inquired into this accident and found that owing to a wiring error by the technicians the facing crossover moved to the reverse position (ie to take a train from the Up line to the Down, or vice versa) but still allowed the signals to clear to Green for movements straight along the Down line and Up line. There was some confusion as to whether the signalman was properly informed by the technician that the repair work had been completed and tested (which it had not). As soon as the signalman cleared the signals for the two standing trains the Liverpool to Hull train set off, but was diverted through the facing crossover into a head-on collision with the other train. Both drivers were killed.

4. Bushbury Junction, near Wolverhampton, 13 August 1979

The 13.29 passenger train was derailed when passing over switch diamonds at Bushbury Junction, about 1½ miles north of Wolverhampton. Defective equipment allowed the signal to show Green even though the points were not fitting correctly. This accident was fully described in *Danger Signals*.

5. Chester, 9 June 1981

The 13.48 DMU from Wolverhampton to Chester was running along the Up Slow line at about 15mph, when the trailing bogie of the first coach, followed by the remainder of the train, was diverted to a different line at a set of facing points. The first coach became derailed. Maj King inquired into this accident and found that the signalling was being converted from a mechanical system to an electrical system, as part of the stage works for the introduction of a new signalbox at Chester, and that earth faults in the equipment allowed the signalman to make an error and move the facing points whilst the DMU was just passing over them. The points should have been electrically locked but the earth faults rendered the safeguards ineffective.

Below:
Recovery of materials proceeds on 13 December, the day following the accident. *Brian Morrison*

10
Purley and Glasgow Bellgrove — Accident or Design?

On 4 March 1989, a perfectly normal Saturday, the 12.50 Southern Region EMU from Horsham to London Victoria, a four-coach set, approached Purley on the Up Slow line. The driver braked for the station stop, and as he did so the signal at the far end of the platform, T170, changed from Red to Yellow, and the junction indicator (a row of white lights) was illuminated to signify that the points ahead were set to take the train through the crossovers on to the Up Fast line. After the normal station stop the driver restarted his train at about 13.36, and took it steadily through the 20mph crossovers.

The signalling in the whole area is controlled from Three Bridges signalbox, and is very modern, being commissioned on 14 January 1984. On the main line from Brighton to London Victoria through Purley, four-aspect colour-light signals are used; the lines are track circuited throughout and are equipped with the BR standard Automatic Warning System. Many of the signals work automatically, and some of the ones which are operated by the signalman can also be set by him to work automatically, which means that they will change to Red as soon as a train passes them, then successively to one Yellow, two Yellows, and Green, as the train passes succeeding signals. The signal at the London end of the Up Fast line platform at Purley, T168, is such a

signal. The signalman had set it to work automatically for a sequence of trains along the Up Fast line, but then he required to switch the Horsham train from the Up Slow line to the Up Fast line, so he restored T168 signal to non-automatic operation after the passage of a Gatwick Airport to Victoria express. This action held T168 at Red and prevented it from changing to Yellow etc. He then set the route for the Horsham train, which was a regular movement every half-hour and should have been perfectly safe provided any driver approaching along the Up Fast line ensured that he stopped his train at T168 signal, but the basic philosophy of BR signalling is that drivers do stop at Red signals and they have the Automatic Warning System to assist them. This system is operated by magnets in the track about 200yd before each signal, which send out an electrical message to be picked up by a receiver mounted

Below:
Purley 4 March 1989. The 12.17 from Littlehampton to Victoria cannoned off the rear of the 12.50 from Horsham (seen top left) and plunged down the steep tree-clad embankment almost into the houses below. The front of the train is shown circled, which indicates that the coach had turned through 180°.
Mail Newspapers PLC

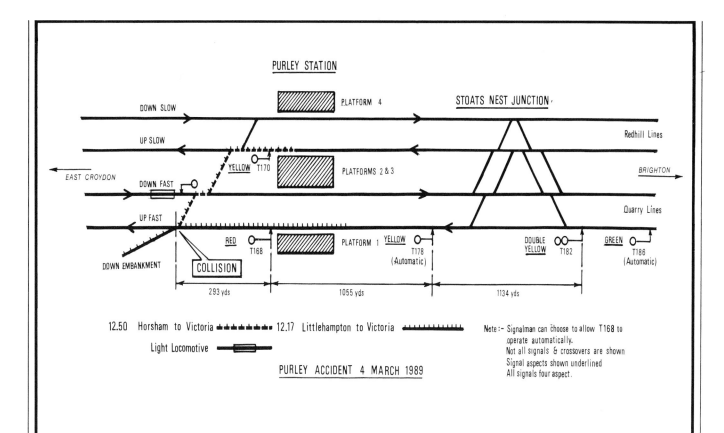

PURLEY STATION

PLATFORM 4

STOATS NEST JUNCTION

DOWN SLOW

Redhill Lines

UP SLOW

YELLOW T170

PLATFORMS 2 & 3

BRIGHTON

EAST CROYDON

DOWN FAST

DOWN EMBANKMENT

UP FAST

RED
T168

COLLISION

PLATFORM 1

YELLOW
T178
(Automatic)

Quarry Lines

DOUBLE
YELLOW   T182

GREEN   T186
(Automatic)

293 yds   1055 yds   1134 yds

12.50 Horsham to Victoria ▪▪▪▪▪▪▪ 12.17 Littlehampton to Victoria ▪▪▪▪▪▪▪▪▪

Light Locomotive ▭▭

PURLEY ACCIDENT 4 MARCH 1989

Note:- Signalman can choose to allow T168 to
operate automatically.
Not all signals & crossovers are shown
Signal aspects shown underlined
All signals four aspect.

Above:
Purley accident 4 March 1989.

Left:
**Purley. The battered first, third and fourth coaches of the
12.17 from Littlehampton.** *Mail Newspapers PLC*

underneath the train. If the signal is at Green the message
causes a bell to sound in the driving cab, but if the signal is
showing any other aspect (ie two Yellows, one Yellow, or
Red) a different message is sent, which sounds a warning
horn. The driver then has 2-3sec to press a button to
acknowledge receipt of the warning and if he fails to do so
the brakes are automatically applied. It is a very valuable
safeguard, but it is cancelled out as soon as the driver
presses the acknowledgement button because he is then
solely responsible for applying the brake and there is no
equipment to check that he actually does so. This is now
becoming widely recognised as a fundamental drawback,
because in the course of a normal day's work drivers
frequently require to press the acknowledgement button
and then find that they have no need to brake, because they
can see the next signal change to a less restrictive aspect (eg
from Yellow to double Yellow or double Yellow to Green).
This oft-repeated acknowledgement not followed by any
action on the driver's part can lure him to disaster if he
should subconsciously press the acknowledgement button
and take no action at the very time he needs to do so.
Collisions have resulted from this situation on a number of
occasions.

When the signalman set the route for the Horsham train
there was indeed a train approaching on the Up Fast line,
the 12.17 from Littlehampton to London Victoria, an
eight-coach EMU, and it was running at high speed down
the favourable grade from Merstham Tunnel, four miles

Above:
Purley. The smashed-in front-end of the 12.17 from Littlehampton, in which the driver survived.
Mail Newspapers PLC

Left:
The Up and Down Fast lines through Purley, looking north towards signal T168 and London. The station buildings on Platform 2 obscure the driver's view of signal T168 owing to the curvature of the line, until he is within 300yd of the signal.
Author

Below left:
Purley. The view north from signal T168. At this point the driver of the 12.17 from Littlehampton would see the 12.50 from Horsham making its way through the crossovers, and realise to his horror that it was crossing on to his line. *Author*

away. The driver of a light locomotive (ie a locomotive without a train) which was standing at a signal on the Down Fast line just north of Purley, saw the Horsham train about to cross in front of him to the Up Fast line. At the same moment he saw the 12.17 approaching the station and realised in a flash that it was coming too fast to stop at signal T168. He was correct. The Littlehampton train ran by T168 and struck the last coach of the Horsham train, which was just coming off the crossovers, a glancing blow, at a speed said by an expert witness at the subsequent public inquiry to have been about 55mph.

The railway lines at this point are on a high embankment, with the Up Fast line on the outside. The Littlehampton train cannoned off the rear coach of the Horsham train and plunged down the tree-clad embankment, leaving only the last coach remaining on the track. Most of the other coaches were strewn at random, some upside down or on their sides. Five passengers died and 87 required hospital treatment, 32 of whom were detained, after being tossed around like peas in a drum inside the crazily tumbling carriages.

Public reaction, with the accident coming so soon after the Clapham disaster only a few miles away, was one of shock and astonishment. How could such a thing happen on a busy railway like the Brighton line with all its modern safeguards? This is what the Public Inquiry, held by Mr Alan Cooksey, Deputy Chief Inspecting Officer of Railways, was set up to establish. BR said that there was no evidence of any malfunction of the braking system or the AWS equipment on the Littlehampton train, nor any signalling operation malpractice, nor signalling equipment defect, and the cause of the crash was an error by the driver. The driver himself declined to give evidence in public, and until the report itself is issued it would be wrong to speculate about what might have caused the driver to pass the signal in error. However, from the evidence given it would seem that, after running on Green signals, he would then have received the normal sequence of signal aspects when approaching T168 at Red, ie two Yellows and one Yellow and that he would have received the normal AWS warning at each. Had he not acknowledged the warning the brakes would have been applied automatically. But in any case, the reason why he passed T168 signal at Danger, whilst interesting, is of no real consequence. The fact is that, for whatever reason, the signalling and AWS system in use failed to ensure that the train stopped at the Red signal, and that is what matters.

T168 signal is obscured by the station buildings and does not come into view from the driver's cab until the driver is within 300yd of it. That fact in itself should be of no consequence if a driver has correctly responded to the warnings at the previous two signals but, it assumes considerable importance if he has not done so, because by the time the Red signal at T168 comes into his view he is likely to be travelling at too great a speed to enable him to stop either at the signal itself or even at the crossover almost 300yd beyond. What is needed is a better Automatic Train Control system which will ensure that a train will stop safely at a Red signal irrespective of anything the driver does or fails to do. On the evidence available there is nothing new or unusual in the circumstances of the Purley accident and the whole subject was thoroughly explored in Chapters 1 and 8 of *Danger Signals*. Serious accidents of this nature are becoming an annual event, although not usually with so many deaths. The nearest parallel in recent years is perhaps the Wembley accident of 11 October 1984 in which a Euston to Bletchley commuter train passed a Red signal and collided sideways-on with a Freightliner train that was just leaving the sidings and was crossing over on to the same line as the commuter train. Three passengers were killed. The driver had received the normal Caution signals of two Yellows and one Yellow but had failed to react positively and had merely acknowledged the AWS warnings as a subconscious reaction. The driver, who was 63 years old, was subsequently examined by a specially constituted medical board who, on the balance of probabilities, believed that he had suffered from an episode of amnesia and confused behaviour which led him to ignore the signals at Caution and Danger, brought about by a rare but well recognised medical condition. Be that as it may, it is quite intolerable that drivers should have to carry such heavy responsibilities for the lives of hundreds of passengers, for which burden they are inadequately remunerated, with reliance upon a warning system which increasingly is showing itself to be ineffective when most needed. It is good to hear, therefore, that BR has decided at long last to install a better system. Let us hope that the work will be carried out with a proper degree of urgency. And in case it should be thought that such a better system is either a new idea or is not yet available, it ought to be pointed out that following a serious collision on the Midland Railway at Aisgill in September 1913 an eminent signal engineer wrote 'We believe we shall eventually develop a genuine speed control system which will in no way interfere with the driver's control if he does his work, but will check him if he exceeds the authorised speeds.' That was 75 years ago, and such systems have existed and have been in use on other railways for many years. And even while BR and the public were still recovering from the shock of the Purley and Bellgrove accidents there were two near misses within the next few days caused by drivers passing signals at Danger. One was at Worle Junction on the Western Region where a train from Weston-super-Mare overran a Danger signal and almost collided with a Penzance to Cardiff train on the main line. The other was many miles away in much more hostile country, where BR was engaged in one of its frequent diversions of West Coast main line services over the Settle-Carlisle line. The signalman had cleared his signals for a Down express to travel over the single line across Ribblehead Viaduct. An Up express came out of Blea Moor Tunnel. Its driver failed to stop at the Up Home signal, which was at Danger, and headed towards the single line and the approaching Down express. It would have made a fitting Wagnerian epitaph for Ribblehead Viaduct — two expresses colliding head-on and plunging to the valley below — but fortunately the signalman was on the alert. He immediately apprehended danger and pulled over his emergency detonator-placing levers, which laid detonators on the line. Their explosion caused the driver to make an emergency stop and there was no collision. On diversion weekends the Settle-Carlisle line attracts large numbers of train spotters, photographers, recorders and other enthusiasts, but they had all gone home. The incident happened during the night.

Emergency detonator-placing equipment was also used in the accident at Glasgow Bellgrove station, two days after the Purley accident, on 6 March 1989, but this time it was ineffective. Bellgrove station lies on the North Glasgow electrified line from Airdrie to Dumbarton and Helensburgh, and is the second station east of Queen Street Low Level station. There is a junction at Bellgrove to Springburn, which was formerly a conventional double-line junction but was remodelled in 1987 to a single-lead junction in preparation for the Yoker resignalling scheme. The question of these single-lead junctions and the safety problems they can cause was fully explored in Chapter 8 of *Danger Signals* but briefly they consist of a short piece of single line connecting the double track main line with the double track branch line. Their particular hazard lies in the fact that if the signal is cleared for a train to proceed off the

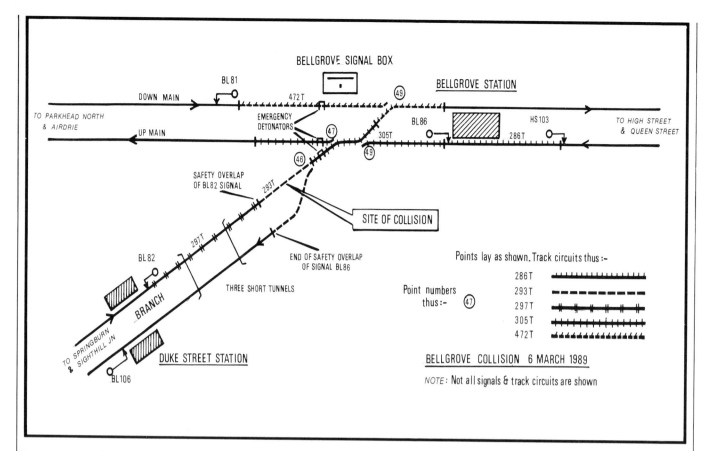

BELLGROVE SIGNAL BOX

BELLGROVE STATION

DOWN MAIN

TO PARKHEAD NORTH
& AIRDRIE

UP MAIN

TO HIGH STREET
& QUEEN STREET

BL81   472T   49   BL86   HS103   286T

EMERGENCY DETONATORS   305T

47

46   49

SAFETY OVERLAP OF BL82 SIGNAL   293T

SITE OF COLLISION

297T

BL82

END OF SAFETY OVERLAP OF SIGNAL BL86

Points lay as shown. Track circuits thus:-

286T

BRANCH

THREE SHORT TUNNELS

Point numbers thus:-   47

293T
297T
305T
472T

TO SPRINGBURN & SIGHTHILL JN

DUKE STREET STATION

BELLGROVE COLLISION 6 MARCH 1989

BL106

NOTE: Not all signals & track circuits are shown

branch on to the main line the points will be set in such a way that if a train on the main line overruns the junction signal at Danger it will automatically be diverted on to the branch line and into a head-on collision with the train coming off the branch. This could not have happened with the previous double-line junction layout as the offending train would have been diverted out of harm's way on to the unoccupied branch line. Single-lead junctions therefore demand a higher standard of obedience to signals by drivers, and the identification and effective treatment of any special hazard at the junction signal.

There was just such a special and well known hazard at the junction signal at Bellgrove, which will become apparent from a description of the circumstances surrounding the accident. Two trains were approaching the junction at Bellgrove simultaneously — the 12.39 from Springburn to Milngavie and the 12.20 Milngavie to Springburn. Each was a three-car electric multiple-unit of 1960 vintage. Although the lines are track circuited throughout they are worked on the Absolute Block System. The signalman accepted the train from Springburn from the Sighthill Junction signalman, and cleared his signals for it to run as far as signal BL82 at Duke Street station. He also accepted the train to Springburn from the High Street signalman, after setting points 47 and 46 to the reverse position so that they lay towards the end of the safety overlap of signal BL86. When the train to Springburn had come to a stand in Bellgrove station, with signal BL86 at Red, the signalman normalised points 46 and reversed points 49 to take the train from Springburn through the junction to the Down Main line and into Bellgrove station. He then cleared BL82 signal and the train set off into the three short tunnels.

At this moment the Bellgrove signalman saw the train to Springburn start to leave Bellgrove station and to his consternation it passed BL86 signal, which, according to his signal lever, was at Red. He immediately pulled over his emergency detonator-placing levers and heard the bang as the train passed over the detonators and exploded them. However, the two trains were now very close to each other and they met head-on at a combined speed of about 30mph. The driver of the train from Springburn, and a passenger on that train, lost their lives.

The question at issue, therefore, is why the train to Springburn left Bellgrove station and passed signal BL86, which the signalling system should have held at Danger and with which no fault could subsequently be found. Events 10 years earlier, and only a few miles away, may provide the answer.

On Easter Monday 1979 the 18.58 from Ayr to Glasgow set off from Paisley Gilmour Street station, wrongly passed the platform starting signal at Danger, and collided head-on with the 19.40 Glasgow to Wemyss Bay, which was just crossing the junction. Seven people died. It was felt that the guard's bell signal to the driver that the train was ready to start had caused the driver to overlook the Danger signal at the end of the platform, and if that may sound strange it has to be said that it was a very well known and recognised situation which had caused many accidents in the past. Indeed, as long ago as 1957, following an inquiry into an accident at Staines, the Inspecting Officer, Brig Langley, had said that the great psychological effect of the guard's 'right away' signal had occasionally allowed drivers to be misled by it. The whole question was examined in detail in Chapter 5 of Danger Signals.

Following the Paisley accident, BR altered the Rules to require the guard to ensure, where practicable, that the platform starting signal (BL86 at Bellgrove) had been cleared before giving the 'Ready to start' signal to the driver. In his evidence at the Public Inquiry into the Bellgrove accident, held by the Chief Inspecting Officer of Railways, Mr Robin Seymour, the guard of the train to Springburn said that he could not remember looking at signal BL86. If he had done so, and if it had been at Red, he

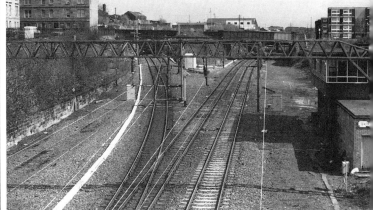

Left:
Bellgrove collision 6 March 1989.

Above right:
Glasgow Bellgrove 6 March 1989. The 12.20 from Milngavie to Springburn and the 12.39 from Springburn to Milngavie meet head-on near the junction. *Mail Newspapers PLC*

Right:
Glasgow Bellgrove, showing the single lead connecting the Springburn Branch (left) with the Airdrie line (right). The collision occurred opposite the white hut (top centre). *Author*

Below:
General view of Glasgow Bellgrove station, looking towards Springburn and Airdrie. The signal at the far end of the platform, BL86, has been cleared for the Class 303 unit to proceed to Springburn. *Author*

should not have 'belled the train away', as he described it, because that would have been against the Rules. Was it practicable for him to see it? That is a matter for the Chief Inspecting Officer to decide. It is on the right-hand side of the line and clearly visible from part of the platform. Where difficulty arises in the visibility of such a signal, it is the practice to provide On/Off electrical indicators to help guards and station staff. There was no such indicator at Bellgrove. But in any event, the responsibility for obeying signals in such circumstances is entirely that of the driver. The Rules tell him that the 'Ready to start' signal indicates only that the station work is complete and that he must ensure before starting the train that the signal is cleared.

However, a wise and prudent management will learn the lessons of history; and, recognising that human beings make human errors, will take whatever steps it reasonably can to guard against such human errors, especially at those locations such as Bellgrove where there is an additional hazard. It is one thing to alter the Rules, but to be effective such alteration needs to be reinforced by training and supervision. How effectively is this Rule applied by guards in the Glasgow area, and how effective is the supervision? It seems that Bellgrove may not have been an entirely isolated case, for there was a near miss a few weeks later at, of all places, Paisley. And what action do drivers take when the Rule is not applied? Are either drivers or guards aware of the provisions of the Health & Safety at Work Act of 1974, Section 7(a), which says:

'It shall be the duty of every employee while at work to take reasonable care for the . . . safety of himself and of other persons who may be affected by his acts or omissions at work'?

Is there any equipment that BR can install to guard against a driver's wrongly passing, at Danger, signals such as BL86? The new Automatic Train Protection System which BR is proposing to install could include such a provision, but several years are likely to pass before the new equipment comes into widespread use. A quicker and cheaper alternative, to be installed at those places where train speeds may be quite high and where there is an additional hazard such as a single-lead or conflicting junction beyond the platform starting signal would be an AWS magnet located immediately beyond the signal. The equipment would give no indication at all if the signal showed anything other than Red, but whilst the signal was at Red the equipment would be de-energised and would sound a warning horn in the driving cab if a driver passed the signal at Danger — sufficient to alert him if he had passed the signal in error.

The 'system' (incorporating signalling, track layout, and operating methods) at both Purley and Bellgrove has been seen to be flawed. It failed to prevent the accidents of 4 and 6 March 1989. So it is reassuring for passengers to hear that BR now intends to take remedial action and install a better system, and if this sounds like closing the stable door after the horse has bolted, one can only retort that there are still plenty of horses inside the stable, whose safety is a matter of some importance, at least to them.

Below left:
A Class 303 unit stands in the platform at Glasgow Bellgrove. The guard is leaning out of the centre coach to make sure that the signal has been cleared for the train to proceed to Springburn. *Author*

Bottom left:
The guard on the Class 303 unit leaving Glasgow Bellgrove for Springburn appears to be making a final check that BL86 signal is still cleared for the train to proceed to the Branch. *Author*

Below:
A view of signal BL86 from the '3-car Stop' position. It is located just at the far side of the overbridge. The junction to Springburn is just out of sight to the left. *Author*

11
Conclusions

What are the impressions gained from the preceding chapters so far as safety is concerned? They fall, I think, into four main areas:

1. Technical Excellence

In 1948, when the railways were nationalised, their equipment and methods had changed but little in the previous half-century. The railwayman of 1900 would quickly have felt at home if suddenly transported to the railway of 1948, and vice versa. Since 1948, however, the railway scene has undergone a major change, whilst engineers and designers have achieved levels of safety standards in respect of the track and rolling stock that might have been thought of at one time as unattainable, especially when one considers the speed of today's trains. This particular area of activity must therefore be judged a resounding success in safety terms. However, it is impossible to guarantee that no more serious accidents will be caused by defective track or rolling stock; in fact history teaches us that one can almost guarantee that there will be further accidents and that some of them will be, in practical terms, unavoidable. To accept that situation is not being defeatist, but merely recognises the inevitability of accidents in the daily transport of millions of passengers and millions of tons of goods.

2. The Hidden Hazards of Technical Innovation and Change

The hidden hazards in this area are nowhere better illustrated than in the story of the development of continuously-welded rail, in which the main line became in effect an outdoor laboratory where experience was dearly bought by a process somewhat resembling that of trial and error. Then, just when engineers were beginning to think that they had at last reached a plateau of success, along came the Motherwell accident in 1986 to remind them of their fallibility. The development of CWR is a fascinating story, with engineers not only pushing at the boundaries of knowledge, but reaching beyond them; then reacting and adjusting as each new hazard revealed itself. Maj Holden's comments at the Public Inquiry into the Motherwell accident seem specially apt in this connection:

'This aspect of track design (ie the particular layout at Motherwell) is, perhaps, more of an art than a science and we may never come to a final mathematical conclusion. It is quite plain that a considerable amount of research needs to be done so that I can make some recommendations to the Secretary of State for Transport.'

3. Human Error

Many of the accidents described in this book confirm yet again that people, being human beings, make mistakes, or are careless. The range of human error is fascinating in its breadth and diversity, ranging from simple forgetfulness to errors of judgement; from lack of care to the jumping to wrong conclusions; and from the man at the bottom to the man at the top. Management, however, has a real responsibility here which it does not always recognise, or having recognised it does not always give it sufficient attention — and that is the responsibility to guard against the frailty of human nature. Technical safeguards are part of the answer, but another important area is that of training. There can rarely be too much of it, but sometimes there is insufficient. It is expensive, and an easy activity in which to economise when costs have to be cut. However, having said that, it must be pointed out that three of the worst accidents in the last 20 years (West Ealing 1973 — 10 killed, Taunton 1978 — 12 killed and Clapham Junction 35 killed) were caused by human errors that might seem almost trivial, but which had the most awful consequences and are exceedingly difficult to guard against.

The accidents at Purley and Bellgrove both demonstrated the still urgent need to do more to help the driver to avoid erroneously passing signals at Danger; a need which BR has at last accepted. Both accidents were clearly foreshadowed in *Danger Signals*, and even though BR is to take action, there are likely to be further accidents before that action becomes wholly effective. One hopes that more urgency will be shown than was the case with the existing Automatic Warning System. The decision to install AWS on the more important lines was taken in 1948. Design, development, testing and proving took 10 years. Installation took the next 30: the programme was not completed until 1988. Such snail-like progress would surely be unacceptable so far as the introduction of a modern Automatic Train Protection system is concerned.

4. Outside Influences

These are staggering in their diversity. They range from government action on the one hand, to lorry drivers bashing bridges on the other. Railways are, and have been for many years, a political football, and if management sometimes gives the impression that it does not know whether it is coming or going, is there any wonder? Furthermore, the situation does not improve. Privatisation, bus-substitution, sell-offs, reviews and inquiries, and fluctuations in capital investment are but a few of the BR Board's current problems. Each time there is a change of minister with responsibility for railways there are further upheavals, and as ministers change office so frequently, that is a major factor. Given Britain's political history, it was inevitable that the railways would be nationalised one day, but many of their problems have stemmed from the Transport Act of 1947, which brought them into public ownership. Prior to 1948 the four main line companies were basically well managed, each in its own particular way, but for historical reasons they were short of investment and their assets were not in a very good state, due to the war and its aftermath. By contrast, the nationalised railway cannot be considered to have been run as efficiently as the private companies were, because of the political interference to which it has been subjected; indeed, one would go further and suggest that BR has at times been virtually unmanageable, despite the considerable efforts of a lot of good managers.

Successive chairmen have come and gone, each one attempting to put things right according to his lights, and each one retiring, defeated. For 40 years BR has been struggling to get its organisation right and it has not yet entirely succeeded; which is a serious criticism because it has done nothing but reorganise since 1948 and it should be sufficiently expert by now. What is more, the railway of today is a much simpler affair than it was 10, 20 or 30 years ago. It must have seemed to the government many times over the last 40 years that the railways were a byword for waste and inefficiency, even though much of it was caused by the government's own policies, and it is hardly surprising that governments have imposed strict and severe financial constraints on the day-to-day activities. This has forced BR to cut its staff to the bone, and its margins below prudent levels in an almost desperate attempt to prove to the government that it deserves to be allowed to embark on a major capital investment programme. The downside of this daily struggle to exist within the government-imposed financial framework is that safety margins may become eroded, and this manifests itself in the long hours that staff have to work to increase their earnings to what they consider to be a reasonable level; in the shortages of key staff because BR cannot afford to pay the going rate in many parts of the country; in the upheaval of constant reorganisations, which distracts line managers from their job of supervising safety; and in the inability of BR to train its staff properly because training costs money which it has not got.

The Railway Inspectorate has voiced its concern over these issues several times in the last few years.

The public voice on railway safety has traditionally been the Railway Inspectorate, and it has fulfilled this role by holding Public Inquiries into accidents, and by publishing reports of those inquiries. Unfortunately the reports are often not published until many months, or even years, afterwards, which is much too late for them to serve their purpose. A more worrying trend in recent years has been the reduction in the number of Public Inquiries held. The average number of inquiries held in the 1970s was 11 per year. The average in the first half of the 1980s was eight. The average for the three years 1985-87 was five. In 1988, for the first time since the Inspectorate was formed in 1840, there was none. (The serious collision at Clapham on 12 December 1988 was followed by a formal inquiry headed by a QC.) This is not an indication that railway safety has improved so remarkably, but is caused by a shortage of staff in the Railway Inspectorate, due to the reluctance of the Department of Transport to pay the rate for the job and to recruit sufficient staff. Public Inquiries are very time-consuming, and in order that the Inspectorate can carry out its responsibilities effectively as the public watchdog on railway safety it needs to be properly staffed. The passenger has a right to know what is being done about his safety.

The Chief Inspecting Officer of Railways, Mr R. J. Seymour, concluded his Annual Report on Railway Safety for 1987 in the following terms:

'1987 brought no grounds for complacency about the safety of railway travel'.

He tempered this remark somewhat by going on to say that a great deal of effort was devoted by the operators and their staff at all levels to maintaining the railways' traditionally high standards. The number of significant train accidents in 1987 was 200, the same as in 1986, and the figure has hovered around the 200 mark throughout the 1980s, after being halved during the 1970s mainly owing to changes in freight train operation. BR appears now to have reached a plateau so far as safety is concerned, and the following figures of passenger deaths in train accidents can only give rise to sober reflection:

Years	No of Passengers killed in train accidents
1900-09	169
1930-39	114
1960-69	134
1980-89 (June)	75

Much of the improvement in the 1980s can be attributed to the stronger coaches now in general use which prevent telescoping, a potent source of death in earlier decades, and it is difficult to see how the high standards of safety which have always epitomised Britain's railways can be greatly improved upon, given the multitude of causes of railway accidents, and the almost trivial but vital errors that caused some of the worst ones. Nevertheless, the unremitting struggle to achieve a safer railway must continue. The price of safety is eternal vigilance, but it would be unrealistic to pretend that we shall ever eliminate accidents altogether. They are the price of mobility.

ADDENDUM

Railway accidents continue to provide an almost voyeuristic fascination for the public, the overwhelming proportion of which now travel by train quite infrequently. Whatever *Schadenfreude* the Motoring Classes might derive from viewing the discomfiture of the rival transport system would, one might have thought, be tempered by a comparison of railway safety with the unremitting carnage on the roads. Yet to most people a railway accident remains a greater novelty, and stimulates proportionally greater publicity than any pile-up in fog on the M25. It would be almost inconceivable to publish an Illustrated Book Of Road Accidents – it would be dismissed as sick and depraved in its purpose, and yet one could stock an entire bookshelf with albums of Trains In Trouble and their ilk.

So what is the fascination? Probably because railways are so relatively safe, and accidents are exceptional, we are more curious as to their whys and wherefores. Pictures of mangled machinery surely cannot in themselves excite much interest, unless one is a complete ghoul. No, surely our interest is more concerned with analysing the background to the event, and the individual or collective responsibilities involved?

Contrastingly, in the case of road accidents – once we have gasped at the horror of compacted metal – we as good as take it for granted that they are the result of someone's individual responsibility having been taken lightly. Then, after the usual "Why-oh-Why?" and "Not Again!" the journalistic inquest is slight and superficial. Individual motorists are, after all, only lightly-trained private citizens, so are not pilloried in the way that British Rail's presumed-professional staff and organisation inevitably are.

A recent controversy in the area of railway safety has, however, no parallel in the world of road transport, and this concerns the high incidence of passengers falling out of trains. Faulty door locks, mainly on Inter-City 125s, but not uncommon in the remaining venerable Mk.I carriages of '50s and '60s construction, are the cause in most cases except suicides. A TV documentary highlighted the issue in a rather scare-tactic fashion – whilst possibly saving a few lives (by discouraging passengers from clustering round the doors of an overcrowded train), one wonders how many potential travellers were cajoled by sensationalist material into deciding never to use a train ever again.

As all new trains are designed with sliding or power-operated doors as standard, the problem is self-solving in the long run. However, the programme of replacement of slam-door stock is unlikely to be completed before the 21st Century. Unless a magical amount of investment in new or re-furbished rolling-stock is forthcoming before then, the demise of the slam-door – in popular esteem the *sine qua non* of modern railway design – will continue to excite the tabloids by its delay in coming about.

Some of the following accidents were widely-publicised at the time they occurred – some were not. Generally, if the public are involved as passengers, the media coverage is far greater. Freight train accidents in relatively inaccessible yards or countryside receive little attention, unless they involve disastrous fire, spillage or pollution...

27th February 1989 – Arpley Yard. Locomotive no.85 020, hauling a Dover-Moss End Speedlink train, ran into the back of a Warrington-Doncaster freight. 85 020's cab was crushed beyond recognition, and its occupants killed.

30th July 1989 – West London Line.
Two railwaymen were killed and a third seriously injured, as two Engineering trains collided. The cab of one of the diesel locos, where the three victims were, was crushed to half its original length. Parts of both trains were derailed, with some wagons breaking through a fence and up onto the platform of West Brompton (LT) Station.

6th August 1989 – West Ealing.
Locomotive no. 50 025 *Invincible*, hauling the 2115(Sundays) Oxford-Paddington service at 70 mph, struck an object placed on the line by vandals, pushing it for a mile before being derailed at points, and sliding on its side onto the platform. The Mk.II coaches of the train formation remained upright, and only seven people required treatment for shock at Ealing Hospital. A flashfire on the wrecked loco narrowly missed damaging a passing IC125 on an adjacent track.

A piece of masonry had been removed from the track earlier in the day, suggesting a serious pattern of vandalism. Putting railway passengers at risk renders one liable to imprisonment, and rewards of up to £10,000 for information leading to a conviction are available.

22nd August 1989 – Hyde North Junction, Greater Manchester.
The 0930 Manchester Piccadilly- Sheffield DMU service was in head-on collision with the 0933 Rose Hill(Marple)-Manchester Piccadilly train. Twenty-six were injured, one seriously.

6th November 1989 – Huddersfield.
A head-on collision, in which a Class 156 Super Sprinter on a Scarborough-Liverpool service rammed into the front of a Class 141 Railbus on the eastern approaches to the station. Eighteen were injured, three seriously.

16th May 1990 – Chorleywood.
Three London Underground staff and one private contractor, on overnight Engineering work, were killed by a runaway wagon. It had gathered considerable momentum after a downhill run of some miles from the point where it had been parked, either unbraked or imperfectly braked.

19th June 1990 – Bessacarr, near Doncaster.
A woman and two children were killed on a gated crossing spanning five tracks. The woman and three children were cycling across, when one child fell. When the woman and one other child went to help, all three were struck by the 1733 Inter-City Kings Cross-Hull service. The driver braked, but too late to stop in time.

8th January 1991 – Cannon Street.
The 0758 Sevenoaks-Cannon Street collided with buffer stops at the end of Platform 3. Despite the low speed of impact, the sixth carriage was lifted up, then dropped onto part of the fifth carriage in front of it. Two passengers were killed and 243 injured, 30 seriously. The leading 4-car unit sustained only minor damage, but the middle unit was compressed, necessitating the cutting away of bodywork to free passengers trapped in the wreckage. Brake failure was not to blame, and at the inquest in July 1991 it was established that the driver had traces of cannabis in his system two days after the accident. He had not been examined immediately afterwards in accordance with the rules, so no charge of driving under the influence of drugs was forthcoming. Another disturbing aspect that was reported was that the driving cab was left unattended after the accident, so that the final position of the controls could not be firmly established.

Much was made in the press concerning the antiquity of the underframes of some of the carriages, none of which were in fact found to be faulty. Frames from 1920s steam stock had been used in the 1950s to construct new EPB units. Newspapers crowed about their "sources of information in BR" and "secret reports", as though the existence of the re-cycled frames was part of a sinister cover-up.

In fact, any half-knowledgeable trainspotter could have told them about this (perhaps commendable?) 1950s cost-cutting exercise, documented quite freely in the enthusiasts' magazines and ABCs of the time.

18th January 1991 – Liverpool Lime Street.
Three S&T engineers were struck and killed on the approaches to the station by an a.c. loco on an empty stock movement from Edge Hill to form an up London Service. The Engineering staff who died had been attending a points failure.

21st July 1991 – Newton, Strathclyde.
The 2055 Balloch-Motherwell service was in head-on collision with the 2155 Newton-Glasgow Central just outside the station. The impact was at 35 mph, and four died, with 30 injured. A possible cause was damaged points on a section of bi-directional track. At the enquiry it was proposed that this single-line working should be restored to double-line.

7th December 1991 – Severn Tunnel.
The tunnel had been re-signalled in 1990 to allow bi-directional working of both tracks. That morning a signal failure had been reported, and the fault was under investigation.

An IC125, stopped at a signal on the tunnel approach, was then instructed to "Proceed With Caution" as per the Rule Book. Moving at about 15-20 mph, three miles into the tunnel and climbing upwards for the last mile, it was struck violently from behind by a Super Sprinter. The latter had been significantly delayed before reaching Temple Meads, and had left there 22 minutes late.

102 passengers and a baby required hospital treatment, 16 being detained overnight, including three with spinal injuries, and others with broken limbs. Neither train was fitted with traditional railway sprung buffers.

An emergency train on stand-by on the Welsh side was used to help bring out the seriously injured, then the IC125 minus its damaged rear power-car took out the rest. The emergency services were praised by Malcolm Rifkind MP, then Minister of Transport. The accident was the first in the tunnel since it had opened 105 years previously.

On the 9th December, BR's Press Office issued a brief statement : "Having ruled out Vandalism, BR have accepted responsibility for the accident in the Severn Tunnel on Saturday 7th December involving the 0700 Portsmouth-Cardiff and the 0830 London(Paddington)-Cardiff."

Index

(Where only passing reference to an accident is made in the text, it is not included below)

Bibliography

Magazines & Periodicals

Modern Railways
Railnews (BR house journal)
Railway Gazette
Railway Gazette International
Railway Magazine
Railway Observer

Books

Biggs Clauses Consolidation Acts 1845-1866: James Biggs (1866).
British Railways Engineering: John Johnson and Robert A. Long (1981).
Danger Signals. An Investigation into Modern Railway Accidents: Stanley Hall (1987).
The First Principles of Railway Signalling: C. B. Byles (1918).
Gradients of the British Main Line Railways: The *Railway Magazine* (1936).
Historic Railway Disasters: O. S. Nock (1966).
Jubilees of the LMS: John F. Clay (1971).
The Law of Carriage by Inland Transport: Dr Otto Kahn-Freund (1965).
The Law of the Railway: Leslie James (1980).
Red for Danger: L. T. C. Rolt (1982).
Trains in Trouble: Vols 1 & 2: Arthur Trevena (1980/81); Vols 3 & 4: Ken Hoole (1982/83).

Reports & Pamphlets, etc

British Railways and Constituent Companies Books of Rules, Regulations & Instructions.
British Standard Code of Practice for Fire Precautions in the Design & Construction of Railway Passenger Rolling Stock (BS 6853: 1987).
The Carriage of Dangerous Goods by Rail: Paper delivered to CIT (Humberside Section) by G. W. Foulger (1978).
It Can Now be Revealed. More about British Railways in Peace and War (1945).
Railways of Central & West Wales: Neil Sprinks (1987).
A Strategy for the Reduction of Bridge Bashing: Report by a Department of Transport Working Party (1988).
Transport of CEGB Irradiated Nuclear Fuel: CEGB (1983).
Transportation of Radioactive Material: NUR (1987).

022971

DATE DUE

0 6 NOV 2019

PRINTED IN U.S.A.